MICROSCOPY
FOR CHEMISTS

MICROSCOPY FOR CHEMISTS

by

HAROLD F. SCHAEFFER

Department of Chemistry
Westminster College
Fulton, Missouri

DOVER PUBLICATIONS, INC.

NEW YORK

This Dover edition, first published in 1966, is an unabridged republication, with minor corrections, of the second printing (1956) of the work originally published by D. Van Nostrand Company, Inc., in 1953.

Library of Congress Catalog Card Number: 66-25955

Manufactured in the United States of America
Dover Publications, Inc.
180 Varick Street
New York, N.Y. 10014

To
KATHERINE ARLENE

PREFACE

"It is rather remarkable how slow American chemists have been in realizing the importance of the microscope as an adjunct to every chemical laboratory. This is, perhaps, largely due to the fact that few of our students in chemistry become familiar with the construction and manipulation of this instrument."[1] Although half a century has passed since this was written, the statement is probably just as true today. While it must be admitted that many microscopes have found their way into chemical laboratories, the application of microscopic methods is by no means general. Just as Chamot mentioned at the turn of the century, relatively few of our students in chemistry are given any systematic training in the use of the microscope. Not infrequently the chemist's only formal training in microscopy is restricted to that acquired in connection with some course in biology; yet it is probably safe to assume that the majority have not had even this advantage.

Such a general lack of training in microscopy is deplorable because there are so many types of chemical problems to which the microscope can be applied advantageously. These applications are not restricted only to samples which are inadequate for conventional methods of analysis. A very important consideration is the fact that frequently the methods of microscopy can effect a substantial saving of time. The minute quantities of reagents required may permit at times the use of desirable chemicals which would be too rare or too expensive to be employed in the amounts needed in corresponding macro methods. In certain instances the microscope *must* be pressed into service because ordinary chemical methods cannot be applied, viz., determining the type of starch in a mixture. A very important fact which is frequently overlooked is that the microscope is a precision instrument which lends itself to certain types of quantitative determinations, especially when a few accessories are provided. It is not surprising that Chamot[2] fifty years ago considered the microscope to be "as much a necessity in every analytical laboratory as is the balance." More recently Adrianus Pijper,[3] in

[1] E. M. Chamot, *Journal of Applied Microscopy* 2, 502 (1899).
[2] *Loc. cit.*
[3] *Journal of the Royal Microscopical Society* 62, 36–50 (1942). Reprinted from the *South African Journal of Science* 26, 58–72 (1939).

addressing the South African Association for the Advancement of Science, went so far as to describe the instrument as "man's noblest, supreme, and most far-reaching tool."

The author feels that intelligent and efficient use of the microscope requires an understanding of its construction and a knowledge of certain underlying principles. As Pijper [4] expressed it: ". . . although there may be many scientists who use the microscope, comparatively few are microscopists." For this reason the present work devotes some attention to the elementary principles of optics and certain other divisions of physics.

The best way to learn the techniques of microscopy is to pursue the work under the personal guidance of a competent instructor. However, the graduate chemist who plans to take up the subject may not always be in a position to avail himself of such personal instruction. With this in mind the author has endeavored to present the material so as to be intelligible to the worker who must depend upon his own resources, without benefit of a mentor.

ACKNOWLEDGMENTS

The author wishes to express his appreciation to Waynesburg College and to the College of Our Lady of the Elms for the use of certain material in their libraries. He is especially grateful to Mrs. Vivien Lawson, reference librarian at the University of Alabama, for her diligence in securing various publications which were not available locally. A word of appreciation is also due to the late Dr. Walter E. Thrun who made available certain facilities at Valparaiso University. A number of manufacturers of instruments and several scientific supply houses have been very generous in providing material for many of the illustrations which appear in the book. Their co-operation is highly appreciated, and appropriate credit lines have been appended to all illustrations thus obtained.

H. F. S.

[4] *Loc. cit.*

CONTENTS

vii

viii CONTENTS

MICROSCOPY
FOR CHEMISTS

Chapter I

PRINCIPLES GOVERNING LENSES

Introductory.—Since a microscope is no better than its optical system, the serious worker must comprehend thoroughly certain fundamental principles concerning the behavior of light and of lenses. As early as the 17th century Chris Huygens, René Descartes, and Robert Hooke maintained that the propagation of light is a wave phenomenon. Although challenged at times by Newton, La Place, and others, physicists of today prefer to treat light as a wave phenomenon when they are interested in the path along which light travels.[1] Practically everyone at present knows of, or at least has heard about, cosmic rays, X rays, ultraviolet rays, infrared rays, and radio waves. None of these can be seen by the eye. In part, visible light rays differ from these others just mentioned in the magnitude of their respective wave lengths. The dimensions of visible light rays lie between those of infrared rays and ultraviolet.

APPROXIMATE WAVE LENGTHS

*Angstrom Units**

Cosmic rays .... between 10^{-5} and 10^{-3}
X rays .... between 10^{-1} and 10
Ultraviolet rays .... shorter than 3800
Visible light .... between 3800 and 7700
Infrared rays .... over 7700 and to approx. 10^6
Radio waves .... between 10^2 and 10^4 centimeters

* An Angstrom unit equals 10^{-8} centimeter, or a hundred millionth of a centimeter.

The phenomenon of refraction.—For any practical purposes it may be assumed that, in any given transparent medium, light travels in straight lines; but, in passing from one medium into another transparent medium, the direction of a beam of light may be changed. Many of the effects of this phenomenon are quite well known. One common example of this

[1] Cf. p. 483 of H. Howe, *Introduction to Physics,* McGraw-Hill, 1948.

1

change in direction is the appearance of various objects submerged in water (Figure 1.1). It should be noted that in the illustration the object on the bottom of the empty beaker would not be seen if the sides were not transparent. Why, then, should the addition of water render the object visible? This may be explained by reference to the diagram in Figure 1.2, where we shall follow the course taken by a ray of light in traveling from a small point on the submerged object O to the eye of an observer. It is customary to express the direction of a light ray in terms of the angle

Fig. 1.1. Refraction. The two small glasses are identical in size and shape. Each contains a 25-cent silver coin. When viewing the top of glass A from the position of the camera, the silver coin cannot be seen. However, by pouring water into the glass, as has been done in B, at the right, the light rays coming from the submerged coin suffer refraction to such an extent that the coin is readily seen through the top of the glass.

which it makes with a line drawn perpendicular to the surface which the ray strikes. In Figure 1.2 the line NN' is perpendicular to the water surface at S, where the ray OS meets the surface. The angle $N'SO$, or θ, is the angle of incidence, and the ray OS is the incident ray (meaning the ray which approaches the surface).

Now, if upon reaching the air the ray OS were to continue along its original course, it would not be seen by the observer unless his eye were somewhere along the line SH. Actually, upon reaching the air, the ray changes its direction. It is bent, or refracted, so that the angle it makes with the normal NN' is greater than the angle of incidence. The new path SE represents the *refracted* ray; the angle NSE is the angle of refraction. Because of refraction the observer at E sees the ray as though it came from a point at O'.

The foregoing conditions could be reversed. Let us assume that in

Figure 1.2 an object is placed in the air at E, and that a ray of light travels from E to the water surface at S. The line ES now represents the incident ray. Upon entering the water, refraction occurs, so that SO represents the path of the refracted ray. If the eye of an observer (a fish, for example) is somewhere along the line SO, the refracted ray from E will be seen.

A very important property of transparent substances is known as *refractive index,* or index of refraction. Assume that a narrow beam of

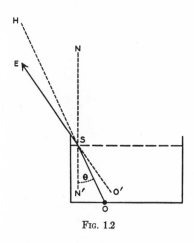

Fig. 1.2

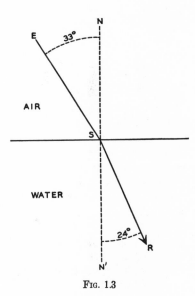

Fig. 1.3

S, surface of water
NN', normal to water surface
ES, incident ray (in air)
SR, refracted ray (in water)
33 degrees equals *angle of incidence*
24 degrees equals *angle of refraction*

light traveling through air strikes the surface of water so as to make an angle of 33 degrees with the normal (Figure 1.3). Approximate measurements will show that in the water the refracted ray makes an angle of about 24 degrees with the normal. In a book of mathematical tables we can find that the sine of an angle of 33 degrees is equal to 0.54464; whereas the sine of 24 degrees equals 0.40674. As our next step we shall divide the sine of the angle of incidence by the sine of the angle of refraction, or

$$\frac{\text{Sine of } 33°}{\text{Sine of } 24°} = \frac{0.54464}{0.40674} = 1.336 \text{ (approximate)}.$$

The number thus obtained is the refractive index of water. Calculations based upon very precise measurements of the angles would give the value

1.333.   According to Snell's "law of sines," for a given pair of transparent media,

$$\frac{\text{Sine of angle of incidence}}{\text{Sine of angle of refraction}} \text{ or } \frac{\sin i}{\sin r} = \text{a constant.} \qquad [\text{I}]$$

This relationship is very important.   If the angle of incidence should be greater or smaller than that given in the foregoing problem, then, natu-

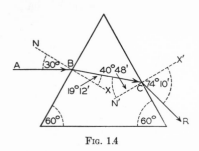

Fig. 1.4

rally, the angle of refraction in the water would likewise have a different value; but the ratio of the sines of these angles would remain the same, that is, 1.333.   It should be noted that the refractive index refers to values obtained when the incident ray travels through air or, more precisely, through a vacuum.   Refraction may occur when light travels from glass to water or even from one kind of glass into another kind, as from crown glass into flint glass.   In expressing the refractive index for a combination of which neither component is air (or vacuum) the value is termed the *relative* refractive index.

Let us now consider what occurs when light rays pass through a glass prism (Figure 1.4).   First we shall use our knowledge of refractive index to trace the path followed when a beam of yellow light, AB, passes from air into the prism.   At B, where the light strikes the side of the prism, we draw the normal NX.   By means of a protractor the angle of incidence ABN is found equal to 30 degrees.   From equation [I], sin i/sin r = refractive index n, we derive

$$\sin r = \frac{\sin i}{n}. \qquad [\text{II}]$$

The sine of an angle of 30 degrees equals 0.5000, and n equals 1.52.   (The refractive index of glass is equal to 1.52.)   Hence,

$$\sin r = \frac{0.5000}{1.52} = 0.329.$$

From reference tables we find that 0.329 is the sine of an angle of about 19 degrees 13 minutes.   This should be the angle of refraction, that is, the angle which the refracted ray in glass makes with the normal NX.

Upon passing from the right face of the prism into air, the ray BC will again suffer refraction. BC now becomes the incident ray, striking the right face of the prism at C.   It can be demonstrated that the angle of incidence BCN' equals approximately 40 degrees 48 minutes.   ($N'X'$

is normal to the face of the prism at C.) The angle of refraction $X'CR$ may now be calculated by applying equation [II], but it must be noted that the value of n has changed. As given before, the value 1.52 represented the refractive index of glass, with the light traveling from air into glass. In the present instance the conditions are reversed, so that the new value n' is the reciprocal of the previous value, or $1/n$. It might be said that this value is the relative refractive index of air compared with glass.

$$N' = \frac{1}{n} = \frac{1}{1.52} = 0.658. \qquad \text{[III]}$$

$$\sin r = \frac{\sin 40° \, 48'}{0.658} = \frac{0.6536}{0.658} = 0.962.$$

Referring to the tables we find the corresponding angle is **74 degrees 10 minutes** (approximate). This is the angle which the refracted ray CR makes with the normal when leaving the glass prism. Observe that, when the light passes from air into glass, the angle of refraction is *less* than the angle of incidence, whereas the converse is true when the light emerges from glass into air. Should the incident ray travel from R to C, the path through the prism would be C to B, whereas B to A would represent the course of the ray emerging from the left of the prism. As an additional illustration the reader may consider the case of a prism having opposite sides in the shape of an isosceles triangle, as diagrammed in Figure 1.5.

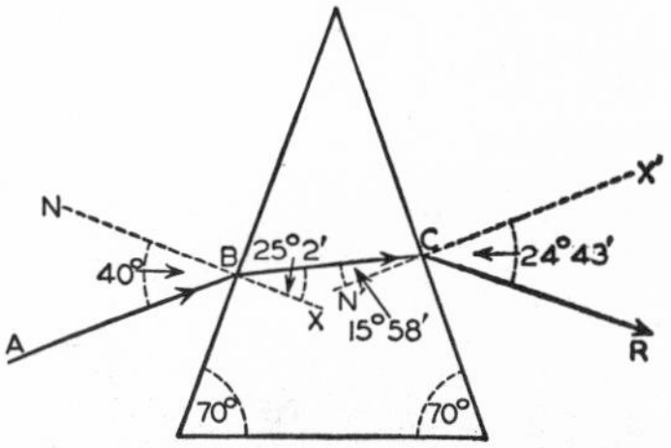

Although two different transparent media may possess refractive indices lying closely together, the respective paths traversed by rays emerging from two such solids may differ considerably.

Having considered refraction in glass prisms, we should next proceed

FIG. 1.5. Incident Ray, AB. Normal to prism surface at B is NX. Angle of incidence, 40 degrees. From equation II, the sine of the angle of refraction CBX equals $\frac{\sin e\ 40°}{1.52} = 0.423$. Corresponding angle is 25 degrees 2 minutes. Normal to surface at C is $N'X'$. Angle of incidence here is BCN' which equals 15 degrees 58 minutes. Refractive index, from equation III, equals 0.658. Sine of the angle of the emerging ray equals $\sin r$; $\sin r = \frac{15°\ 58'}{0.658} = 0.418$. Corresponding angle, RCX', equals 24° 43' (approx.).

to a figure having a curved surface as one of its boundaries. By means of a diamond pencil the section STV has been cut from a disc of thick glass (Figure 1.6). What should result when rays enter the glass somewhere along the curved surface?

For the present purpose we shall restrict ourselves to a consideration of only such incident rays as are parallel with ray PV. Since OV is the radius of the arc TVS, it must likewise be the normal to the arc at V. Whenever an incident ray is perpendicular to the surface of the medium, it will not suffer refraction upon entering the latter. The ray in this case, therefore, maintains its original course in traversing the glass. For similar reasons the ray which emerges at E is not diffracted but continues in the same direction along EO and beyond.

In the case of incident ray AB, conditions are entirely different. The normal to the curved surface at B is NX, which lies along the radius of the arc. If the angle of incidence ABN is 30 degrees, then the angle of refraction in glass is 19 degrees 13 minutes, as shown previously in the discussion

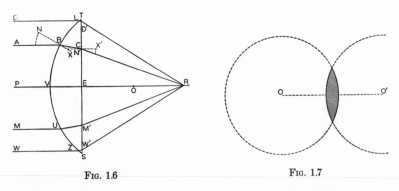

FIG. 1.6   FIG. 1.7

of Figure 1.4. It can be shown that the refracted ray BC should make an angle of 10 degrees 47 minutes with $N'X'$, which is the normal to the plane surface TS. By the same method employed in connection with Figures 1.4 and 1.5 we find that the emergent ray CR makes an angle of 16 degrees 31 minutes with the normal $N'X'$.

Near the end of the arc, the ray DL makes an angle of 50 degrees with the normal. After passing through the glass the emergent ray $D'R$ makes an angle of 30 degrees 55 minutes with the normal to the plane surface TS. The angles for rays MU and WZ are equal to those of AB and DL respectively. The interesting feature to be observed here is that the refracted rays intersect at point R, and in this respect our segment of a plate glass disc bears some resemblance to a lens. In fact, if we had chosen the segment of a glass sphere, we would have a lens.

Simple lenses and their properties.—We now ask the question: "What is a lens?" Fundamentally, a lens must provide two surfaces, one of which must be curved. For our purpose one surface may be thought of as the curved boundary of the segment of a sphere, while the other surface may be plane or spherical. The lenses may be divided into two main classes, according to their effect on parallel rays of light. Lenses which cause parallel rays to converge, as shown in Figure 1.6, are called *converging lenses;* those which cause parallel rays to spread apart are called *diverging* (or dispersing) *lenses.* The two groups may likewise be referred to as positive or negative lenses, depending upon whether or not they form *real* images.

Among the converging or positive lenses may be included the following.

1. *Plano-convex.* This is the segment of a sphere   The cross section of such a lens is represented in Figure 1.6.

2. *Double convex.* In this type both surfaces are derived from part of a sphere (Figure 1.7). In the illustration given both spheres have the

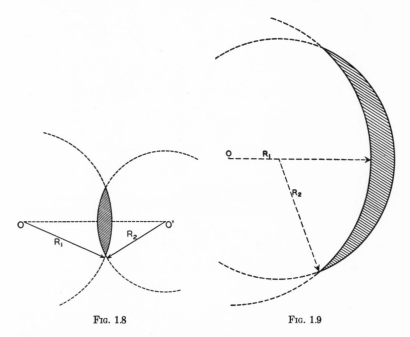

FIG. 1.8   FIG. 1.9

same radius, but such is not always the case. In Figure 1.8, for example, the ratio between the two radii is about 8 to 10. Although the cross section of this lens appears to differ only very slightly from that represented in the previous figure, the actual optical properties of two such lenses will differ appreciably.

3. *Concavo-convex.* For this type of lens the centers of curvature for both surfaces are on the same side, and the distance between surfaces is greatest in the center (Figures 1.9 and 1.10).

The following are examples of negative or diverging lenses.

1. *Plano-concave.* This lens (Figure 1.11) is just the opposite of the plano-convex. If this lens were used as a mold into which melted wax were poured, upon cooling, the solidified wax would resemble a plano-convex lens (Figure 1.6).

2. *Double concave.* If the plane surfaces of two plano-concave lenses were cemented together, the resulting figure would resemble a double

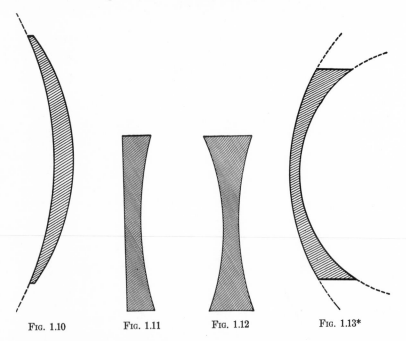

FIG. 1.10   FIG. 1.11   FIG. 1.12   FIG. 1.13*

concave lens (Figure 1.12). In fact, if properly cemented together, this combination would serve as a double concave lens.

3. *Convexo-concave.* The reader may be tempted to consider this lens the same as a concavo-convex lens. Observe, however, that the convexo-concave lens is *thinner* at the center. Contrast Figure 1.13 with Figures 1.9 and 1.10.

Nearly everyone is familiar with some of the properties of the double

* For the reader who doubts that there is any difference between the properties of a concavo-convex lens and those of a convexo-concave, it will be an interesting exercise to carry out an investigation by means of diagrams. After drawing fairly large figures to represent the two lenses, apply the same general procedure referred to in connection with Figure 1.9. The convexo-concave lens is also known as a diverging meniscus lens.

convex lens because this type is so commonly employed in a wide variety of ways. As cheap magnifiers they can be purchased for only a dime; a better quality is sold for use as reading glasses; some of the folding pocket-lenses used by biologists are double convex lenses of small diameter. Most schoolboys seem to know how to apply the fact that, if parallel rays enter one side of such a lens, the rays emerging from the other side will converge. Furthermore, they know that, for a given lens, these converging rays meet at a certain definite distance.

The foregoing statements may be amplified thus: The sun is so far distant that its rays upon entering a lens are practically parallel. If a sheet of paper is placed behind the lens, there will be found a certain distance at which the emerging rays will form the smallest (and also the brightest) disc of light. In other words, the rays have been focused. Since this spot of light will be very hot, a hole may be burned through the paper if sufficient time is allowed; hence the term "burning glass" was frequently used until recent decades.

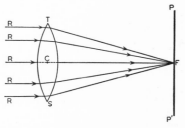

Fig. 1.14. *R*, parallel rays of light, as from the sun, entering the double convex lens.

C, optical center of the lens.

F, focal point, or principal focus of lens, where the refracted rays meet.

CF, focal length of the lens.

P P', focal plane, or image plane. This plane is perpendicular to the axis *CF*.

In the foregoing instance the locus where the sun's rays converge to the smallest disc is known as the focal point of that lens (Figure 1.14). The distance from the optical center of a given lens to the focal point is the focal length. The focal point lies in the *focal plane*, which is also known as the image plane. If, instead of allowing parallel rays of light to enter the lens, one places a source of light at the principal focus, the paths of the rays will be opposite to those represented in Figure 1.14. Rays emerging from the lens will then be parallel. In many projection lanterns and photographic enlargers this principle is employed to form parallel rays through the agency of "condensing lenses."

Image formation.—Our next concern shall be the formation of images by a converging lens. A convenient way to form these images would be to have the lens attached in front of the bellows of a camera provided with a ground-glass focusing screen. Let the position of the lens be so adjusted that the distance to the screen is equal to the focal length. If we now direct the lens toward a tall tree two hundred feet away, an image will be formed on the ground-glass screen. This image will be *inverted* and, of course, very much smaller than the original object. Another interesting fact becomes evident when the camera is taken closer to the tree. In order to obtain a clear image it will be found necessary to move the lens farther away from the screen as we approach the object. In other words, the image is no longer in the plane of the principal focus. This is demonstrated by Figure 1.15. Meanwhile the image becomes larger.

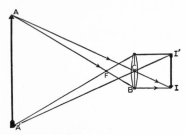

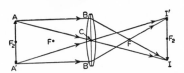

FIG. 1.15. CONVERGING LENS FOCUSED ON A DISTANT OBJECT AT $A A'$. It will be recalled that, as shown in Figure 1.14, rays which pass through the principal focus to a lens surface will emerge on the opposite side in the form of rays parallel with the optical axis. Hence AB, which passes through the principal focus F, will emerge as ray $B I$, parallel with the axis. The ray from A to the optical center C should emerge from the opposite side to continue in the same direction. Where the rays $B I$ and $C I$ intersect, the image I of point A should be in focus. By a similar procedure it is found that there should be an image of A' at I'. It will be found that the image is inverted and smaller than the object. This image would be seen on a screen (such as a white card or a sheet of ground glass) placed in the plane of $I I'$. For this reason it is considered a *real* image.

FIG. 1.16. DISTANCE FROM CONVERGING LENS TO OBJECT EQUALS TWICE THE FOCAL LENGTH OF THE LENS. Let F, F represent the principal foci on either side of the lens; F_2, F_2 are separated from the center of the lens by a distance equal to twice the focal length $C F$. $A A'$ represents the object. When rays which are parallel to the optical axis enter the lens, they emerge at such an angle that they pass through the principal focus F. This is true for the ray $A B$, coming from point A. Upon emerging on the other side it travels through the principal focus F. The *ray of minimum deviation*, passing through C, continues in a straight line until it meets the first ray at I, where the image of point A should be in sharp focus. Rays from A' will come to a focus at I'. Here, as in Figure 1.15, the image is *real* and inverted. The important difference is that the image is the same size as the object.

When the image becomes larger, let us assume that the lens is more specifically focused on a relatively small object, such as an individual leaf. Eventually it will be found that the screen image is exactly the same size as the object. The distance from the optical center of the lens to the object will then be identical with the distance from the lens to the image. Under ideal conditions this distance equals twice the focal length of the lens (Figure 1.16). This furnishes another practical method for determining the focal length of a lens. From what has been stated it follows that when the size of the screen image is identical with that of the original object, the two must be separated by a distance equivalent to four times the focal length of the lens.

To continue our experiment with the lens, if the lens is moved closer to the object, so that the distance is less than twice the focal length, the resulting screen image will be larger than the object. The magnification is increased as the lens is moved closer, until the distance to the object is equal (approximately) to the focal length. From here on, no matter how far the screen is moved away from the lens, no image can be projected.

It is important to keep in mind the fact that in the examples just considered the images formed by the lens can be focused on a screen. Such an image is known as a *real* image.

If we now remove the lens and merely employ it as a hand lens to read a page of print we find that the type is magnified. The magnified image thus obtained will not be inverted; it will be upright. Measurements would show that the distance from the lens to the printed words is *less* than the focal length. Furthermore, the image *could not* be caught on a screen. Such an image is known

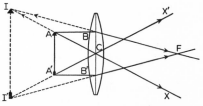

FIG. 1.17. PRINCIPLE OF THE SIMPLE MICRO-SCOPE. The distance from the object $A A'$ to the lens is less than the focal length of the latter. Let $A B$ represent a ray parallel with the optical axis; the refracted ray should pass through the principal focus F. From point A, the ray of minimum deviation through C continues unaltered in its course toward X. Obviously, $B F$ and $C X$, the rays coming from point A, are divergent and therefore will not meet. The same is true for $B' F$ and $C X'$, coming from point A'. On the side of the lens opposite the object, therefore, no image will be formed on a screen. Nevertheless the observer's eye will see a magnified upright image of the object. This *virtual* image $I I'$ appears to be on the same side as the object. The apparent position of image point I is found by projecting rays $B F$ and $C X$ behind the lens.

as a *virtual* image, to distinguish it from a real image. When a converging lens is used to magnify objects placed within the focal distance, it is actually serving as a simple microscope. The principle can be understood from Figure 1.17.

With the compound microscope we can obtain a real image; that is, the magnified image can be projected on a screen. Fundamentally, the real image produced by a converging lens of considerable magnifying power is further magnified by a second lens placed in an appropriate position. Before the compound microscope could be made entirely satisfactory for critical work two very serious faults had to be overcome. For a better

understanding of the lens system of the compound instrument we should
first make a brief study of these shortcomings.

Aberrations and their correction.—The reader may recall that when
we discussed the refraction of a beam of light in traveling through a prism
(page 4) we specified yellow light. Should one employ daylight, for
example, the results would be quite different. As demonstrated by Sir
Isaac Newton, the light emerging from the prism would be not merely a
refracted beam of "white light"; instead, there would be a fanshaped
group of rays (Figure 1.18). If a white screen were placed in their path
these rays would form a spectrum, that is, a band of different colors ranging from deep red at one end, through yellow, green blue to violet. For
us, the important conclusion to be drawn here is that violet rays are

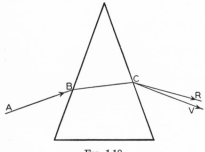

Fig. 1.18

refracted to a greater extent than are the red rays; or, in general, the
angles of refraction are greater for the shorter wave lengths. (It must
be remembered that the wave lengths of rays near the red end of the
spectrum are longer than those toward the violet end.) This property of
a transparent medium to separate emerging light into the various components of the incident ray is known as *dispersion.*

Since the very principle of a lens depends upon the refraction of light,
this unequal refraction of different colors means that for any single lens
there is a different focal length for each color. When rays of white
light, parallel to the optic axis, fall upon a converging lens, the violet
components come to a focus closer to the lens, while red wave lengths are
focused farther from the lens (Figure 1.19). If this simple lens were
employed to magnify an object illuminated by white light the image
would exhibit color fringes around the edges. The reader may have observed this phenomenon in the use of a large reading lens or a pair of low-
priced opera glasses. This peculiarity is known as *chromatic aberration.*

The ray which coincides with the optic axis *CR* (Figure 1.19) suffers
no refraction; consequently there is no dispersion. One way to overcome

chromatic aberration to some extent is to employ a diaphragm in front of the lens, so that only a small central portion is actually used. Unfortunately, the use of such a diaphragm as the sole means to overcome chromatic aberration is not too satisfactory. The serious disadvantage of the method is that in many instances it does not pass sufficient light through the lens.

A practical solution to the problem depends upon the fact that the degree of dispersion varies in different media. Different kinds of glass which have practically the same index of refraction may present considerable differences in their degree of dispersion. A glass having a high refractive index may also exhibit a high degree of dispersion, while another variety with the same refractive index may show only slight dispersion. Numerous combinations of these two properties are possible. Thus, by combining two lenses of different types of glass it is possible to obtain a lens system in which the dispersion of one element is at least partly neutralized by the other. A lens combination which has been corrected so that various colors have practically the same focus is known as an *achromatic* lens. Incidentally, if the combination consists of two lenses it is referred to as a *doublet,* or, in the present instance, as an *achromatic doublet.*

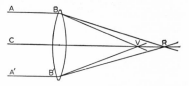

FIG. 1.19. CHROMATIC ABERRATION. Let $C R$ represent the optical axis of the double concave lens. $A B$ and $A' B'$ are rays of white light parallel to the optical axis. When $A B$ emerges on the right side of the lens, the violet component will take the direction $B V$ while the red component assumes the course $B R$. In similar fashion the violet component of the ray $A' B'$ will be refracted along $B' V$. Where $B V$ and $B' V'$ meet, the violet rays are brought to a focus; or one may say that point V represents the principal focus of the violet rays. The red rays apparently will be in focus at R. In the diagram the distance between V and R has been exaggerated.

There is another important particular in which a simple lens differs from the ideal which we have been discussing. If parallel rays of light enter a converging lens, those which emerge near the periphery will cross the principal axis, or, in other words, will be brought to a focus, closer to the lens than those rays which emerged from the central portion of the lens. This *spherical aberration,* as it is called, is sometimes remedied, at least in part, by using only a part of the lens near the center. The more practical method for correcting this type of aberration is to combine several different lenses, just as in the correction of chromatic aberration. By selecting appropriate types of optical glass an optician can correct the spherical aberration in a convex lens. This correction may be accomplished by combining the convex with a concave lens possessing an equal and opposite spherical aberration, without destroying the convergent effect of the convex lens. Such a corrected combination is known as an *aplanatic lens*, or, merely, an *aplanat*.

In some instances the correction in an aplanat is not complete, so that rays emerging near the edge of the lens still come to a focus closer to the lens than the other rays. Such a lens is said to be *undercorrected*. On the other hand, the degree of correction may be such that marginal rays come to a focus slightly beyond the focus of rays from the central portion of the lens. This is *overcorrection*. Its practical usefulness will be referred to later.

Since the production of highly corrected lenses is rather expensive, it is customary to limit the degree and the kind of correction according to the purpose for which a given lens is desired. As the human eye is most sensitive to the yellow-green region of the spectrum, correction for spherical aberration is commonly made for only this portion. Such lenses in which spherical aberration has been corrected for only one color are *achromats*. In *apochromats*, however, the spherical aberration has been corrected for two colors.

Two other serious aberrations in single lenses are *curvature of field* and *distortion*. The image formed by a single lens does not really lie in a perfectly plane field; instead, the field in which a sharp image is formed is curved. This means that if the image is to be projected on a plane surface, as on a sheet of photographic film, it will not be critically sharp unless the lens has been corrected for curvature of field. Distortion has been observed by everyone who has employed a simple magnifying glass. Quite frequently the object appears to undergo a higher degree of magnification near the rim of the lens than toward the center.

Study Problems

1. Explain the difference between refraction and dispersion.

2. Given a glass prism which has a cross section represented by an isosceles right triangle. The incident ray *AB* is normal to the face *HT*. Assuming the glass has a refractive index of 1.5, trace the path followed by the light as it travels through the prism. (Sines of angles may be obtained from a geometry text or from a book of mathematical tables.)

What practical applications can you suggest for such a prism?

3. Show how the results would differ in the foregoing problem if the prism were made of glyptal resin, which has a refractive index of 1.57.

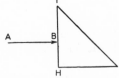

PROB. 2

4a. Referring to Figure 1.3, and to pages 3 and 4, diagram the course of the refracted ray when the angle of incidence, *NSE*, is 40 degrees.

b. Trace the course of a refracted ray if the liquid in part (a) were carbon bisulfide. (Refractive index = 1.628.)

5. Referring to Figure 1.4, trace the course followed by the refracted rays if the prism were a diamond. (Refractive index, 2.417.)

6. Draw up a list of the more common aberrations of lenses.

7. Distinguish between a *virtual* image and a *real* image.

8. When using a simple reading lens, the eye sees an erect image of the print. Under what conditions could the same lens yield an inverted image? Would these images (the erect and the inverted) be *real* or *virtual?*

9. A double convex lens was mounted between a movable white screen and an illuminated cross. By adjusting the screen and cross it was possible to find an arrangement where the screen image was the same size as the cross. The two were then 14 inches apart. Find the focal length of the lens. How far was the image from the optical center of the lens?

10. Describe the effect produced (in problem 9) if the object were placed farther from the lens. Could the image be focused on a screen?

11. Pure ethylene bromide and ethylene chloride are colorless. A colorless crystal of pure sodium chloride is practically invisible in the former but distinctly visible in the latter. Explain why.

12. Explain how a simple reading glass and a candle or a flashlight bulb could be employed as a source of parallel rays.

13. Explain or describe the following terms: (a) Meniscus lens; (b) achromatic doublet; (c) positive lens; (d) principal focus; (e) focal plane.

14. Explain the difference between spherical aberration and curvature of field.

Chapter II

GETTING ACQUAINTED WITH THE MICROSCOPE

The parts of a microscope.—Essentially, the microscope consists of the following parts.

1. A lens system.
2. Some provision for focusing the lens system.
3. A stage on which to place specimens.
4. Some device for providing satisfactory illumination.

As might be expected, these features may be had in various degrees of refinement, and in many instruments additional facilities are furnished. The design of instruments currently employed varies somewhat according to the maker, date of manufacture, cost, and intended use. Practically all, however, follow certain general trends in design. Names of the various parts of the instrument are given in Figures 2.1 and 2.2.

The lens system ordinarily consists of two types of lenses, namely, objectives and oculars (or eyepieces). The objective is the lens just above the specimen. The ocular, or eyepiece, is the lens found in the upper end of the draw tube. Its function is to magnify further the image formed by the objective. As will be seen later, the ocular also serves certain other purposes. In order to provide several different degrees of magnification the microscope may be equipped with two or more objectives. To facilitate changing from one objective to another several objectives belonging to the same instrument may be mounted in a *revolving nosepiece,* as in Figure 2.3. When a different objective is required, one need merely rotate the nosepiece until the desired lens is in position. Although the degree of magnification can also be varied by the use of different oculars, it is not as practicable to mount these in any device comparable with the revolving nosepiece employed with the objectives. (However, it has been done.) No serious handicap is involved, however, because an ocular is very easily inserted in the draw tube of the microscope.

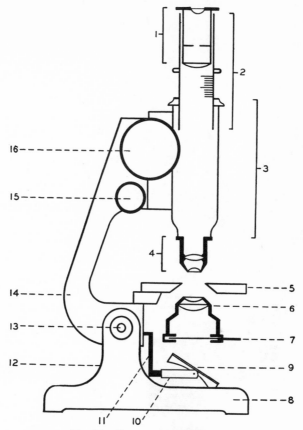

FIG. 2.1. PARTS OF THE MICROSCOPE

1. Ocular
2. Draw tube
3. Body tube
4. Objective
5. Stage
6. Substage condenser
7. Diaphragm
8. Base

9. Substage mirror
10. Mirror fork
11. Mirror arm
12. Pillar
13. Inclination pin
14. Arm
15. Fine adjustment knob
16. Course adjustment

The *coarse adjustment* knob serves to focus the microscope on the specimen by raising or lowering the lens system. In the less elaborate low-power instruments this may be the only focusing device provided, but in microscopes designed for higher magnification the final critical focusing is done by means of the *fine adjustment*.

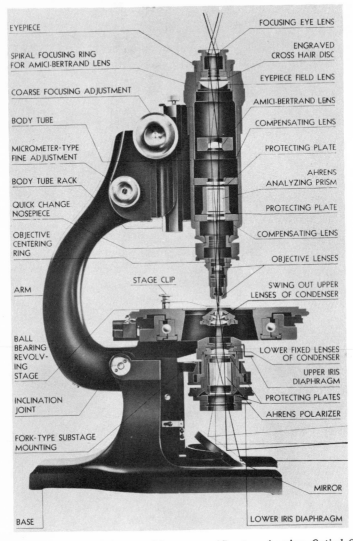

EYEPIECE

SPIRAL FOCUSING RING
FOR AMICI-BERTRAND LENS

COARSE FOCUSING ADJUSTMENT

BODY TUBE

MICROMETER-TYPE
FINE ADJUSTMENT

BODY TUBE RACK

QUICK CHANGE
NOSEPIECE

OBJECTIVE
CENTERING
RING

ARM

BALL
BEARING
REVOLV-
ING
STAGE

INCLINATION
JOINT

FORK-TYPE SUBSTAGE
MOUNTING

BASE

STAGE CLIP

FOCUSING EYE LENS

ENGRAVED
CROSS HAIR DISC

EYEPIECE FIELD LENS

AMICI-BERTRAND LENS

COMPENSATING LENS

PROTECTING PLATE

AHRENS
ANALYZING PRISM

PROTECTING PLATE

COMPENSATING LENS

OBJECTIVE LENSES

SWING OUT UPPER
LENSES OF CONDENSER

LOWER FIXED LENSES
OF CONDENSER

UPPER IRIS
DIAPHRAGM

PROTECTING PLATES

AHRENS POLARIZER

MIRROR

LOWER IRIS DIAPHRAGM

FIG. 2.2. PARTS OF A PETROGRAPHIC MICROSCOPE. (*Courtesy American Optical Co.*)

The plate on which the specimens are placed for observation is known as the *stage*, which may be rectangular or circular in form. Glass slides may be held firmly in place by means of the *spring clips*. The *substage mirror* serves to reflect light up toward the stage when one is observing transparent material. Although various appropriate light sources will be discussed later, for his first efforts the novice may confine himself to almost any readily available type of illumination. In daytime it may be sufficient to place the microscope on a table near a window. Direct sunlight should be avoided. Certain types of study lamps form very serviceable sources of artificial light for the less critical types of work. The lamp should be provided with a shade, so arranged that the eyes are protected from glare. A high-powered bulb is not recommended.

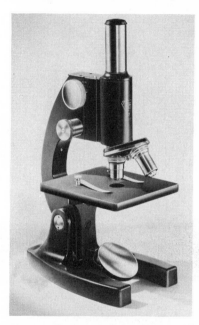

FIG. 2.3. BAUSCH & LOMB "MODEL A" MICROSCOPE. This type is adequate for some of the less exacting work. However, this instrument is not equipped with substage condenser. (*Courtesy Bausch & Lomb.*)

FIG. 2.4. BAUSCH & LOMB "MODEL A" MICROSCOPE WITH SUBSTAGE CONDENSER AND TRIPLE NOSEPIECE. (*Courtesy Bausch & Lomb.*)

At this point the student should actually start working with the microscope in order to become thoroughly acquainted with it. At all times it is necessary to keep in mind the fact that the microscope is a precision instrument which possesses a number of delicate parts. It is easily damaged, but with reasonable care will remain serviceable for decades.

Cleaning and setting up the instrument.—The first task will be to clean the instrument. The ocular is easily removed from the draw tube by merely lifting it out. Dust may be removed from the lens surfaces

by means of a small camel's-hair brush. If fingermarks or a greasy film
should be present, the surface can be cleaned with lens tissue (or Kleenex
tissue) moistened with a drop or two of xylol. The exposed surface of
an objective can be cleaned in the same manner. **Do not unscrew the
objectives,** unless it is with your instructor's permission. If you are
working independently and it seems necessary to remove any dust particles
which have lodged inside the lens mount, enlist the aid of someone with

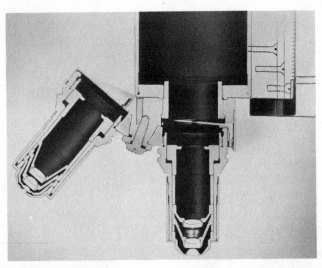

Fig. 2.5. Revolving Nosepiece. Cross-sectional view showing 97-× oil immersion
objective and 43-× dry objective. (*Courtesy Bausch & Lomb.*)

experience. Your local camera shop (not the drugstore camera clerk), an
optician, or a jeweler should be able to help.

If several oculars are available, choose one marked 5× or 6×. On
the older instruments the oculars may be marked 1, 2, or 3; in this case
select number 1. The nosepiece should be turned so that the objective
which is brought into position directly below the body tube bears the
notation "16 mm." If you are working with one of the older instruments
the corresponding objective may bear the notation "2/3." (Two-thirds
of an inch is the practical equivalent of 16 mm.)

If the microscope is provided with a draw tube, it should be drawn
out of the body tube until the 160-mm graduation just shows (Figure 2.6).
On certain older instruments (Zeiss) the draw tube should be extended to
the 170-mm mark.

When making observations through the microscope, both eyes should
be kept open. It will be found that working with the unused eye closed

eventually becomes very fatiguing. A very simple device can be used to overcome the tendency to squint (Figure 2.7). After working with this shield for a time, it can be dispensed with.

Whenever a specimen is to be observed microscopically, it is placed on a clean object glass (microscope slide) which is then laid on the stage so that the part to be examined is directly below the objective. By means of the coarse adjustment the objective is lowered to within a few millimeters of the specimen. Now, while peering into the ocular of the

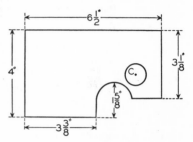

FIG 2.6. GRADUATED DRAW TUBE. (*Courtesy Bausch & Lomb.*)

FIG. 2.7. SHIELD. The shield is cut from a sheet of cardboard measuring 4 by 6½ inches. After the card has been cut to the outline shown in the diagram, it must be provided with a one-inch circular opening as shown at *C*. The center of the circle should be 1¼ inches to the left of the vertical edge and 1⅛ inches above the lower short edge. By removing the ocular the shield can be slipped over the draw tube. As shown here the shield permits the right eye to make observations through the microscope. By turning it over, the left eye may be used instead.

microscope, the concave surface of the substage mirror is adjusted to secure adequate illumination. For the present purpose, if the light which enters the lens system proves too intense, it may be dimmed by moving the light-source farther from the instrument. More detailed directions on the subject of illumination are to be discussed later.

Proper focusing procedure.—The coarse adjustment knob is next turned very slowly to raise the objective above the specimen until the latter is brought into sharp focus. The fine adjustment may be employed for the final critical focusing of different planes of the specimen. Generally, with a well-trained hand, it is not necessary to use the fine adjustment when working with a 16-mm objective. A very important habit to acquire is this—while looking into the microscope turn the coarse adjustment only in the direction which will raise the objective. Always focus **up.** If the objective has been raised so high that the specimen is no longer in focus, it should be lowered only while the worker is actually watching the objective and the stage. The statement just made bears repetition. When lowering an objective toward the stage, the observer should not be peering into the eyepiece. Instead he should carefully watch the objective and the stage. If the objective is lowered while one is peering into the eyepiece, there is a risk of actually ramming the lower lens against the specimen slide. Such an accident can be serious for several reasons.

1. The specimen may be ruined. This necessitates the preparation of a new specimen, which may be expensive or, in certain instances, even impossible.

2. Some of the specimen (if not covered) may adhere to the front element of the objective, in which case time will be lost in cleaning the latter.

3. If the specimen was immersed in an organic liquid, which is the case in certain crystal preparations, the liquid may attack the cement employed in making intimate contact between the various components of the objective lens. This may render the lens useless.

4. If the slide contains corrosive inorganic liquids on its surface, the metal lens mount may be attacked.

5. Some of the specimens examined may contain hard, gritty particles. If the objective is rammed down on such abrasive material, the front lens may be scratched.

If, inadvertently, the objective has been run against the slide the former should be cleaned with lens tissue **immediately.**

Having brought the specimen into focus, one should observe the effect of moving the slide. In what direction does the image move when the slide is made to travel from right to left, or to and from the observer? Notice, also, that unless the object under examination is very thin not all planes or levels are in equally sharp focus. Slight turning of the fine adjustment knob will bring other strata of the specimen into critical focus.

Eyepoint.—By the time the student has completed Experiment 1 (see Part II: Laboratory Manual), he should have become aware of the fact that the relative distance between the eye and the ocular is of some importance. A certain distance above the eyepiece there is a horizontal plane in which the rays from the optical system cross. The region where these rays cross is known as the *eyepoint,* or *Ramsden disc.* To receive light from all parts of the field the pupil of the eye should be placed at (or very close to) the eyepoint. The position of the latter is not the same for all lens combinations, although its distance above the ocular is of the same general magnitude for the eyepieces most commonly employed. There are available, however, special oculars which have an unusually high Ramsden disc or eyepoint. Their usefulness lies in the fact that when the observer's pupil is placed at the eyepoint there remains ample

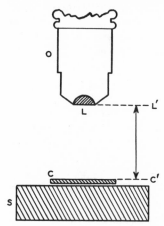

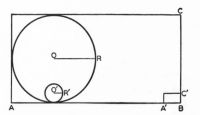

FIG. 2.8. WORKING DISTANCE. *L* represents the front element of the objective *O*. *S* is a slide bearing a specimen over which lies the cover glass *C*. When the specimen has been brought into proper focus, the distance between the top of the cover glass and the front lens of the objective, as represented by the arrow joining lines *C'* and *L'*, is the working distance of the objective. This assumes, of course, that the objective is one which has been corrected for cover-glass thickness.

FIG. 2.9. DEGREE OF MAGNIFICATION. In the large rectangle the side *A B* is ten times as long as the corresponding side *A' B* of the small rectangle. Likewise, *B C* is ten times the length of the side *B C'*. If the larger figure were the enlarged image of *A' B C'*, the degree of magnification would be ten diameters or, as commonly expressed, 10-×. If the small circle were magnified to yield the image represented by the larger circle, the magnification would be five diameters, or 5-×, because the image radius *O R* is five times as large as the object radius *O' R'*.

space for spectacles.   With the ordinary oculars it is rather awkward to make observations while wearing spectacles.   There is a constant risk of striking a lens of the latter against the draw tube of the microscope.

Working distance.—In working with objectives of different focal lengths it will be found that after a slide has been properly focused the distance from the latter to the front element of the objective is not always the same.   The distance is least for objectives having the shortest focal lengths.   In other words, for a 4-mm lens the *working distance*, that is, the height of the front element of the lens above the cover glass on a properly focused specimen, is less than the working distance of a 16-mm objective. This may not be so very important when working with lenses of low magnification or long focal distance, but the working distance *does* become a significant factor when one employs the higher powers.

The chemical microscopist frequently must work with specimens containing liquids. If these give off corrosive fumes the latter may eventually exert a damaging effect on an objective which has too short a working distance. This is particularly true if one must regularly deal with hot liquids or with reacting mixtures which evolve gases. Inadequate working distance makes it rather awkward, sometimes impossible, to proceed with certain manipulations of the specimen while it is in focus. When it is necessary to resort to objectives of higher magnifications, there may be insufficient space for a cover glass with certain types of material. In chemical microscopy, however, most work does not require an objective having a focal length shorter than 4 mm; hence there is usually ample space for a cover glass when one is required.

Degree of magnification.—Quite commonly the tendency of the novice is to strive for the greatest degree of magnification possible with the equipment at his disposal. For a number of reasons this is not a sound practice to follow. While it is preferable to postpone the discussion on magnification, for the present purpose the following table of approximate values may be used. It should be understood that whenever the magnification is expressed as, let us say, 10-×, it means ten diameters (Figure 2.9). If an object has been magnified ten diameters, the image formed is ten times as long and ten times as wide as the original.

Ocular	Objective	Magnification (diameters)
5-×	16-mm	50
6-×	16-mm	60
10-×	16-mm	100
5-×	8-mm	105
10-×	8-mm	210
5-×	4-mm	215

Ordinarily the best practice is to resort to the least magnification which enables the microscopist to discern adequately the features presented by the specimen under investigation. With higher powers the field of view is decreased, the working distance becomes less, and the depth of focus is greatly diminished. Other disadvantages will become apparent after the student actually tries out the lenses of higher magnification.

Diameter of field; field of view.—It will not require a great deal of experience for the student of microscopy to discover that the area of a specimen revealed by different objectives varies. For example, if a given

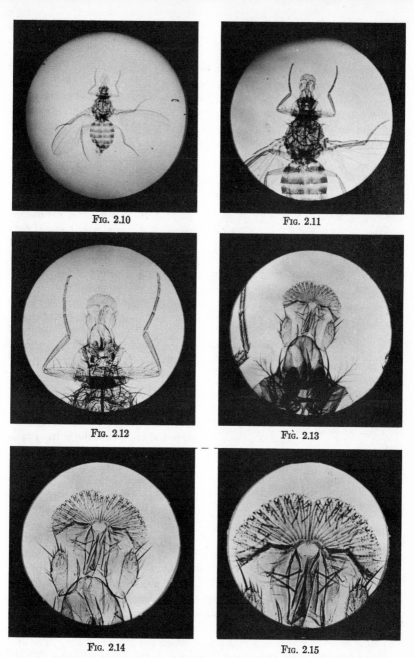

Fig. 2.10

Fig. 2.11

Fig. 2.12

Fig. 2.13

Fig. 2.14

Fig. 2.15

Fig. 2.10 to 2.15. Drosophila Collaris, or Vinegar fly (female). Views of mounted specimen as seen through the microscope at different magnifications. (*Courtesy American Optical Co.*) These photomicrographs show the advantages of different magnifications. While the lower magnifications show a greater portion of the specimen, the higher magnifications reveal greater detail. The microscopist must select the magnifications which best serve the requirements of the specific problems under consideration. The magnifications here represented are 3.2-×, 6-×, 12-×, 22.5-×, 36-×, and 54-×.

specimen were to be viewed first through a 16-mm objective, and then through an 8-mm objective, the latter would be found to reveal a smaller portion of the specimen, although the degree of magnification in the latter case would be approximately doubled. The area which can be brought within the focus of an objective is known as the field, ordinarily measured as the "diameter of field" of that objective. In general, the diameter of field becomes less as the focal length of the objective is decreased or as the degree of magnification is increased. To express it another way, a 10-× objective, of 16-mm equivalent focus, would reveal features lying outside the area constituting the field of a 20-× objective of 8-mm equivalent focus.

It should be noted, however, that the diameter of field of a given objective is not necessarily identical with the diameter of the area actually seen by the observer. The latter area, which may be called "the field of view," is modified by the eyepiece used with the objective.

FIG. 2.16. DEPTH OF FOCUS. Although the glass bowl and the tall blossom in the center are in sharp focus, some blossoms which are closer to the camera are blurred or out of focus. The background design is likewise out of focus. Depth of focus refers to the *depth* of the region within which all objects appear in sharp focus. In this instance it equals approximately 9 inches, or the distance from the front of the flower bowl to the rear. Objects closer than this, or farther away, appear blurred or out of focus. A similar phenomenon applies to objects viewed through the microscope, only here the depth of focus is very much smaller.

Depth of focus.—Another important feature in which various types of objectives differ from each other is depth of focus. When the microscope is focused on a specimen, it may be observed that, although certain portions of the material may be in reasonably sharp focus, those which lie above or below a certain restricted region appear blurred.

Critical focus is not confined to features lying in one single plane devoid of depth. Rather, at a certain minimum distance from the lens, there is a plane within which the eye sees all features in sharp focus; for a short distance beyond this plane objects continue in focus. However, there is a certain maximum distance beyond which objects are no longer in sharp focus. In other words, in front of the objective there are two parallel planes between which lie all the points which are in sharp focus. The distance between these two planes is known as the *depth of focus* (Figure 2.16). The depth of focus of a high-power objective is extremely small, whereas that of a low-power objective may be relatively large. In the case of two objectives which have the same focal lengths but different numerical apertures (see page 29), the depth of focus is less for the lens having the higher numerical aperture.

Study Problems

1. From memory, draw a rough sketch of a microscope and label the various parts.

2. Explain the meaning of (a) working distance; (b) eyepoint.

3. State the purpose of an ocular.

4. Can magnified images be observed by employing the objective without an ocular?

5. What is meant by the term *focusing down?*   State why it is generally inadvisable to focus down while peering into the microscope.

6. A certain microscope is equipped with objectives having the following respective focal lengths: 32 mm, 16 mm, and 8 mm.   How could you distinguish the three unmarked objectives from each other merely by external appearance?

7. Which of the above objectives would one expect to have the greatest working distance?

8. State how magnification of objectives generally varies with focal length.

9. A crystal seen under the microscope measured 1.2 mm in length and 0.2 mm in width.   In a photomicrograph of this specimen the image of the crystal measured 78 mm in length.   Calculate the degree of magnification in terms of diameters. Calculate the width of the enlarged image.

Chapter III

PROPERTIES OF OBJECTIVES AND OCULARS

If one is to attain a reasonable degree of proficiency in microscopy and to take full advantage of all its inherent possibilities, it will be necessary to give additional attention to the optics of the instrument. Since there are certain definite limitations to the possible performance of a microscope, it is important to know the nature of some of these limitations, instead of endeavoring to achieve the unattainable through a blind groping in the dark.

Variations in working distance.—It has previously been stated (Chapter II) that for an objective of high magnification the working distance is shorter than for a low-power lens. This, of course, could be anticipated from a general knowledge of simple lenses. It should not be assumed, however, that the distance from the lens to the object on which it is focused will necessarily be equal to the focal length of the objective. Since we are not concerned here with a rather thin simple lens, but rather with a highly corrective objective which consists of a number of individual components, the center from which the focal length is measured lies some distance above the front element. Thus a 16-mm objective supplied by one of the well-known optical companies is in focus when the front element is only 5.5 mm above the object, while a certain 8-mm objective is in focus at a distance of 2 mm. An objective having an equivalent focus of 4 mm may be in focus when less than a millimeter separates the front element from the specimen. Ordinarily objectives are corrected for use with cover glasses. For such objectives the working distance refers to the distance between cover glass and the front component of the objective when the latter has been properly focused. Certain objectives are intended for use without cover glasses, in which case the working distance refers to the distance between the front lens component and the object on which it is focused. Metallographic microscopes employ objectives of this type.

Parfocal objectives.—A great convenience on the modern microscope is the parfocalization of its objectives. This applies especially to instruments which have their most frequently used objectives mounted in a double-, triple-, or quadruple nosepiece. If one has focused a specimen under the 16-mm objective and then has occasion to employ a higher power, such as the 4-mm objective, it is a very simple matter to obtain the new focus. Generally the mounts of objectives in a given series are so adjusted that, when one of them has been focused, each of the others will be very nearly in correct focus when it is brought into position by revolving the nosepiece. Critical focus is then obtained by a slight turn of the fine adjustment screw. Objectives which have been designed thus are referred to as *parfocal* objectives. In certain kinds of work this is more than a mere convenience; it may prove very important because there are occasions when the time consumed in refocusing another objective could result in the loss of the specimen sought.

Although the revolving nosepiece is so commonly found on modern microscopes, it should not be thought that all good instruments are thus equipped. Some microscopists prefer what are known as bayonet mounts and sliding objective changers. These may prove more adequate for high precision work where the most accurate centering of objectives is essential.

Importance of numerical aperture; image brilliance; resolving power.—On modern objectives the manufacturers engrave not only the magnification and the equivalent focus but also the numerical aperture. Unfortunately, to many laboratory workers who merely "pick up" their knowledge of the instrument the N.A. (designation for numerical aperture) imparts no information whatever. In the words of Belling, however, numerical aperture "is the most important figure connected with the microscope." This statement is particularly true for the higher magnifications.

At an early date it was seen that the brilliance of the image formed by an objective depends upon the light-gathering ability of the latter. The bundle of rays of light proceeding from a specimen to the objective under which it is focused may be considered as being confined within a cone. For any given objective the angle subtended by this cone is known as the angular aperture. During part of the 19th century this expression was considered a significant index of the quality of a lens. Abbe, however, arrived at a more practical system of expressing this light-gathering property. He introduced what is known as numerical aperture. This figure became especially important with the development of better condensers and immersion objectives.

The N.A. is defined as the number obtained by multiplying the sine of one-half the angular aperture of the lens by the refractive index of the medium through which the light travels to reach the objective. Since most of the work of the chemist does not involve high-power microscopy, the medium between specimen and objective will be air, the refractive index of which is practically equal to 1. For such objectives (dry objectives) the N.A. will be equal to the sine of one-half the angular aperture. In view of the fact that half the angular aperture can never quite approach 90 degrees, the N.A. of a dry objective is always less than 1.00, which is the sine of an angle of 90 degrees. For some of the 3-mm or 4-mm objectives the N.A. is about 0.95, which corresponds to an angular aperture of approximately 143 degrees. A 32-mm objective, on the other hand, might have a N.A. of 0.10, indicating an angular aperture of 11½ degrees.

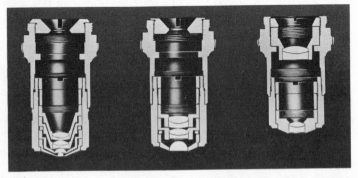

Fig. 3.1. Sectional View Showing Construction of Spencer Objectives. Focal lengths, reading from left to right, are 1.8 mm, 4 mm, and 16 mm. (*Courtesy American Optical Co.*)

A high N.A. signifies a high angular aperture. Obviously, the greater the numerical aperture of an objective, other factors remaining unchanged, the greater will be the light-gathering properties. The intensity of the light passed by objectives which are similar in other respects varies as the squares of their numerical apertures. In order to acquaint himself further with the full significance of this specific property of numerical aperture, the serious worker or student should compare various objectives by actually working out their relative image brilliance.

By way of illustration, let us compare two 8-mm objectives whose respective numerical apertures are 0.50 and 0.65. If the two lenses are identical in all other respects, is this difference in N.A. of any great importance? It was stated previously that the light-collecting powers of otherwise similar lenses varied as the squares of their numerical apertures. The ratio in this case should be

$$\frac{(0.65)^2}{(0.50)^2} = \frac{0.4225}{0.2500} = 1.69.$$

Accordingly, the objective of N.A. = 0.65 will pass 1.69 times as much light as its companion with N.A. = 0.50. This is nearly 70 per cent more light.

To compare the two in another way, it can be shown that the objective with the smaller aperture passes barely 60 per cent as much light as the other one. This difference could be very important when working with deeply colored or thick specimens, when requiring special light filters, or when taking photomicrographs.

Does the foregoing mean that an objective which has a N.A. of only 0.25 or 0.10 must be an inferior piece of equipment? The answer depends upon other factors. In the case of a 32-mm objective giving a magnification of 5 diameters, a N.A. of 0.10 should prove quite adequate, whereas a very serviceable 16-mm objective may have a N.A. of 0.25. Other conditions being the same, the brilliance of the image formed varies inversely with the square of the magnification. A 16-mm objective magnifies about 10 diameters, whereas an 8-mm objective gives a magnification of about 20 diameters. If the two lenses were similar in all other respects, the image formed by the 8-mm objective would be only about one-fourth as bright as the image formed by the other objective; this follows from the fact that the one with the shorter focal length gives twice the magnification given by the other lens. If the 16-mm objective yields an image of sufficient brilliance, then under similar conditions the 8-mm objective might produce an image which would be too dark.

This condition can be avoided. One of the 8-mm objectives on the market has a N.A. of 0.50. The 16-mm objective, it was assumed, has a N.A. of 0.25. Recall that earlier it was shown that image brilliance varies with the square of the N.A. Dividing the square of one N.A. by the other, we obtain

$$\frac{(0.50)^2}{(0.25)^2} = \frac{0.2500}{0.0625} = 4.$$

Hence, while doubling the magnification reduces the brilliance of image to one-fourth the original value, changing the N.A. from 0.25 to 0.50 increases the intensity of the illumination four times. Therefore it follows that under similar conditions an 8-mm objective of N.A. = 0.50 yields an image of the same brilliance as that formed by the 16-mm objective of N.A. = 0.25. Because more light is required to obtain brilliant images as the degree of magnification is raised, the various optical manufactures provide proportionately higher numerical apertures in their higher-power lenses.

Another property which varies with numerical aperture is degree of resolution, or resolving power. Resolving power is the capacity for distinguishing between points or lines which lie very close together. What would appear as a chain of minute spheres when observed through a good objective of high resolving power, might be imaged merely as a fuzzy line by a lens of the same magnifying power but inferior resolving power. Soon after the introduction of achromatic objectives it was noted that, other factors being the same, the lenses of large angular aperture had the highest resolving power. Later it was shown that resolution varies with N.A.

One may well raise the question, "What distance must separate two lines or points in order that they can be distinguished as two different structures?" For a properly corrected lens, the answer can be determined from the equation

$$D = \frac{\lambda}{2 \text{ N.A.}},$$

where D represents the distance between adjacent points, and λ is the wave length of the light employed. This equation assumes, of course, an adequate light source, which will be discussed later. Assuming proper lighting conditions have been provided, using green light having an average wave length of 5200 Angstrom units (or 5.2×10^{-4} mm), we shall determine the resolution that is possible with an 8-mm objective of N.A. = 0.50. Substituting in the foregoing equation, we find that

$$D = \frac{0.00052}{2 \times 0.50} = 0.00052 \text{ mm, or } 0.52 \text{ micron.}$$

(This value is equivalent to about 1/50,000 inch.) If the distance between two adjacent lines or points should be less than this distance, they would not be resolved into two separate structures. With an 8-mm objective of N.A. = 0.65, using the same light, under favorable conditions, D would equal 0.40 micron instead of 0.52. This lens could yield distinct images of certain delicate features which would not be resolved by the lower N.A., in spite of the fact that both objectives give the same degree of initial magnification. From this it may be concluded that mere magnification, without adequate resolution, does not determine a good objective.

Numerical aperture is of greater significance than magnification. The simple lenses of Leeuwenhoek (1632–1723) gave an initial magnification of close to one hundred diameters, which would correspond to modern objectives of 1.5-mm to 2-mm equivalent focus. However, according to Rooseboom the N.A. of these early lenses was not in excess of 0.15. The resolution obtainable by Leeuwenhoek therefore was no better than that of a good modern 28- to 32-mm objective giving magnification of approximately 5 diameters. In fact, the N.A. of an objective actually determines the maximum limit of its useful magnification. Although the method of derivation need not be discussed here, it is generally conceded that the maximum useful magnification is about 1000 × N.A. (Cf. Beck, *The Microscope*.) Using an ocular which yields a greater magnification may form a larger image, but the actual detail will not be increased. The greater magnification may be justified at times because it may render less fatiguing the observation of very fine structures over a long-continued period.

According to the resolution equation given above it would appear that finer structures could be resolved by a lens if the illumination consisted of shorter wave lengths. Quite early it was believed, therefore, that ultraviolet illumination would afford greater resolution. On the basis of theoretical considerations this was a valid deduction, but the application of the principle was hampered by certain difficulties. Since ordinary optical glass does not transmit ultraviolet radiation efficiently, a quartz optical system was required, and quartz objectives necessarily are quite expensive. A given objective, furthermore, could be used only within a relatively narrow band of ultraviolet. As the ultraviolet lies beyond the visible portion of the spectrum images would have to be recorded photographically (unless they could be observed by means of a special fluorescent screen).

Quartz objectives were made available early in the present century, but, in general, ultraviolet microscopy did not prove very satisfactory. More recently the subject has been attacked from a different angle, namely, by the use of *reflecting* objectives instead of the usual *refracting* systems. Even so, the equipment for ultraviolet microscopy remains quite expensive, and its usefulness is somewhat restricted.

To date, this tool has been applied chiefly in the field of biology, and even here its importance has not been associated primarily with increased resolution. Ultraviolet has been able to reveal certain cell structures not observed in visible light because they exhibit preferential absorption for various wave lengths in the ultraviolet region.

Corrections for chromatic aberration.—At this point it may be well to recall the fact that lenses vary in their corrections for chromatic aberration (see p. 12). Achromatic objectives are only partially corrected for color. For wave lengths approaching the extremes of the spectrum the correction is less complete than for the intervening colors. These deficiencies become especially apparent when using the higher-power oculars.

For the best rendition of color it is necessary to resort to the use of apochromatic lenses. Under favorable conditions these lenses give admirable results even when employed in combination with compensating oculars of 20- or 30-diameter magnification. The color correction extends fairly uniformly over the whole of the visible spectrum. Naturally, apochromats are much more expensive than are the achromats.

Where utmost precision is not essential it is possible to employ objectives in which correction for chromatic aberration falls about midway

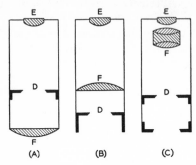

Fig. 3.2. Common Types of Oculars, in Cross Section

A. Huygenian eyepiece (Negative). B. Ramsden eyepiece (Positive). C. Compensating eyepiece. Also known as compensation eyepiece, or as compensator. In each of these schematic diagrams E represents the eyelens; D indicates both the diaphragm of the ocular, and also the image plane of the objective; F is the field lens. Observe that in the compensating ocular, the field lens D is a corrected combination of three elements.

between the correction in achromats and that in the apochromats. These are the semi-apochromatic, or fluorite, objectives. (Fluorite is crystalline calcium fluoride.) These lenses cost somewhat less than apochromats.

Fig. 3.3. Four Types of Eyepieces. Reading left to right, these are Huygenian, Wide Field, Ramsden, and Compensating. (*Courtesy American Optical Co.*)

Different types of eyepieces.—Although it is true that a magnified image is formed by the objective when used alone, the versatility and general usefulness of the microscope are greatly enhanced by the addition of an ocular or eyepiece. Primarily the function of the ocular is to magnify further the image formed by the objective. As imaged by an objective alone, certain fine structures may not appear as distinct features to the human eye. As will become apparent, however, the ocular serves other purposes.

The most common type of ocular, as well as the least expensive, is the Huygens or Huygenian eyepiece. These oculars are primarily intended for use with achromatic objectives. Their magnifying power may be from 5 to 15 diameters. Examination of such an eyepiece will reveal that the essential parts with which the tube is equipped are two

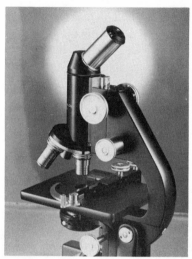

Fig. 3.4. Inclined Monocular Eyepiece. (*Courtesy Bausch & Lomb.*)

plano-convex lenses placed on either side of a circular diaphragm (Figure 3.2A). It should be observed that the convex side of each lens faces down. The field of view is restricted by the size of the circular opening in the diaphragm. The position of the latter is approximately at the focus of the eyelens. It is also in the plane of the image formed by the objective.

Although both the eyelens and the field lens of the Huygenian ocular are simple, uncorrected lenses, the aberrations of one are partly offset by imperfections in the other, so that taken as a unit, the ocular is sufficiently corrected for most medium-power work. Cross hairs, ocular micrometers, and special scales, when used in a Huygenian eyepiece, are placed on the diaphragm. In special micrometer oculars the eyelens is placed in a focusing mount so that the micrometer scale can be brought into sharp focus for any observer's eye.

A very appropriate type of ocular for use with micrometer scales is the Ramsden eyepiece (Figure 3.2B). This is a positive combination; that is, it can be employed as a simple magnifier. Its two plane-convex lenses are placed with the convex surfaces facing each other. The ocular diaphragm, which lies in the plane of the real image formed by the objective, is placed below both lenses of this eyepiece. If an ocular micrometer is placed on the diaphragm, any imperfections in the performance of

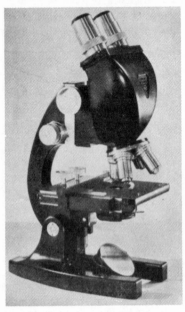

FIG. 3.5. INCLINED BINOCULAR EYEPIECE. (*Courtesy Bausch & Lomb.*) Since the image-forming rays pass through only one objective this instrument does not give the true stereoscopic effect obtained with a stereoscopic microscope; i.e., one which employs two paired objectives.

the eyepiece will affect the micrometer scale and the objective image equally.

To obtain satisfactory results when employing an apochromatic objective the microscope should be equipped with a compensating eyepiece (Figure 3.2C). With aprochromats the magnification is not the same for all wave lengths, so that when used with ordinary eyepieces color fringes result. Compensating oculars are over corrected,[1] so that the final image seen by the observer appears well corrected. Although intended primarily for use with apochromats, compensating eyepieces yield good results with

[1] See page 14. Chapter 1.

fluorite objectives and with achromats of high magnification. However, they should not be employed with the lower-power achromatic objectives. The magnification of compensators as catalogued by the various optical companies commonly ranges from 5 to 25 diameters.

The image plane obtained by combining a compensating eyepiece with an apochromatic objective may not be very flat. Special "flat field" oculars have been designed to overcome the difficulty. Color compensation, however, lies about midway between the Huygenian ocular and the

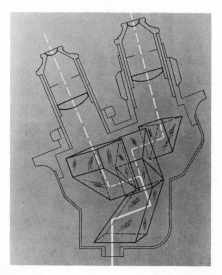

Fig. 3.6 Path of Light Through Inclined Binocular Body. Observe the number of special prisms required. (*Courtesy American Optical Co.*)

compensating type. Flat field eyepieces are especially useful in projecting images for photomicrography. In cost they are comparable with compensating eyepieces. Their field is somewhat larger than in a corresponding Huygenian ocular. Flat field oculars work very well in combination with high-power achromatic and fluorite objectives.

The cover glass as part of the optical system.—A very real part of the optical system which is frequently ignored, is the cover glass. Although it is true that in many instances its effect is negligible, this does not justify the microscopist in discounting completely the importance of the cover glass. An indication of its significance may be inferred by considering light rays which are traveling from a small point directly beneath the cover. An oblique ray will travel through the glass, along a certain path, until it reaches the surface. When the ray emerges into the air its direction changes because of refraction. Aberrations result as shown in Figure 3.8.

If objectives were fully corrected, the use of cover glasses would result in spherical aberration. Ordinarily the objectives are slightly under-

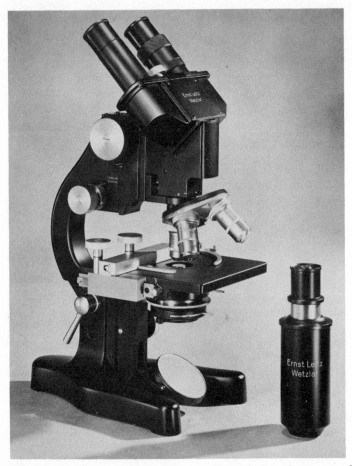

FIG. 3.7. INCLINED BINOCULAR MICROSCOPE WITH GRADUATED FINE ADJUSTMENT, MECHANICAL STAGE, SUBSTAGE CONDENSER, ETC. The monocular tube at lower right is readily inserted in place of the binocular unit. (*Courtesy E. Leitz.*)

corrected, thus yielding proper definition when used in combination with cover glasses. As a result, however, such an objective, when employed without a cover glass, forms an image which suffers from loss in definition.

Not just *any* cover glass will serve the intended purpose; it must be of the proper thickness.   Generally the cover glass correction on an objective is for a thickness of 0.17 or 0.18 mm, depending upon the manufacturer.   Optical companies claim that the use of a cover slip which varies from this thickness by so much as 0.03 or 0.04 mm will appreciably impair the image quality.   Concerning an achromatic fluorite objective, having an equivalent focus of 4.4 mm and a N.A. of 0.85, Zeiss claims that cover thickness must not vary over 0.01 mm from the 0.17-mm correction.   On the other hand, for their 4.4-mm achromatic objective of N.A. = 0.65 this firm claims that image quality is "not appreciably affected by variations in cover glass thickness within the usual limits."

Belling feels that with dry objectives the consistent use of 0.15- or 0.16-mm cover glasses will produce the best results. Naturally the most serious effects resulting from the failure to use a cover glass with dry objectives will be experienced with the higher powers.   In chemical studies there are occasions when the use of a cover glass would be awkward, to say the least.   In such cases even so high a power as the 8-mm objective may prove quite useful, although workers in certain fields insist that a cover glass must be employed with any objective having a focal length of 16-mm or less.

If one plans to restrict his work in microscopy to some field in which the very nature of the specimens renders cover glasses unnecessary, it is possible to procure objectives which are not corrected for cover glass thickness.   In metallography, for example, short mount objectives are constantly employed without covers.

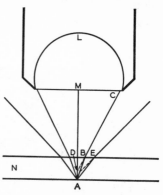

FIG. 3.8. ABERRATION CAUSED BY COVER GLASS. Front lens of high power objective is represented by *LM,* and the cover glass by *N.* The specimen is at *A,* touching the lower surface of the cover glass. After traveling through the cover glass, the ray *AB,* upon emerging into the air, is bent from its original course to follow the path *BC.* As viewed from above (i.e., through the microscope) the ray would appear to come from point *B.* Similarly other diffracted rays would appear to originate from various loci within the cover glass, rather than from the object at *A.* The only exception is the ray *AM,* which is perpendicular to the plane of the cover-glass surface. It naturally follows that an objective which has been corrected for use with a cover glass will not yield the best image if the cover is omitted.

An unfortunate situation in connection with cover glasses is the fact that they are marketed in three degrees of thickness.   Size 1 may vary from 0.15 to 0.17 mm; number 2 covers may range from 0.17 to 0.25, while size 3 includes glasses up to 0.50 mm.   The thickness generally desired with high-power objectives is really a borderline size. Fortunately, in chemical microscopy size 1 is generally adequate. When the work demands a high degree of precision, it is necessary to select the proper thickness by actually measuring the glasses. Various types of cover glass gauges are on the market, but where there is only an occasional need,

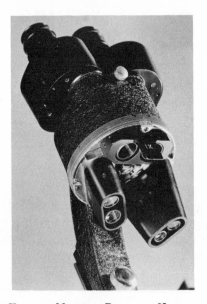

Fig. 3.9. Close-up View of Multiple Revolving Nosepiece of a Stereoscopic Microscope. Note that the objectives are used in pairs; hence the observer sees two images of the specimen just as in normal vision of large objects. This produces the "stereoscopic" effect, which is not really obtained with binocular microscopes using a single objective. The stereoscopic microscope is employed for the examination of objects which do not require a high degree of magnification, such as mineral specimens, metal castings, insects, food samples, etc. (*Courtesy American Optical Co.*)

they can be measured as directed in Experiment 14C (see Part II: Laboratory Manual).

Part of the cover-glass problem can be avoided by using objectives provided with correction collars. These lenses can be adjusted to accommodate cover slips of different sizes. For those who must constantly employ high-power objectives the additional cost of such correction collars may be a very sound investment. Generally, however, such precision is not called for in chemical work. To some extent it is possible to make allowance for incorrect cover-glass thickness by adjusting the height of the drawtube of the microscope. Shortening the tube length will in-

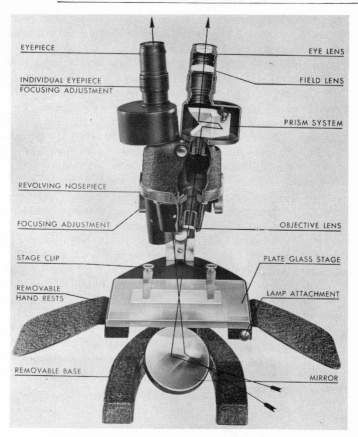

EYEPIECE

EYE LENS

INDIVIDUAL EYEPIECE
FOCUSING ADJUSTMENT

FIELD LENS

PRISM SYSTEM

REVOLVING NOSEPIECE

FOCUSING ADJUSTMENT

OBJECTIVE LENS

STAGE CLIP

PLATE GLASS STAGE

REMOVABLE
HAND RESTS

LAMP ATTACHMENT

REMOVABLE BASE

MIRROR

Fig. 3.10. Path of Light Through a Stereoscopic Microscope. (*Courtesy American Optical Co.*)

troduce the undercorrection required to make up for abnormal thickness of a cover glass.

Immersion objectives.—Since the N.A. of a dry objective must always be somewhat less than one, the degree of resolution (using green light, as in the previous discussion) would appear limited to lines or dots which are at least 0.26 micron apart. According to the resolution equation,

$$D = \frac{\lambda}{2 \text{ N.A.}},$$

it would be possible to go beyond this limit if there were some means of constructing objectives of higher N.A. For the purpose of high-power microscopy this is achieved in the immersion objectives. Their principle will be taken up rather briefly because these objectives are not required in ordinary chemical work.

Lenses which give very high magnifications have extremely short working distances. A 3-mm objective, giving a magnification of about 60 diameters, may have a working distance of 0.15 or 0.20 mm. This is of the same order of magnitude as the thickness of a cover glass. For the 90-× and 120-× objectives the working distance is even less. It is so small, in fact, that a drop of liquid, such as water, glycerine, or certain oils, could fill the space between the cover glass and the front lens of the objective. If the liquid should have a refractive index equal to that of the cover glass, then a ray of light from the specimen could reach the objective by traveling in a straight line, instead of being bent from its original path upon emerging from the cover glass. Reference to Figure 3.8 will explain how a lens employed in this manner could have a numerical aperture greater than one. Objectives designed for such use are termed *immersion* objectives. Many of the immersion lenses are intended for use with cedarwood-oil, which has a refractive index nearly equal to that of glass. Among these oil immersion objectives a N.A. of 1.25 to 1.40 is not uncommon. They are especially useful in the fields of bacteriology and histology. Immersion objectives, it should be noted, *do not* give satisfactory results if used dry or if used with the wrong immersion fluid.

Theoretically, slight variations in cover-glass thickness should have no appreciable effect on the performance of an oil immersion lens; but Belling claims that, even here, best results are obtained by consistently adhering to a specific thickness, namely, 0.17 mm.

Study Problems

1. Explain why the working distance of an objective is less than its equivalent focus.

2. Is your microscope provided with parfocal objectives? On what do you base your decision?

3. The following notations were found engraved on an objective mount.

$$8 \text{ m/m} \quad 0.50$$
$$21\text{-}\times$$

Explain what information is conveyed.

4. Would a substage mirror, without condenser, furnish adequate illumination for maximum performance of the objective described under the above problem? Defend your answer.

5. On a microscope equipped with apochromatic objectives the 16-mm lens with a magnification of 10-× had an N.A. = 0.30. The 8-mm objective with 21-× magnifying power had an N.A. = 0.65. Assume that the intensity of the light source remains the same, but an appropriate condenser cone is employed with each objective. Which of the two yields the brighter image?

6. The ridges on a certain diatom specimen are 6×10^{-6} mm apart. Calculate the minimum N.A. required in an objective capable of resolving these lines. Assume that the illumination is by green light of average $\lambda = 5200$ A. (An Angstrom unit is equivalent to 10^{-7} mm.)

7. On your own microscope, what is the rated initial magnification of the lowest objective which can resolve the features of the specimen described in Problem 6?

8. In a certain manufacturer's catalog three 4-mm dry objectives are said to meet the following specifications.

Objective	Type	N.A.	Magnification	Working Distance (mm)
(a)	achromat	0.65	43-×	0.55
(b)	achromat	0.85	43-×	0.30
(c)	apochromat	0.95	43-×	0.20

Tabulate the advantages each objective has over the other two.

9. Compensating oculars are more expensive than the usual type. Explain any disadvantage which would arise in using such oculars with all of the objectives on your microscope.

10. It has been suggested that a microscope having three different objectives should be equipped with one ocular of appropriate power, in order to avoid the inconvenience of changing from one eyepiece to another. Assume that your instrument were equipped with 32-mm and 8-mm achromatic, and a 4-mm apochromatic objectives. Their respective N.A. ratings are 0.10, 0.50, and 0.95. Make a list of serious objections to the use of only one eyepiece with this microscope.

11. Assume that the foregoing microscope were available with your choice of any two oculars. To get the utmost out of your instrument, which oculars would you select, assuming that the cost is immaterial? Give ample reasons to justify your decision.

12. Suppose that you were permitted to have only two oculars on a microscope provided with 32-mm, 16-mm, and 8-mm objectives. What kind would you select as the most useful? State reasons for your decision.

13. A research worker was interested in obtaining colored photomicrographs (Kodachrome) of specimens requiring an 8-mm objective in combination with a 15-× ocular. Describe in detail the type of objective and ocular you would recommend, giving ample reasons for your selection.

14. In a research project which required a magnification of approximately 300 diameters it was decided to employ a 15-× ocular in combination with a 21-×, 8-mm objective of N.A. = 0.50. What reasons would there be against the choice of a 30-× ocular with a 10-×, 16-mm objective of N.A. = 0.25? (The latter would cost less.)

15. The special cover glasses furnished for use with various counting cells (for blood, etc.) may measure 0.40 or 0.50 mm in thickness. Why are such cover glasses not recommended for more general use? Prepare a diagram to illustrate the nature of the error resulting from the use of such covers.

Chapter IV

ILLUMINATION: EQUIPMENT AND PRINCIPLES

A. CONDENSERS AND LIGHT SOURCES

For much of the work encountered in chemical microscopy the substage mirror of the microscope may serve as an adequate means for directing the necessary light to the specimen. For certain purposes, however, a more efficient device must be provided. This problem is usually solved by employing special substage lenses or condensers. The simplest, and most common, is the ordinary Abbe condenser (Figure 4.1). Essentially

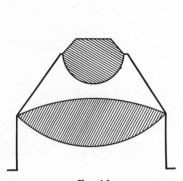

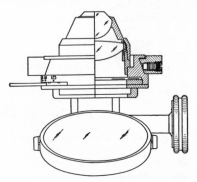

FIG. 4.1

FIG. 4.2. SIMPLE SUBSTAGE, SHOWING MIRROR AND N.A. 1.25 CONDENSER, PARTLY IN CROSS SECTION. (*Courtesy American Optical Co.*)

this consists of two lenses in a suitable metal mount, beneath which there is an iris diaphragm. The size of the diaphragm opening can be varied to suit the requirements of the occasion. The N.A. of this type of condenser is practically equal to one, so that it should be suitable for all dry objectives.

Because of the spherical aberration inherent in the Abbe condenser, where a high degree of resolution is desired an *aplanatic* should be employed. This type differs from the Abbe in being constructed of several corrected lens combinations. For anyone who plans to do very much work requiring a high degree of resolution the additional cost of such a corrected condenser is a good investment. Generally two or three different focal lengths are possible with these condensers because one or two of the lens combinations can be removed. For use with oil immersion objectives (not generally required for chemical work) it will be necessary to have a condenser of high N.A. value.

Concerning the question of a light source, it might be said that, in spite of the attitude taken by some extremists, much work continues to

Fig. 4.3. Substage Condensers. (*Courtesy Bausch & Lomb.*)

A	B	C
1.25 N.A.	1.40 N.A.	1.40 N.A.
Abbe	Abbe	Achromat
Condenser	Condenser	

be performed with a light source no more modern than daylight. Since, however, the latter is not always available when and where required, even the earliest microscopists attempted to adapt artificial illumination to their purpose. Even the lowly candle had its day. Various types of oil lamps followed. In England, it seems, the kerosene lamp continued in favor until rather recently, although some workers preferred a gas light with an inverted mantle. Where the current is available, electric lighting is, of course, the most convenient.

Supply houses offer quite a variety of lamps which are intended for use with the microscope. The ideal lamp for the purpose should be provided with an arrangement for regulating the diameter of the aperture through which the light issues. There should be some provision for controlling the luminosity, as well as a device for accommodating colored light filters.

The first of these requirements can be met by means of an iris diaphragm. Preferably, the rim along which the control knob moves should bear numbers so that certain desired apertures can be duplicated readily. A simpler device, and less expensive, is a rotating disc provided with a graduated series of circular openings. The substage diaphragms on some of the older microscopes are of this latter type (Figure 4.6).

FIG. 4.4. SPHERICAL MICROSCOPE LAMP. (*Courtesy Bausch & Lomb.*) Note that this lamp is equipped with iris diaphragm and has provision for accommodating glass light filters.

FIG. 4.5. This versatile lamp is equipped with an aspheric condenser, filter slot, iris diaphragm, 6.5 volt bulb which can be focused in a range from 6 inches to infinity, and a transformer for operating on a 110 volt A.C. line. Suitable for Koehler or critical illumination. (*Clay-Adams Co., New York.*)

The two other requirements can be taken care of by providing an appropriate holder in which one can place small squares (or discs) of glass. In order to increase the light intensity a neutral tint filter is placed in the holder. Such filters are supplied by the Eastman Kodak Co. Ground glass or opal glass will likewise decrease the luminosity, although this method is unsuited to some work. Photographic film which has been just slightly exposed before developing may serve quite effectively. By combining several sheets of such light gray film a range of any desired number of degrees of light intensity can be secured. The color of the light can be varied by inserting Wratten light filters in this same holder.

A very common type of lamp sold for use with the microscope is simply a small rectangular metal box provided with a 10- or 15-watt clear glass bulb and a small polished metal reflector. The light issues from a small circular opening which is screened by a thick plate of white or blue ground glass. The lamp-house is sufficiently small to permit its being placed directly beneath the stage of the microscope if the sub-stage mirror is swung aside or removed. More often its light is directed into the mirror. The chalet lamp is essentially a large metal housing with a ground-glass window on one side. The top of the housing projects over this window so as to

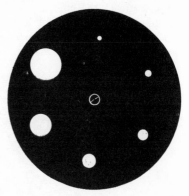

Fɪɢ. 4.6

serve as a shade. An ordinary incandescent bulb can be used. Some companies supply a microscope lamp which is essentially a "flexible goose neck" type of study lamp, provided with a frosted bulb. All three of these lamps can be quite serviceable for a great deal of microscopic work, but where special conditions must be met they are by no means ideal. More details will be given later.

B. LIGHTING THE SPECIMEN

Obtaining an adequate light cone.—For really serious work the problem of securing satisfactory illumination is more important than most students realize. The greater share of responsibility falls directly upon the individual, because the mere purchase of recommended equipment will not solve the problem. In order to arrive at some understanding of the relative merits of various lighting methods it is important actually to study their possibilities and limitations.

The objective should receive light in the form of a cone of adequate diameter. Too large a cone may be as undesirable as one which is too small. It is likewise important that the entire field of view be supplied with light. After an objective has been focused on the slide, a convenient way in which to determine whether the light cone is of proper diameter is to remove the eyepiece and peer down the draw tube. If the back lens of the objective is receiving sufficient light, then the entire combination is sufficiently lighted.

One might reason that the angle of the cone of light should approximate the angular aperture of the objective employed. Flooding with so much light, however, has tendency to cause glare. For this reason it is preferable, in actual practice, to have the light cone slightly smaller than the aperture of the objective. Many microscopists feel that generally best results are secured with a light cone of approximately 9/10 or 4/5; that is, the illuminated disc seen on the back lens of the objective should have a diameter about eight- or nine-tenths as great as that of the lens

FIG. 4.7. "MICROLUX" GENERAL PURPOSE MICROSCOPE LAMP. (*Courtesy E. Leitz, Inc.*) The knob at the side of the lamp operates a rheostat by means of which the intensity of the illumination supplied by the low voltage bulb can be varied. At its maximum setting the light is of the proper color temperature (3200° K) for use with Kodachrome film (Type B) without the use of auxiliary filters. The lamp is provided with a short focal length condenser, slot for filters and an iris diaphragm. The lamp housing can be tilted at practically any desired angle.

(Figure 4.9). This is achieved by closing down the iris diaphragm of the condenser until the luminous disc, as seen by looking into the microscope tube, appears of the correct diameter. The method just described is a fair approximation of what is referred to as "critical illumination." It meets the requirements of most of the work of chemical microscopy.

If, when the diaphragm is closed down, the luminous disc seen in the back lens is not in the center of the shaded ring (Figure 4.9D), the diaphragm is off center. Before it can render proper service such a diaphragm will have to be recentered. It may not be advisable for the novice to undertake this task unless the diaphragm is in a mount provided with centering screws.

With objectives of small N.A. the substage mirror and light from a window may provide ample illumination. Since, however, the N.A. of the mirror is rated at about 0.25, it is quite obvious that as the numerical aperture of the objectives increases the mirror becomes inadequate. Although one may be able to see images when using higher N.A. objectives with a relatively small light cone, resolution will suffer.

As pointed out previously, the maximum useful magnification, resolving power, and numerical aperture are all interrelated. In practice the maximum useful magnification is often considered equivalent to about

FIG. 4.8. LEITZ RESEARCH MICROSCOPE, ORTHOLUX MODEL II. (*Courtesy E. Leitz, Inc.*) This "reversed" type of microscope represents a radical departure from the conventional design. Both the coarse and fine adjustment knobs are placed in a low position. The source of illumination *is built into the microscope.* A simple lever adjustment at the base permits rapid change from transmitted light to reflected light. The substage is equipped with two iris diaphragms, the lower one constituting the field diaphragm and the upper one an aperture diaphragm. The top element of the condenser system itself can be swung out, so that, without removing any part of the condenser, one can employ all of the objectives, whether achromatic or apochromatic, from the lowest to the highest powers. The microscope can be employed as a monocular instrument if desired by replacing the binocular tube with a single tube.

a thousand times the N.A. of the objective. (Although for some purposes it may be convenient to resort to greater magnification, there would be no additional resolution.) If therefore a 4-mm objective having a magnifying power of 43-× should be employed with a light cone permitting a working aperture of, let us say, 0.45, the maximum useful magnification would be 450-×. This would be attained (nearly) by using a 10-×

ocular with the objective. Such a degree of magnification would be justified only if other conditions were ideal. Normally such objectives have an N.A. of 0.65, so that under favorable conditions a useful magnification of 650-× should be possible. With certain specimens this additional resolution may reveal features not brought out by the smaller light cone.

It was for the purpose of providing an adequate light cone that Abbe brought out his now well-known condenser (Figure 4.1). Although the latter serves for certain purposes, a corrected condenser is much to be

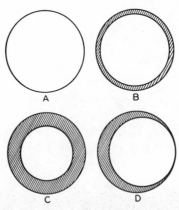

FIG. 4.9. A. When the entire back lens of the objective is filled with light the luminous disc shows practically no shaded border. B. For best results the used aperture should light up about $9/10$ of the objective. In this case the luminous disc seen on the back lens will be surrounded by a narrow shaded rim. C. Sometimes workers try to increase contrast by employing a relatively small light cone. Here the cone is about $2/3$ of the objective aperture, which is the least recommended for general work. It should be noted that the increase in contrast resulting with a small light cone (or small condenser cone) is obtained by sacrificing resolving power. D. When the shaded border seen on the back lens of the objective appears like this, the iris diaphragm (or the condenser) is not properly centered.

preferred (see p. 45). Reference has already been made to the importance of having the substage diaphragm perfectly centered. When a condenser is employed, centering is equally important. Regardless of the quality of the equipment available its efficiency is decidedly impaired if the condenser and its diaphragm are not centered.

Critical illumination.—Although the foregoing approximation to critical illumination may prove adequate for most chemical work, it does not permit maximum resolution. One method for securing a high degree of resolution is to resort to correct critical illumination. This requires a lamp capable of providing rays which are parallel, or nearly so. The position of the light source should be such that the condenser, when racked up or down, will focus an image of the source in the plane of the object on the slide. Light which comes through ground glass is not ideal for this method. If an electric light bulb is to serve as the illuminant, the bulb must be of clear glass. This means that an image of the lamp filament is projected on the object slide. It will be found that in ordinary incandescent lamps the filaments are too small to provide a light cone sufficiently large to illuminate the field to be observed. For this purpose special bulbs have been designed, such as the ribbon filament bulb. In order to benefit from the advantage of having parallel rays coming from the lamp condenser, it is important that the light beam fall directly on the center of the substage mirror.

Another method for obtaining critical illumination of the specimen is frequently referred to as the Koehler method. For this purpose the light need not be parallel, but the rays should constitute a single cone. Diffuse lighting, such as obtained through ground glass, is not appropriate. The lamp condenser is focused so that the image of the diaphragm in front of it appears in the object plane. Ideally, upon looking into the draw tube with the ocular removed, an image of the lamp filament appears to lie on the back lens of the objective. It may be necessary to make some slight adjustment of the substage condenser to achieve this result. Since the filament image may prove objectionable, the condenser is racked up or down just enough to throw the filament image out of focus.

The light focused on the object slide should cover about the same area as the field of view. As stressed by Wright, Brewster, Gage, and others, impairment of image quality results when too much stray light is present. This is one reason why light from a large window is not desirable for certain critical observations. In order to confine the illuminated area to the field of view there should be an iris diaphragm close to the light source. If such is not already provided, it may be possible to arrange a rotating disc which has been drilled with a series of holes of different diameters (Figure 4.6). For work involving high-power microscopy (about 1000-diameter magnification) Belling suggests a light source as small as 3 mm in diameter. In this case the lamp must be fairly close to the microscope.

When working with a substage condenser, the objective must be furnished with an adequate cone of light, just as was suggested in connection with the use of a substage concave mirror. The appropriate condenser cone, as this light cone may be called, is obtained by adjusting its iris diaphragm while the observer peers down the draw tube, just as described earlier (see page 48). When using a condenser some workers suggest closing the iris until the *used* aperture is as small as two-thirds of the objective aperture. This, of course, decreases the resolving power of an objective, but it offers the advantage of greater contrast. Similar results are achieved by lowering the condenser slightly.

Control of brilliance.—The actual luminosity or brilliance of the light required will vary with the nature of the specimen and with the particular lens system involved. For any given combination of lenses the least intense illumination will be necessary for transparent objects, such as colorless, plate-like crystals. As the specimens increase in thickness, and as they become more intensely colored, light of greater brilliance must be provided. Some of the microscope lamps are furnished with an appropriate rheostat for controlling the power supplied to the incandescent bulb. A disadvantage encountered with this system is the fact that the color of the light emitted is not the same when the lamp filament operates at different temperatures. This would be a serious objection where color values are of great importance. A simple, although effective, method for regulating the intensity of the light is the use of neutral density filters. Frequently, of course, it is quite feasible to control brilliance by the simple expedient of varying the distance between the microscope and the light source.

At this point the author wishes to reiterate the fact that the *intensity* of illumination is **never** to be controlled by means of the condenser diaphragm or by means of the diaphragm placed near the light source. As explained previously, the respective functions of these two diaphragms are (1) to control the condenser aperture and (2) to regulate the diameter of the illuminated area on the object slide. Intensity should be controlled as outlined in the foregoing paragraph.

Use of filters; monochromatic illumination.—An important means for controlling contrast in certain specimens is the judicious use of colored filters. This applies in visual work and also in the recording of photomicrographs. Those who have worn sun glasses of various colors are aware of the fact that the relative contrast of certain colored objects may be decidedly altered. Filters may be obtained in the form of colored glass, or as sheets of colored gelatin mounted between plane glass squares or circles known as optical flats. Wratten filters have been well standardized and can be supplied in various sizes. Gelatin filters must be protected from excessive heat and from moisture.

The following table gives an indication of the general type of filter to employ in order to obtain more contrast with specimens in which a certain color predominates.

Color of Specimen	Suggested Filter
Red	Green
Yellow	Blue
Green	Red
Blue	Yellow, red, or orange
Violet	Green

It frequently happens that the appropriate filter must be determined by trial, since several colors may be involved in the specimen under investigation.

In spite of the fact that objectives have been corrected for chromatic aberration, the correction may not be equally good for the different wave lengths. For this reason, when the specific color of a specimen is not of prime importance, monochromatic illumination may improve objective performance. A green filter is frequently employed in front of the light source when circumstances permit.

The use of a filter which transmits only the shorter wave lengths of the visible spectrum can also increase the resolving power of an objective. The reason for this relationship can be seen by referring to the equation for resolution,

$$D = \frac{\lambda}{2 \text{ N.A.}}.$$

Yellow-green or green light combines low wave length with high visibility. Some microscopists recommend blue. Although it is true that the latter represents a shorter wave length, the author has found green easier to work with.

If for some reason it is found inconvenient to employ glass or gelatin filters, these may be substituted by various colored solutions contained in suitable glass cells or troughs. A flask or trough of saturated cupric acetate solution serves as an effective blue-green filter. A solution of sodium or potassium dichromate is sometimes used where yellow light is desired.

Whenever critical work is to be done by transmitted illumination, the microscopist should exclude all light excepting that which passes up through the substage diaphragm. The stage itself should be protected from any bright source of illumination, because otherwise the material on the slide will be seen by both reflected light and transmitted light. There are occasions when this may lead to an incorrect interpretation of the resulting image. This precaution may be particularly important when one is working near a very bright wall lamp or ceiling light. Further, if the work table is rather strongly illuminated, the microscope image will not appear as distinct as otherwise. This is for the same reason that we shade the eyes in order to discern objects which must be viewed by gazing in the direction of the sun. This does not mean that the room must be practically dark; the lighting should be sufficiently subdued to prevent the pupils from contracting too much, and to prevent any pronounced image from being formed by rays reflected by the specimen.

Other types of transmitted illumination.—Thus far the discussion on illumination has been restricted to transmitted "axial" lighting. This refers to the fact that, when the plane surface of the substage mirror reflects parallel rays up into the object plane, the rays are parallel with the optic axis of the microscope. To be more specific, this type is known as *parallel axial* illumination. Whenever the specimen is illuminated by means of the concave substage mirror or by means of a properly focused substage condenser, the effect is a cone of rays which converge toward a point in or near the object plane. With the mirror or condenser properly centered the focus of such rays should be at some point along the optic axis of the microscope. The result is *symmetrical convergent* illumination. If desired, it is possible to obtain substantially parallel rays with the substage condenser. These are obtained by racking the condenser somewhat below its normal focal position and reducing the diaphragm aperture. Whether the rays are parallel or convergent, the characteristic of all symmetrical illumination is that the specimen is lighted uniformly from all sides.

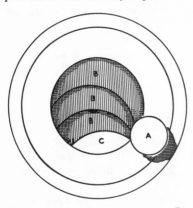

FIG. 4.10. DIAPHRAGM FOR OBLIQUE ILLUMINATION. (*Courtesy American Optical Co.*) This device is entirely independent of the iris diaphragm. It consists of three bronze leaves (B), which rotate on a common axis at one end of each leaf; by turning the button (A), these leaves close the aperture from one side only, leaving an opening (C) for the decentered light to strike the condenser. For the same amount of obliquity, the volume of light is three times that admitted when the iris is decentered. The apparatus is highly effective although simple to manipulate.

There are occasions when symmetrical illumination fails to yield the most satisfactory results. To bring out relief or greater contrast in some specimens it may prove desirable to resort to *oblique* illumination (sometimes called *unilateral oblique* illumination). This kind of illumination refers to an arrangement which causes uneven lighting of the object. The light comes from one side. When using a substage condenser, oblique illumination can be obtained, by closing part of its diaphragm opening with a small card. A more convenient method is to insert in the filter holder a portion of a cardboard disc. With some microscopes a similar result may be attained by decentering the condenser. If the illumination is by means of the substage mirror alone, the effect can be achieved by swinging the mirror to the right or left of its usual position. (This may not be possible with some microscopes which are normally equipped with condensers.)

For the sake of completeness another type of transmitted illumination should be considered.   Let us assume that an object is being examined by symmetrical convergent illumination, as obtained by means of a substage condenser.   Under the condition of critical illumination the condenser furnishes a light cone of dimensions adequate to fill the aperture of the objective employed.   Rays in excess of the required aperture are shut out in order to prevent glare.   By this method the specimen is observed as lying in a brightly illuminated field.   Highly transparent portions of the

specimen may appear as bright as the field itself, while those parts which are less transparent necessarily appear darker than the field.

Now suppose that in the diaphragm opening there were an opaque disc.   The latter would obstruct the passage of the central rays, even if the iris diaphragm were opened to a greater aperture.   Only the annular rays could reach the object slide.   Under proper conditions, a clean blank slide when viewed by such illumination would exhibit a dark field.   This is because the rays constituting the usual light cone are held back, in spite of the fact that there is an abundance of light rays outside the central cone of darkness.

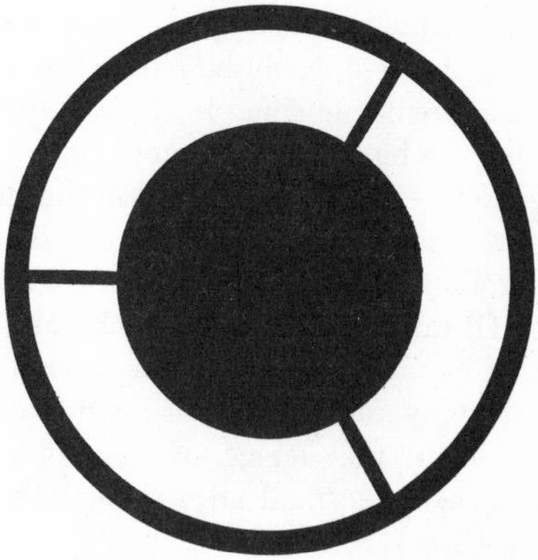

It must be recalled that rays which reach the slide surface at an angle in excess of the angular aperture of the objective cannot reach the latter directly.   If, however,

FIG. 4.11. OPAQUE STOP FOR DARK-FIELD ILLUMINATION.   Metal stops of this type can be inserted in the filter holder beneath the condenser.   These stops are available with central opaque discs of different sizes.   In the Travis Expanding Stop, the size of the central disc can be varied.   This is made possible by providing the center with a number of thin, movable leaves, which operate on the same principle employed in the iris diaphragm.

such rays pass through a specimen on the slide, they may be refracted to such an extent that they are transmitted to the objective.   In consequence the specimen then appears to be the source of such rays.   The observed effect is that of an illuminated specimen resting on a dark field —hence the term *dark-field illumination.*

Dark-field illumination can be secured by inserting a metal stop (Figure 4.11) in the filter slot below the substage condenser.   If one of the conventional stops is not available, similar results can be obtained by attaching a disc of metal foil or opaque paper to a circle of glass (or to a circle of heavy cellophane) which fits the filter holder.   For magnifications beyond those of the 8-mm objective, satisfactory results require the use of a special dark-field condenser.   The chief advantages of this *dark-ground illumination,* as it is sometimes called, appear in certain fields of high-power microscopy.   Some types of bacteria are best seen against dark-ground illumination.

An interesting variation of dark-field illumination is known as Rheinberg illumination.   If the dark-field stop were employed in combination with a green filter, the specimen would yield a green image on a dark field; with a red filter the result would be a red image on a dark ground.   If instead of an opaque stop the central disc were to consist of transparent red glass, the field would be red instead of dark.   In actual practice one may cut a circular opening in the center of a green filter disc, and a small red filter can be placed in the opening.   When such a combination, known as a Rheinberg disc, is inserted in the substage filter holder, the observer can view a green image against a red background.   Rheinberg discs are commercially available in various color combinations.

Illumination of opaque objects.—When working with opaque objects it will be necessary to make observations by reflected light.   The method to employ and the type of lamp to use will depend upon the nature of the specimen, the degree of magnification desired, and the result to be achieved.   A small adjustable spot light, similar to that shown in Figure 4.4 or 4.5, may serve the requirements of a great variety of work.   It will be seen, of course, that such a source is restricted to oblique illumination.   When working with low-power objectives it is possible to come fairly close to vertical illumination with this type of lamp, but it will be only an approximation.   In the case of a high-power objective the working distance is so short that vertical illumination can be secured only by means of special devices.   Oblique illumination is excellent for showing up relief in opaque materials.   If the relief is very slight, it may remain unobserved unless the angle of obliquity of the rays approaches 180 degrees, that is, nearly horizontal.

Oblique rays will not penetrate to the depths of narrow cavities, depressions, or scratches.   If these are to be studied, vertical illumination should be employed.   Some of the vertical illuminators are in the form of a short cylinder which can be introduced between the objective and the body tube of the microscope.   Inside there is a small, transparent reflector, which may be a very thin plate of glass set at a 45-degree angle.   Light entering the illuminator from the side is reflected through the objective to the specimen.   Ordinarily, chemical work does not require this type of lighting.   Fields which require it can be served best by specialized equipment, namely, some type of metallographic microscope.   For a more extensive treatment of vertical illuminators the reader may consult Chapter IV in Volume 1 of Chamot and Mason.

Study Problems

1. Explain what is meant by each of the following terms.

Numerical aperture   Neutral density filter
9/10 Light cone   Oblique illumination
Resolution   Symmetrical convergent illumination
Condenser cone   Dark-field illumination

2. A certain microscope was equipped with an 8-mm objective (N.A. = 0.50), but there was no substage condenser. Why would this combination reveal no more detail than a 16-mm objective of N.A. = 0.25?

3. A student was making observations through a microscope equipped with a 16-mm objective and a substage mirror. When the illumination proved too intense, he decided to decrease it by closing down the substage diaphragm. Criticize this procedure and recommend correct methods for maximum resolution.

4. Tell how to obtain a 9/10 light cone.

5. Determine the effective aperture when using a 9/10 light cone with an 8-mm objective of N.A. = 0.50.

6. (a) Calculate what would probably be the maximum useful magnification to be attained with the arrangement in Problem 5.

(b) To realize such magnification, what power should the ocular be, assuming the objective yields a magnification of 20 diameters?

7. What advantage may result from the use of a relatively small light cone?

8. Briefly outline the procedure for securing approximately critical illumination.

9. What is the function of a diaphragm on the light source?

10. Explain the value of colored filters.

11. What type of illumination would you recommend for observing the depth of fine scratches on a polished metal plate? State your reasons.

12. Explain why one would expect the shorter wave lengths of monochromatic light to yield better resolution.

13. Outline several methods for obtaining monochromatic light.

14. Many microscope lamps have no provision for varying the luminosity. Explain how this lack may prove to be a disadvantage.

15. By means of a diagram explain why a specimen appears luminous by dark-field illumination although the rays which enter the specimen are in a cone outside the angular aperture of the objective.

16. Explain the principle of Rheinberg illumination.

17. When employing a Rheinberg disc consisting of a blue center and a red outer ring, the image will not be the same red as the color of the ring. Explain why.

Chapter V

PERMANENT RECORDS: PREPARATION OF SKETCHES AND PHOTOMICROGRAPHS

Aids in sketching.—There are numerous instances in which it is desirable to keep permanent records of specimens which have been subjected to microscopic examination, because mere verbal descriptions may prove inadequate. If no special facilities are available, the situation on many occasions is met by sketching with a pencil what the eye sees upon peering into the microscope. Some people possess a natural bent for such work and others may develop a technique through practice. The observance of a few simple "tricks" should greatly facilitate this type of sketching.

FIG. 5.1. SPENCER CAMERA LUCIDA, ABBE TYPE. (*Courtesy American Optical Co.*)

Those who experience difficulty in making freehand sketches will find that a net micrometer can be of considerable help. With such a micrometer in the eyepiece the image resembles a drawing on cross-section paper. By actually using cross-section paper there should be very little difficulty in obtaining satisfactory sketches of most specimens.

The simplest procedure would be to allow a single square on the paper to represent one of the micrometer squares. The dimensions of the proposed sketch can be calculated in advance. If it is desired to have a larger or smaller sketch, one merely allows a larger or smaller number of paper squares to represent one micrometer square.

An advantage of sketches made by the aforementioned procedure is that they will be drawn to scale. Even the angles between adjoining crystal edges can be represented with a fair degree of accuracy. This may at times be of importance for purposes of identification. If the paper is ruled

58

in light blue, photographic copies taken on a color-blind film will record the sketch without rulings. In most cases, of course, only one copy is required for record purposes. Should the appearance of ruled squares prove undesirable, the sketch can be made on thin paper placed over cross-section paper. For this purpose, however, the rulings should be in black or some other intense color.

If a net micrometer is not available, an ordinary cross-hair ocular can be employed to advantage. Two fine lines on the drawing paper are allowed to represent the cross-hairs. With their point of intersection as the

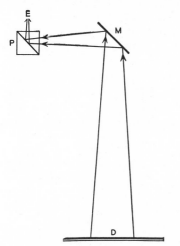

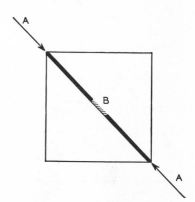

FIG. 5.2. CAMERA LUCIDA.
E, Eye of observer.
P, Prism.
M, Reflecting mirror.
D, Drawing surface

FIG. 5.3. PRISM OF CAMERA LUCIDA. Arrows A, A point to film of metallic silver which separates the two halves of the prism. B, the shaded area, indicates small area not covered by silver film.

center, a circle is drawn to represent the field seen in the eyepiece. Various lines of the specimen image can be compared with the length of a cross-hair. Thus a crystal edge might appear to be one-half or two-thirds as long as a cross-hair. Although angles may be estimated, the results can be only approximate. The estimations will most likely be in terms of fractions of a right angle.

One precision method for preparing sketches of microscopic objects requires the use of a *camera lucida* (Figure 5.1). With this device acceptable sketches can be produced even by those who boast no skill in freehand drawing. This method saves time and insures correct proportions. It is important, however, that the artist has the ability to interpret properly what he sees in the microscope, since otherwise the sketch may be misleading.

A common form of the Abbe camera lucida is ordinarily employed with the microscope in vertical position, while the drawing surface is in horizontal position (Figure 5.2). Fundamentally, this device consists of a mirror which reflects an image of the drawing surface into a specially designed prism. While the Abbe prism permits the observer to see an enlarged image in the usual way, it also reflects upward the image of the drawing surface. In effect, the image of the sketching pencil appears superimposed on the image presented by the microscope. Tracing the outlines of the specimen image thus becomes a relatively simple procedure.

The mirror must be inclined at an angle of 45 degrees; otherwise the drawing will represent a distorted view (Figure 5.4). In certain instances it may happen that the stage of the microscope extends into part of the drawing field. This may be avoided by inclining the mirror of the camera lucida at an angle of less than the usual 45 degrees. Whenever this is done, the drawing surface must be appropriately inclined to prevent distortion. With the mirror set at an angle of 40 degrees, for example, the drawing surface should be raised to an angle of 10 degrees with the horizontal. Some manufacturers provide special drawing boards which can be adjusted to various angles of inclination, but ordinarily this added expense is not essential.

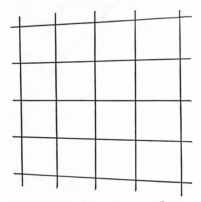

If the image formed by the microscope is of greater brilliance than the reflected view of the drawing paper and pencil, the latter may be difficult to see. Likewise, if the drawing surface should be too brightly illuminated its reflected image may obscure the image of the specimen. To prevent any obscuration, most cameras lucidas are provided with some means for decreasing the brilliance of drawing paper image. This may be accomplished by inserting neutral density filters between the mirror and the prism of the camera lucida. On the other hand, if the microscope image should prove too brilliant, the illumination may be reduced by the usual methods.

Fig. 5.4. Distortion Caused by Inclining the Reflecting Mirror at Incorrect Angle. This shows result obtained in drawing a portion of an ocular net micrometer. Observe that not one single unit is a true square. Measurements based on such a drawing would be unreliable.

Not all cameras lucidas are provided with mirrors. Those supplied by some manufacturers are in the form of a very compact apparatus which employs a specially constructed reflecting prism above, or very close to, the eyepiece.

When the nature of the specimen permits the microscope to be used in horizontal position, projected images may serve as an aid in drawing. For this purpose one requires a reflecting prism or suitable mirror which can be conveniently attached near the eyelens of the ocular [1] (Figure 5.5). The source of illumination must be sufficiently intense to project a distinct

FIG. 5.5. PROJECTION PRISM #346 ATTACHED TO TUBE OF MICROSCOPE. (*Courtesy American Optical Co.*)

image on the drawing surface. The same objective and ocular can yield projected images of various dimensions by changing the distance between the reflecting prism (or mirror) and the drawing surface.

Photomicrography; equipment required.—Frequently photomicrographs may serve as an ideal type of permanent record. The advantages of such records were recognized quite early in the history of photography, as is evidenced by the fact that practically the first use of photography in the scientific field was to obtain photomicrographs. They were made by Wedgwood and Davy as early as 1802,[2] but the images were not permanent because the art of fixing the silver image had not yet been discovered. In

[1] The Central Scientific Company supplies such a prism in a light metal holder which can be clamped to the draw tube.

[2] Cf. Walter Clark, *Photography by Infrared*, Wiley, 1946.

1837 Reade, who had discovered the use of hypo, prepared the first permanent photomicrographs.

For those who already possess a microscope the principal additional equipment required for taking micrographs will be a camera, an appropriate support for the same, and, possibly, some device for coupling the

Fig. 5.6. Solar enlarger adapted for use as a photomicrographic camera. (*Courtesy Burke & James, Chicago.*)

eyepiece of the microscope with the front of the camera. Procuring the foregoing need not involve any great expense.

No doubt the major single item to provide is a camera. There is a very wide range from which to choose. In size, the format may vary from the 35-mm type, up to the $3\frac{1}{4} \times 4\frac{1}{4}$ or 4×5 inch sizes. Larger cameras may be employed, but their bulk renders them more difficult to provide with a sufficiently rigid support. If one intends to rely entirely upon contact prints, it is better to employ a camera which takes negatives measuring $2\frac{1}{4} \times 3\frac{1}{4}$ inches or even $3\frac{1}{4} \times 4\frac{1}{4}$. Those who plan to enlarge most of their micrographs may use smaller cameras. Although some workers are not very enthusiastic over the 35-mm negatives, it must be admitted that the only sizes in which Kodachrome roll film is available today are the 35-mm and the closely similar Bantam size.

Excellent results can be obtained, whether the camera is designed for roll film, film packs, or cut film. Each has certain advantages. For those who are interested in taking micrographs in color, it should be mentioned that professional Ektachrome is available as cut film in sizes ranging from 2¼ × 3¼ inches upward.

It is an advantage to employ a camera provided with a ground glass focusing back, but this is not essential. In fact, good results can be ob-

A   B

FIG. 5.7. ONE METHOD FOR MOUNTING SMALL REFLEX TYPE OF CAMERA (EXAKTA) FOR TAKING PHOTOMICROGRAPHS. A. As viewed from table level. A–1 is square of stiff cardboard which supports camera on iron ring. The camera lens has been replaced by an extension tube which surrounds upper end of drawtube of the microscope. A–2 is sheet of cardboard placed around drawtube to prevent any stray light from entering camera. B. Same assembly as A, but viewed from above. *Note:* Many iron rings used in the laboratory are unsuited for use in the above assembly. It is necessary that the focal plane of the camera be parallel with the microscope stage.

tained with a box camera. It is preferable to have an instrument on which the shutter can be operated by a cable release. In many respects, the ideal camera for this work is the single-lens reflex type. (Pilot, Graflex, Korelle, Exakta are examples.) Here one can see the image to be recorded until the very moment the shutter is tripped. For those who plan to do very much of this work it will frequently prove advantageous to have a shutter with automatic timing for exposures of one second and one-half second.

Since it is the optical system of the microscope which forms the image to be recorded, the aperture of the camera lens is of little importance. Actually, one may as well remove the lens if this can be done without disturbing the shutter. If the microscopist does not possess a camera, and if he wants one solely for taking micrographs, he should be able to obtain a very serviceable piece of equipment from some second-hand dealer. Since the lens is not required, it is usually possible to find a good bargain, especially if one is willing to consider an old model plate camera. Occasionally it is also possible to find a Graflex or other single-lens reflex type camera which is no longer suitable for ordinary photography, but which still possesses an undamaged plate adapter, good bellows and a working "reflex" unit. Many very serviceable cameras of this type antedating World War II are being offered at a mere fraction of their original cost because the present day photographer prefers a less bulky instrument. The prospective purchaser should keep in mind the fact that in some types of reflex cameras the mirror does not spring into focusing position when the film plane is horizontal. Such a camera would not function properly if used in vertical position over the microscope.

Some device must be provided for supporting the camera above the microscope. The support should be quite rigid, so that the camera will not vibrate during exposures. The stands of certain photo-enlargers can be adapted as supports for this work without much difficulty. In fact, a few enlargers which have been on the market can readily be converted into efficient photomicrographic cameras. Regardless of the method of mounting the camera, care must be exercised to have the focal place of the camera parallel with the image plane of the microscope. Failure to observe this precaution will result in distortion of the image.

In the case of certain small roll-film cameras the mounting may be accomplished by means of a small, cardboard adapter tube. First, a tube

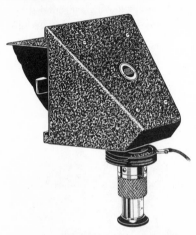

FIG. 5.8. "MICAM" CAMERA ATTACHMENT. (*Courtesy E. Leitz, Inc.*) This versatile accessory can be employed in photomicrography, microprojection and as a viewing screen. It can be attached to any microscope using eyepieces of standard diameter. The shutter can be set for time exposures or for automatic exposures from $\frac{1}{100}$ second to $\frac{1}{2}$ second. The plate holders accommodate $3\frac{1}{4} \times 4\frac{1}{4}$ plates or cut film.

is made which fits snugly around the ocular of the microscope. This is easily done by winding several turns of adhesive tape around the cardboard while rubber bands hold the latter in position around the ocular. A convenient length for the adapter tube is about 2 inches. If the lens barrel of the camera likewise fits inside this adapter, the next step is to glue a narrow band of cardboard inside the latter. This band may be about ⅛ inch wide; its distance from the end of the tube should equal, or very slightly exceed, the width of the lens mount. In use, the adapter is placed over the ocular of the microscope, after which the barrel of the camera lens is introduced. The object is to have the camera rest on the adapter tube. The narrow band which has been securely glued inside the tube prevents the lens of the camera from touching the eyelens of the ocular. Obviously, if the center of gravity of the camera is too far to one side of the focal plane, it will not be advisable to attempt balancing the instrument on the adapter tube. This method of mounting is likewise inadvisable if the draw tube of the microscope moves too freely.

One appropriate method for supporting the Argus, Exakta, Pilot–6, Voigtlander Brilliant and similar cameras makes use of an iron ring clamped to a heavy ring-stand. A sheet of plywood or heavy cardboard is placed on the ring to form a shelf. An opening of appropriate dimensions must be cut in the shelf in order to accommodate the lens mount. There should also be a small hole or notch to admit the cable release. The ring stand should be of the type having a rectangular metal base of adequate proportions to accommodate the microscope. The entire system must be so arranged that the camera lens and the microscope ocular are centered in respect to each other when a micrograph is to be taken. In other words, the optic axis of the microscope should pass through the center of the camera lens and should be perpendicular to the picture plane. If at all possible, the base of the support stand should be provided with guide bars, so that the microscope can be moved into correct position without losing much time. Furthermore, when one wishes to look directly into the microscope, it should be possible to swing the camera around so as to provide free access to the ocular. Afterward it should be possible to swing the camera back into the exact "taking" position without requiring any tedious adjustments.

In the case of a camera which is equipped with bellows the iron ring will not prove feasible. Depending upon the design of the camera, the shelf on which it rests may have to be a board with an appropriate rectangular opening; or in some cases it may have to be a U-shaped board. It is important that the focal plane of the camera is perfectly horizontal when used with the microscope in vertical position.

It is of the utmost importance that the assembly of apparatus used in photomicrography be free from any tendency to vibrate. For this reason the work should be done in a building which is not jarred by the operation of heavy machinery indoors, or by the passing of trucks, and other heavy traffic outside. It may even be necessary to confine the work to times when such disturbances are absent. In certain instances a basement room may be less subject to vibration. For extreme conditions Gage and others have advised mounting the apparatus in a box of sand or sawdust, or on a sponge rubber base. A ready-made device which has been found to be quite serviceable is the "Vibradamp," sold by the Fisher Scientific Co. This consists of a heavy cast iron plate supported by four rubber cushions; it was originally designed as a support for analytical balances.

Taking a photomicrograph.—Let us assume that a micrograph is to be taken by means of a camera which is not provided with a focusing back. Unless it is a box camera or some other "fixed focus" model, it is set for infinity. The support is then adjusted so that the lens of the camera is about ⅛ inch above the eyepiece of the microscope. Having swung the camera aside, the specimen beneath the objective is focused in the usual manner. Until some experience has been acquired, it may be desirable to restrict all work to the use of a 9/10 light cone (cf. p. 48). For the initial trials a 16-mm objective and a 5-× or a 10-× ocular are suggested. It must be remembered that the depth of focus is not very great, and the camera can record distinctly only those portions of the specimen which lie within a very shallow field. This makes it imperative that the microscope be focused very carefully on the plane which is to be recorded by the camera.

When the specimen has been properly focused, the camera is swung around into "taking" position. The shutter is set for "time" and the diaphragm (of the camera) is at its maximum aperture. All bright lights in the room, including the microscope lamp, are turned off. Total darkness is not essential, of course, provided the room lighting is properly controlled. A low wattage amber bulb, such as sometimes used in photolaboratories, will afford sufficient illumination by which to see the watch dial, etc., without appreciably affecting the results obtained.

After the shutter is opened the microscope lamp is turned on for the proper length of time. That is, if the exposure is to be for 5 seconds, the light is turned out promptly at the end of 5 seconds. Finally the shutter is closed. It will be evident from the foregoing that the length of exposure is controlled by the light switch, rather than by the shutter release. If the camera is not mounted rigidly it may be jarred by the operation of the shutter. The method here suggested eliminates this source of vibration during exposures.

At this point it might be of interest to mention a procedure which has been employed successfully by Benedetti-Pichler. Instead of focusing the microscope image directly on the ground glass screen of a camera, or on the photographic film, he projects the image on a vertical screen in a darkened room. It is then a simple matter to photograph the large projected image with any camera. This method, of course, requires an efficient microprojection assembly.

Rather complete records should be entered for all exposures, since such data may serve as an invaluable guide to better future work (Figure 5.9).

No. .... Date ....
Subj.   Oc.   Tube   Filter

....
Obj.   L. Cone   Lamp   Exp.

....

Dist. ....

Remarks ....

....

....

FIG. 5.9. FORM FOR RECORDING EXPOSURE DATA.

A very practical system is to file each negative in its own numbered glassine envelope. If an appropriate form is mimeographed on a filing card, or on a sheet of paper, all of the pertinent data can be enclosed with the negative. If opaque envelopes are employed, the form may be printed on the outside. Even if the negative is filed with the exposure record, it is desirable that the latter include some statement concerning the results. Certain information is not readily obtained by merely glancing at the negative. Under REMARKS it may frequently be desirable to note suggestions for better results in the future. Until the novice has acquired some familiarity with the process, it is advisable to adhere to a uniform procedure in taking photomicrographs. After some experience he may work toward different effects by varying such factors as light cone, intensity of illumination, and types of filters.

Other types of cameras.—Certain advantages are offered by a camera which possesses a ground glass focusing screen. For one, it is more convenient to get the desired image centered on the plate or film. The final critical focusing can be observed on the ground glass. Then, if it appears desirable to do so, the object slide can be adjusted to a more favorable position on the stage, thereby bringing the appropriate portions of the specimen into the center of the field of view. A further advantage comes into play when it is not necessary to photograph the entire field. By using a longer bellows extension the camera will form a larger image of any recorded portion. In this case, of course, the ground glass enables one to adjust the specimen so as to obtain the best view of the desired portion. This type of camera also makes possible the use of a sensitive photo-electric type of exposure meter.

Inspection of the ground glass image should be done with the aid of a hand lens or a reading glass. This will greatly facilitate the problem of securing critically sharp focus of the image, thus rendering possible clear-cut enlargements of the resulting negative. The lens employed for this purpose may be one giving a 4-× or 6-× magnification. To save time, it is desirable that the lens be in a tube or frame of just the correct height. The latter is achieved if the ground glass image is in focus when the magnifier is placed on the screen. The micrographer should test and adjust such a magnifier to suit his own requirements, or purchase one specifically designed for this purpose. Even very fine ground glass appears coarse-grained when viewed through a hand lens. To improve results it is suggested that a clean cover glass be cemented to the center of the ground surface, using Canada balsam for the purpose.

In certain respects a single-lens reflex camera is almost ideal for this work. Since this type is usually equipped with a focal plane shutter, the lens may be removed for taking the micrographs. An important advantage is the fact that the ground glass image can be observed until the moment when the shutter is released. This advantage is of particular significance when working with fresh crystal preparations which are slowly changing. With a reflex camera the exposure can be made as soon as proper focusing has been accomplished. No time need be lost in placing a plate holder or film pack adapter in position. There are occasions when the time required for inserting a plate holder and removing the dark slide may result in the loss of a picture.

Degree of magnification—Unless the camera employed permits a bellows-extension of about 10 inches, the photographer may be disappointed to find that the recorded image is much smaller than promised by the rated magnifying power of the optical system of the microscope. Ordinarily, when using a 10-× ocular with a 16-mm objective the worker looks for a magnification of about 100 diameters. This applies when the image is observed by the eye, assuming a normal viewing distance of 10 inches, or 250 mm. A micrograph, however, is the result of a projected real image, in the formation of which the eye plays no part. Therefore, if the film or the focusing screen is placed at a distance less than 10 inches from the eyepoint the magnification cannot equal that obtained when the observer peers directly into the microscope.

It is generally desirable that the exact degree of magnification be known. With the help of a stage micrometer and a drafting compass this is readily determined for any desired arrangement of camera and microscope. The micrometer is placed on the stage and its image is brought into exact focus on the ground glass of the camera. The points

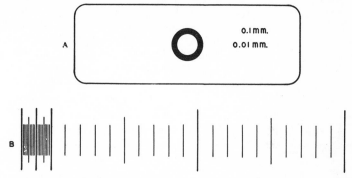

FIG. 5.10. STAGE MICROMETER. A. Appearance of the slide, which has the ruled scale mounted within black circle. B. Enlarged view of the actual rulings.

of the compass are made to span any convenient number of the scale divisions on the screen, after which the exact length of the span is measured on an appropriate rule. Let us suppose that the image of ten of the

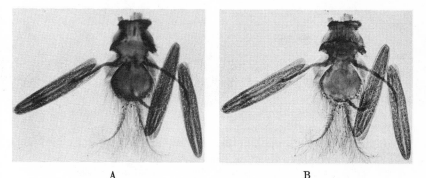

A   B

FIG. 5.11. A. Wheat Flower (triticum), 24-×. Carmine stain. Photograph on ordinary plate. B. Wheat Flower. Taken on "M" plate, with K 2 filter. (*Reproduced with permission from "Photomicrography," published by Eastman Kodak Company.*)

1/10-millimeter scale divisions should cover a span of 3.8 cm on a metric scale; this would mean an actual magnification of 38 diameters. The careful worker will keep a record of the objective and ocular used, position of the draw tube, and the position of the camera. Then, in all subsequent work he will know the magnification obtained when working with this particular system.

Some workers prefer to restrict the magnification of their micrographs to certain specific values divisible by the number five or ten. In the instance just given, for example, a slight change in the position of the camera or in the length of the draw tube (or both) may give a magnification of exactly 35 or 40 diameters. If, in addition, one can also use a 12.5-× ocular, the final magnification may be extended to exactly 50 diameters. Incidentally, the American Society for Testing Materials has

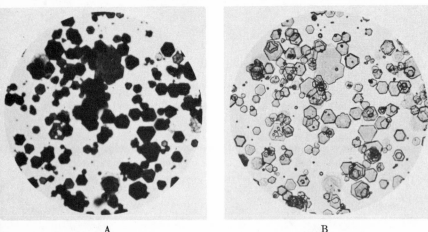

                    A   B

Fig. 5.12. A. Lead iodide precipitate as photographed by an ordinary plate or film (250-×). B. Lead iodide precipitate as photographed on "M" plate, using B filter. (250-×). (*Reproduced with permission from "Photomicrography," published by Eastman Kodak Company.*)

recommended the following as standard magnifications: 10; 25; 50; 75; 100; 200; 500; and 1000 diameters.

It may so happen that the camera which is to be used is not provided with a focusing back. When such is the case, one solution is to take a micrograph of the stage micrometer. The negative image then supplies the desired information. If one prefers, a ground glass of proper dimensions is carefully placed over the rectangle which ordinarily masks the film during an exposure. Obviously the ground surface must face toward the lens. From this point on the procedure is similar to that followed when the camera is provided with a focusing back. In fact, we have here a makeshift focusing back.

It may be well to include a few statements concerning one other phase of the subject of "degree of magnification." The diameter of the circular field projected into the focal plane of the camera is not necessarily proportional to the magnification. If different oculars are employed with the same objective, the circles projected at a certain fixed distance may be found to vary only slightly. The circle formed when using the 10-× ocular may have very nearly the same diameter as that projected through a 5-× eyepiece; but any image in the former circle will have twice the diameter it would have when projected through the lower-power ocular. This indicates that when using a higher ocular in order to increase magnification, a much smaller area of the specimen is projected. This serves to illustrate one advantage of having a camera with a long bellows extension. By doubling the distance from eyepoint to film plane the 5-× ocular will yield the higher degree of magnification and still project the relatively large area of the specimen. There are instances in which this is desirable. In general, it should be remembered that with a given lens combination the magnification of a projected image is proportional to the distance from the eyepoint to the screen or film.

Filters and emulsions.—Just as in regular photography, filters can be employed to vary the contrast of different portions of the specimen or to obtain proper rendition of colors. The same principles apply, but the situation is somewhat simplified by the fact that the micrographer has more complete control over his lighting. A detailed discussion on the use of filters hardly belongs within the scope of this work, although a few of the pertinent facts may bear repetition here. The sensitivity of the emulsions used on early photographic plates was confined toward the blue-violet end of the spectrum. Since satisfactory rendition of colored objects was impossible with such plates, they were referred to as "colorblind."

Eventually the manufacturers developed emulsions which were sensitive not only to violet and blue, but also to wave lengths in the green and yellow regions of the spectrum. These *orthochromatic* emulsions, as they are called, are much more sensitive to the blue and violet portions of the spectrum than to the green-yellow region; however, the use of appropriate filters results in the absorption of part of the shorter wave lengths. This allows the photographer to expose the plate long enough to enable the green-yellow rays to affect the sensitive emulsion. Even these orthochromatic emulsions are unable to give a satisfactory rendition of colors which lie in the orange-red end of the spectrum. A later step in the development of photosensitive materials was the *panchromatic* emulsion, which is sensitive to practically the entire visible spectrum as well as to part of the ultraviolet portion. However, even in the panchromatic plates the greatest sensitivity lies toward the blue-violet region. For this reason, if one wishes to obtain the proper rendition of all colors, it is necessary to employ filters which absorb some of the blue-violet wave lengths.

In general, the work of the micrographer is simplified by the fact that the colors in a given specimen usually lie within a relatively small portion of the spectrum. In fact, when working with crystals and fibers much of the work requires no color correction whatever. When working with color-sensitive emulsions, in order to decrease the effect of blue-violet wave lengths, a yellow filter is indicated. This permits the recording of more detail in parts of the specimen which show other colors. If more contrast is desired, that is, if a certain color in the specimen is to appear darker in the final positive print, one selects a filter which absorbs that particular color. To illustrate, if it is desired to accentuate pale green crystals, the use of an orange-red or light red filter may achieve the result. However, those who are unfamiliar with the photographic use of filters should consult "The Photography of Colored Objects" and "Photomicrography," both of which are issued by the Eastman Kodak Company.

Plates and films employed in photomicrography should possess a fine-grain emulsion. This is especially true if the negatives are to be used in preparing enlarged prints. As a rule this means that high-speed emulsions are to be avoided, since these tend toward coarser grain. Specifically developed for micrography is the Wratten-M plate. This fine-grained panchromatic plate has a sensitivity extending beyond the visible spectrum, into the ultraviolet and the infrared regions. The negatives show a fairly high degree of contrast. It yields satisfactory results in most micro work. If less contrast is desired, the Wratten panchromatic plate is recommended. Although the sensitivity of this plate does not include quite the same range as the "M" plate, it possesses the advantage of greater speed. Both of these plates are manufactured by the Eastman Kodak Company.

One cannot always predict the type of illumination which will yield the most satisfactory results. In fact, it may even be necessary to take several different micrographs in order to reveal the various features of a given specimen. In order to determine the most appropriate lighting for any specific case it is desirable to resort to visual inspection of results produced by various filters. This does not necessarily involve a large number of filters or a large investment. For a modest sum one can obtain a series of nine "M" filters, which should prove adequate for general micro work. Their uses are given in the table on p. 73.

The less expensive sets of filters are supplied in the form of 2-inch gelatin squares. Naturally these must be handled very carefully to prevent damage. A more expensive series is available in the form of 33-mm discs. These are quite thin, so that several may be placed in the filter ring of the substage condenser. Although these filters are mounted in glass, they must be protected from heat. Water and other liquids should not be permitted to touch their edges.

For those workers who prefer cut film, Eastman Panchromatic Process film and Eastman Panatomic film are suggested. The latter yields less contrast. In place of the "D. C. Ortho" plates, one may use Eastman Commercial Ortho cut film. In cameras which do not accommodate plates, very good results can be obtained with the fine-grain roll film supplied by several manufacturers. Eastman Panatomic-X, and Agfa Finopan are popular brands of panchromatic films, while Verichrome and Plenachrome are examples of orthochromatic emulsions.

Filter No.	Color	Use
78	Blue	Valuable for long continued visual work. Primarily for conversion of light from metal filament lamps to equivalent daylight.
38A	Blue	Increases apparent contrast in light yellow and orange specimens. Improves resolution of fine details.
45A	Blue-green	Dominant wave length is about 470 Angstroms. Transmits no red. Useful whenever high resolving power is required.
66	Light green	Increases contrast when used with pink and red specimens. Also appropriate for general work in place of no. 78.
58	Green	Used with faint pink or red specimens. Increases contrast.
15	Yellow	Both of these are for increasing contrast in blue specimens.
22	Orange	
25	Red	A contrast filter; for use with blue and with green preparations.
96	Neutral tint	For varying the intensity of illumination. Available in a number of different densities which transmit from 0.01% to 50% of the incident light.

Micrographs in color.—Although good black-and-white micrographs may serve a very useful purpose, there are innumerable instances in which the natural colors would enhance their value immeasurably. The processes employed in ordinary natural-color photography can be adapted to the rendition of microscopic subjects. Undoubtedly the most popular medium for color photography currently available is Eastman Kodak Company's *Kodachrome*, which is available in the 35-mm and *Bantam* size roll film. (The Kodachrome professional sheet film has been discontinued.) Two types of Kodachrome are sold. One is for use in daylight while the other is designed for electric illumination, as, for example, Fotoflood bulbs. Because of the complex nature of the process exposed Kodachrome film must be returned to the manufacturer for finishing. The record obtained on Kodachrome is a color transparency. Prints and enlargements can be made by the wash-off relief process, but the method is rather tedious and expensive. Copies on Ansco Company's *Printon* can be obtained at reasonable cost from many commercial finishers, but color rendition is not accurate. Another color medium manufactured by Eastman Kodak Company is *Kodacolor* film. This is available in the more popular roll film sizes and produces a negative from which the manufacturer can obtain any desired number of color prints. However, the nature of the Kodacolor process precludes faithful color rendition.

Ektachrome, which is available in various sizes of roll film and sheet film, is capable of excellent color rendition. Processing of the film and preparation of the prints may be carried out by the individual worker or by any one of the numerous commercial color laboratories.

Ansco Color, manufactured by the Ansco Company, is available in popular roll film sizes and sheet film sizes, and produces attractive positive color transparencies. This film can be processed by the amateur photographer if he wishes to take the time to do so; many commercial finishers are equipped to process Ansco Color for a reasonable fee.

Recently the Polaroid-Land Camera has become available with an appropriate accessory for taking photomicrographs. This should be of interest to those who could benefit by having a finished positive print available within a very few minutes.

For a comprehensive treatment of the subject of photomicrography the reader should consult *Photomicrography in Theory and Practice*, by Charles Patten Shillaber, published by John Wiley & Sons, Inc.

Study Problems

1. Explain the principle of a camera lucida.

2. Explain the circumstances under which the drawing surface may be other than horizontal.

3. Tell what undesirable results accompanies overintense illumination of the drawing surface. Explain how this can be remedied without changing the lighting of the specimen.

4. State the advantage of having long bellows on a photomicrographic camera.

5. (a) A certain camera designed to take a picture 6×9 cm was provided with a 7.5-cm lens. (When set for "infinity" focus, the optic center of the lens was 7.5 cm from the film plane.) A student took a photomicrograph by placing the lens of this camera just above the ocular of a microscope. The latter was provided with a 5-$\times$ ocular and an 8-mm objective (approx. 21-$\times$). The resulting photograph was *considerably* less than a 100-diameter magnification. Explain why.

(b) Other factors remaining unaltered, would the removal of the camera lens result in a different magnification in a photograph taken with the equipment mentioned in part (a)?

(c) In general, what arrangement of film and microscope is required to obtain a magnification comparable with the ratings of the objectives and oculars employed?

6. A simple dissecting microscope was equipped with a $4\frac{1}{2}$-$\times$ lens. After a zoology student had placed an interesting specimen beneath this simple microscope, he decided to obtain a photomicrograph by supporting a fixed-focus camera above the magnifier. Comment on this procedure.

7. What type of film or plate would be satisfactory for photographing the following in black and white?

(a) White crystals, by reflected light.

(b) A mixture of white crystals and pink crystals, by reflected light.

(c) Red crystals in a pink solution, by transmitted light.

(d) A mixture of nickel nitrate and cobalt nitrate crystals, by transmitted light. In each case justify your answer.

8. State why certain filters might be employed to advantage in the cases mentioned in Problem 5.

Chapter VI

QUANTITATIVE MICROSCOPY

Determining linear dimensions.—Although many chemists appear oblivious to the capacities of the microscope in connection with quantitative determinations, the fact is that this instrument is admirably suited for carrying out certain types of measurements with a fairly high degree of precision. There are instances in which, if the utmost in precision is not required, the microscope may take the place of an expensive piece of specialized equipment. This is particularly important in laboratories which have only rare occasion to employ certain apparatus of limited applications, viz., a refractometer.

Among the simpler quantitative determinations are length and area. Lengths of microscopic objects may be measured by several different methods. For making approximate estimates, no special equipment is required. If the diameter of the field has been determined for a given lens combination, it is a fairly simple matter to compare the length of a specimen with the diameter of the field in which it is found. Let us assume that a certain crystal is about one-fourth as long as the diameter of the field. If this diameter was previously found equal to 2 mm, the crystal must measure about 0.5 mm in length. Such approximations may be quite useful in innumerable instances. Where a greater degree of precision is demanded, more exact methods are available.

Some microscopes are equipped with a graduated mechanical stage, but instruments which are not thus provided can enjoy the same advantage by obtaining a detachable mechanical stage. Both types are provided with a graduated scale along the rear and one along the side. By means of two knobs the slide holder, which is part of the mechanism, can be moved either from right to left, or from front to rear. The vernier arrangement permits readings to tenths of a millimeter. For work with a graduated mechanical stage the ocular should be provided with cross hairs —or, at least, with one hair line.

To measure the length of a specimen, the slide is placed in the holder of the mechanical stage; then by means of the appropriate knobs the slide is moved sidewise or back-and-forth until one edge, or a point, of the specimen just coincides with the cross-hair in the ocular (Figure 6.2A). After recording the scale reading the slide is moved along until the opposite end of the specimen (Figure 6.2B) coincides with the cross-hair of the ocular. The difference between this second scale reading and the first one should represent the length of the specimen. Because of slight lag in

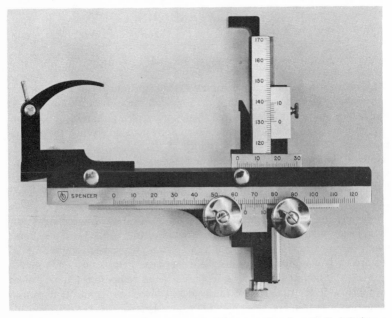

FIG. 6.1. GRADUATED MECHANICAL STAGE. (*Courtesy American Optical Co.*)

the mechanism of the stage it is important to turn the knob slowly, in the desired direction, and to stop promptly when the slide has traversed the required distance. If the slide has been moved too far in a given direction, it is not advisable to attempt a correction by merely turning the knob in the opposite direction until the image appears in proper position; instead, it must be moved back to the original position, and the entire procedure must be repeated.

Readings are taken as on any other vernier scale. It will be seen that the ten divisions on the short movable scale span only nine of the divisions on the fixed scale. When any measurements are made with this device, the division on the fixed scale which exactly coincides with the zero line of the vernier is taken as the correct reading. In Figure 6.3A the reading is 2.0. More frequently, however, the zero of the vernier will lie somewhere between two of the scale divisions, as shown in Figure 6.3B. Here, it will be noted, the vernier scale zero lies between 2.1 and 2.2 cm. To find the figure which represents the decimal place, glance along the vernier scale to see which division exactly coincides with a division on the stationary scale. In the illustration given this turns out to be the fourth division beyond zero. The correct reading, therefore, is 2.14 cm. As in so many other laboratory procedures, one should take the mean of several measurements. These do not require much time once the operator has become accustomed to the use of the apparatus.

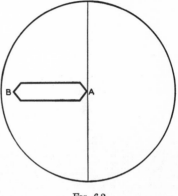

Fig. 6.2

Although the graduated mechanical stage offers a very convenient method for measuring lengths, there are certain disadvantages. Where microscopic objects are concerned, one-tenth of a millimeter is a rather large unit of measurement. For the precise measurement of very minute specimens one may employ a stage micrometer or an ocular micrometer. The former may be a metal plate on which a very fine scale has been engraved, but more commonly the micrometer is ruled on glass, as described on page 190 (Experiment 14).

Since the glass stage micrometer is quite easily damaged, its principal use is for calibrating an ocular micrometer. The latter is a thin glass disc on which there has been ruled a scale. This may be 5 mm in length, with each millimeter subdivided into halves, quarters, and twentieths. On some of the ocular discs the millimeters are subdivided into tenths. Care should be exercised in handling these discs, and when not in use they should be stored in a suitable box or case.

Before an ocular micrometer can be used for actual measurements, it must be calibrated against a standard, such as a stage micrometer. The eyelens (top lens) of an ocular is unscrewed. After removing dust and fingermarks from the micrometer disc by means of a soft brush or lens tissue, the disc is carefully dropped into the ocular tube. Although these micrometers vary in diameter, they are sufficiently large to rest on the ocular diaphragm. The eyelens is replaced, and the eyepiece is inserted in the microscope draw tube. The latter should be set at the usual length of 160 mm if it is movable. (170 mm for some Zeiss objectives.) When

the instrument is now focused on the stage micrometer, both scales should
be visible. If the figures on the scale of the ocular micrometer are reversed, the disc must be removed and turned over. Considerable time
can be saved if a small ink spot is placed near the edge of the disc to indicate which surface must be uppermost.

The stage micrometer is adjusted so the scale is just above or just
below the ocular micrometer scale, and parallel with it. In addition, the

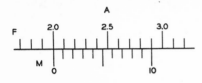

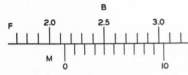

FIG. 6.3. READING A VERNIER SCALE.
A. Here *F* represents a portion of the
mechanical stage, while *M* represents the
movable vernier scale. *F* is graduated in
centimeters. As shown here the reading
is 2 cm. B. Here the zero line of the
vernier scale is a short distance beyond
position 2.1 of the fixed scale. The first
(and only) division of the vernier to coincide with a line of the centimeter scale is
number 4. This indicates that the zero
line of the vernier must be 0.4 of the way
between the *F* scale readings 2.1 and 2.2.
The exact reading, therefore, is 2.14 cm.

zero line of the ocular scale should
be exactly opposite one of the graduations of the stage micrometer.
The ocular scale is next examined
to find some other line which exactly corresponds with a division
on the stage micrometer. Knowing
the exact length of any definite
portion of the ocular micrometer,
the exact equivalent of one division
can be evaluated. Let us assume
that in a specific case the 5-mm
scale spans exactly 0.3 mm (according to the image of the stage micrometer). If the ocular disc is
graduated into twentieths, there
must be a total of one hundred divisions. Therefore each division
actually represents a length of
0.3/100, or 0.003 mm. If, however,
the scale on the disc is graduated in
tenths, with a total of 50 divisions,
then each is equivalent to 0.3/50, or
0.006 mm.

It will not always happen that
the ocular scale is equivalent to an
integral number of tenth-millimeter divisions. In such instances one may
use that portion of the stage micrometer which is graduated into 0.01-mm
divisions. One might find that the ocular scale extends over 0.34 mm of
the stage micrometer image. In this case 0.34 is divided by 100 or 50 to
find the equivalent of each division of the ocular micrometer. This would
give the values of 0.0032 or 0.0064 mm. When dealing with dimensions
of such small magnitude the constant use of fractional values may become
irksome. For this reason microscopists have resorted to a smaller unit,
namely the micron, which is equal to 0.001 mm. On this basis one division of the scale in the example just mentioned would be equivalent to

three microns. The symbol for micron is the Greek letter mu, written μ. In the foregoing example, therefore, the value of each division could also be expressed as 3.2 or 6.4 microns.

When the ocular scale is not exactly equivalent to a whole number of one-tenth millimeter divisions of the stage micrometer, some workers prefer to employ a different method of calibration. This simply consists in raising or lowering the draw tube to such height that the 5-mm scale is exactly equivalent to an integral number of the stage micrometer divisions.

Having determined the precise value of the ocular micrometer it is necessary to record this together with the objective and ocular employed, as well as the tube length. The calibrations will then apply to this system whenever measuring specimens under a cover glass. (Since objectives are corrected for use with a cover glass, the stage micrometers have also been provided with a cover.) In case one should plan to work with some other objective or ocular, or at a different tube length, another calibration is necessary.

If the scale of the ocular micrometer cannot be brought into sharp focus, the condition may sometimes be remedied by partly unscrewing the eyelens of the ocular. Some oculars which are designed for use with a micrometer permit focusing the eyelens up and down. This does not change the values of the micrometer scale; the latter is affected to the same extent as is the image of the stage micrometer.

Instead of placing an ocular micrometer in one of the regular oculars, it is possible to purchase a special eyepiece in which a micrometer has been permanently mounted. These *micrometer oculars,* as they are called, are provided with focusing eyelenses to accommodate individual differences in eyes. Calibration is achieved in the same manner as described previously.

The length of an object to be measured will not always be equivalent to a whole number of divisions of the ocular micrometer. Of course, when the value lies part way between two divisions, the observer may estimate the fractional portion. Although this is not a highly precise method, the actual error introduced need not exceed the limits permissible for most work. To illustrate, let us assume that the length of a specimen was estimated as the equivalent of 10.8 divisions, whereas 10.7 would be the correct value. Here the error would be less than one part in one hundred; in most cases an error of this magnitude could be ignored. After all, this would be similar to an error of one inch in measuring the length of a 9-foot rug! Naturally, the percentage of error would be greater in measuring very short specimens.

Where the nature of the work demands a higher degree of precision one may employ a filar micrometer ocular (Figure 6.4). This device offers convenience and precision, but it is rather expensive. In one form of this instrument the ocular is provided with a graduated scale which must be calibrated against a stage micrometer. In addition there is also a very fine cross hair, which can be moved across the scale by rotating a small drum attached to the side of the instrument. The dimensions are so adjusted that one complete turn of the drum moves the cross hair over a distance represented by one whole division of the scale in the ocular. Since the rim of the drum is divided into one hundred equal spaces, one can measure to the one-hundredth part of an ocular division.

FIG. 6.4. FILAR MICROMETER EYEPIECE.
(*Courtesy Bausch & Lomb.*)

To use the filar micrometer the object slide is so placed that the image of one edge or extremity of the specimen to be measured *exactly* coincides with one of the ruled lines of the ocular scale. The number of whole scale divisions spanned by the image is observed and recorded. To determine the fractional division to be added, the micrometer screw is turned to cause the cross hair in the ocular to coincide with the ruling which bounds the whole number of scale divisions just recorded. Then the screw is slowly turned until the cross hair meets the edge of the object image. The fraction is then read on the drum. The average of several such readings should be taken.

A second form of filar micrometer eyepiece is provided with a movable scale instead of a traveling cross hair. In using this instrument the micrometer screw is turned until the drum

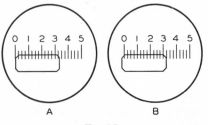

A   B

FIG. 6.5

reading is at zero. The object image is so arranged that one extremity coincides with the zero line of the eyepiece scale. After noting the number of whole divisions spanned by the image, the micrometer screw is turned so as to move the ocular scale toward the right. When the ruling which originally marked the number of whole divisions previously noted meets the edge of the object image, the drum reading is taken.

The foregoing procedure may be clarified by reference to A in Figure 6.5. In this particular case a thin plate-like crystal is to be measured. The image extends across 13 whole divisions on the scale, that is, one whole division beyond line number 3, but there are four scale divisions to each of the numbered units. To find the fractional division covered beyond or in excess of 13, turn the micrometer screw until the thirteenth division is superimposed on the edge of the image, as in B, Figure 6.5. The reading on the drum indicates how many hundredths to add to 13 to obtain the total length. If the drum reading should be 42, the total number of scale divisions spanned by the image would be 13.42. Knowing the number of microns represented by each scale division, the actual length can be found by multiplication.

One method, which has certain advantages, makes use of the camera lucida. The divisions of a stage micrometer, as seen through the microscope, are drawn on a sheet of paper. Since the exact values of the micrometer divisions are known, one can readily calculate the relationship between the length of any image drawn on the paper and the length of the actual specimen under observation. Obviously, this relationship applies only when using the same optical system. That is, the same objective, ocular and tube length must be employed. In one specific case the data obtained were as follows:

Objective	Ocular	Tube Length	Object Length/Image Length
16 mm	5-$\times$	160 mm	$1/52.5 = 0.01904$

In other words, 1 mm of the stage micrometer, when drawn on paper with the foregoing optical arrangement, spanned a length of 52.5 mm. This span indicates a magnification of 52.5 diameters. To find the length of the specimen, the length of the sketched image is divided by 52.5, or multiplied by its reciprocal, 0.019. Once the factor has been determined for a given lens combination the dimensions of any specimen can be determined very promptly. If a complete sketch is not desired, one need merely record small points at the extremities of the image to be measured.

A variation of the foregoing method is to prepare a drawing of the micrometer scale on a narrow slip of paper, using the camera lucida for the purpose. Later this scale can be used in measuring distances on any camera lucida sketches which have been made under similar conditions. Since lengths can be read off directly in microns or in fractions of a millimeter, this method obviates the necessity of multiplying by a factor each time a measurement is made.

The methods just described can be employed with any of the conventional microscopes. With instruments which are equipped with a substage condenser it is possible to project a scale image directly on the object slide. At an appropriate distance from the substage mirror there is placed a glass slide on which a scale has been ruled. By means of the substage condenser an image of the scale is projected into the field occupied by a stage micrometer. The latter is employed for calibrating the divisions of the projected scale image. Thereafter, provided the distance from the scale to mirror is not varied, specimens on the stage of the microscope can be measured with any desired combination of objective, eyepiece, and tube length, because the projected scale image is subject to the same magnification as is the specimen. This device is sometimes referred to as a *ghost micrometer*.

Measuring depth and volume.—Many microscopes are provided with a graduated fine adjustment which makes it convenient to measure verti-

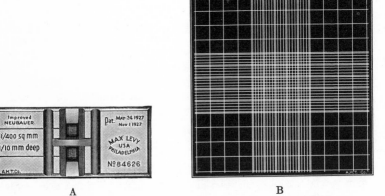

A   B

FIG. 6.6. A. Neubauer haemacytometer or counting chamber. B. Enlarged view of ruling on Neubauer counting chamber. (*Courtesy Arthur H. Thomas Co.*)

cal distances on microscopic specimens. Essentially, the procedure consists in getting an accurate focus on a point in the plane from which the height is to be measured. After noting the reading of the graduated fine adjustment screw, the latter is turned so as to raise slowly the objective until sharp focus is obtained on a point in the upper plane of the object to be measured. The difference between the final reading of the fine adjustment and the initial reading represents the height of the specimen. The graduations may be in terms of microns, but if no information is available calibration is possible by measuring wire of known gauge, or the thickness of a cover glass of known dimensions. If no suitable objects are available, the diameter of any wire or of thin glass thread, etc., may be determined first by the use of an ocular micrometer. This value can then be applied in calibrating the fine adjustment graduations. Measurements with the fine adjustment require the use of objectives having very small depth of focus or low penetrating power. Obviously, the greater the depth of focus of the objective used, the greater will be the error involved.

In certain types of work it is necessary to determine the number of fine particles suspended per unit volume of liquid. Several methods are available for performing such determinations, one method being similar to that employed in making a blood count.[1] The latter generally involves the use of a special slide, such as the Neubauer haemacytometer (Figure 6.6). The important feature of this device is a small, ruled stage ex-

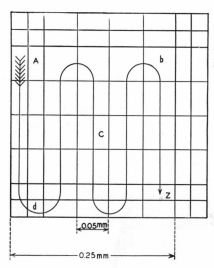

FIG. 6.7. PORTION OF A HAEMACYTOMETER. For greater convenience every fifth row is double-ruled. In the diagram, one block of 25 smaller squares is traversed in following the arrow from A to Z. When only five squares are to be counted, those marked A, b, C, d, Z may be taken.

actly 0.1 mm below the main portion of the slide. By covering this stage with a carefully polished cover glass one obtains a shallow counting cell of known volume. The central portion of the cell is divided into 16 squares covering a total area of one square millimeter. Each of these is further subdivided into 25 smaller squares having an area of 0.0025 sq mm each. With the plane cover glass in place, the volume of liquid confined over this central ruled area of the haemacytometer is equal to 0.1 cu mm.

When the particles to be counted are fairly large, one may count all that lie in the square millimeter area. However, if they are rather small

[1] James Campbell Todd and Arthur Hawley Sanford, *Clinical Diagnosis by Laboratory Methods,* 8th ed., Saunders, 1937, pp. 230 ff.

and very numerous, satisfactory results are obtained by counting the number found in five of the larger squares (see Figure 6.7) and multiplying by the number four.   Having found the number of particles in 0.1 cu mm, it is a simple matter to calculate the number per cubic centimeter.   In many instances the number may be so large that an accurate count seems impossible because of overcrowding.   This difficulty is readily overcome by diluting the sample.   To illustrate, if one milliliter of the original fluid is diluted to ten, the correct final result is obtained by multiplying the actual count by ten.   Naturally, the diluting liquid must be one which has no effect on the components of the sample.

In making a count some definite system should be adopted and adhered to regularly.   A common practice is to traverse 25 small squares of a given block in the direction indicated by the curved arrow in Figure 6.7. Another custom concerns particles which do not lie wholly within any one square.   In such cases all particles which touch on the left side and those which touch on the lower edge of a square are counted, while those which touch the right edge or the top are ignored.

Dilution, when necessary, can be effected by means of pipets and flasks ordinarily employed in volumetric analysis.   In special cases, however, when very minute amounts of sample are available, blood diluting pipets may be employed.

Determination of refractive index.—In the identification of organic liquids and certain crystalline substances information on refractive index frequently proves to be an important aid.   While it is true that for liquids the refractive index can be found with greater accuracy by means of a refractometer, nevertheless many laboratories are not able to afford this apparatus.   When the values need to be known only to the second or third decimal place, the determinations can be made under the microscope.

For those microscopes which are not provided with a graduated fine adjustment, refractive index must be measured by an immersion method. Every user of the microscope has observed that not all transparent colorless specimens appear equally distinct even though all may be mounted in the same colorless liquid medium.   In general, the greater the difference between the refractive index of a specimen and that of the surrounding medium, the more distinct its outline will appear.   If the index of a colorless crystal and that of the surrounding medium are equal, the crystal will be practically invisible.   It would therefore appear that one method for determining the refractive index of a liquid is to find an isotropic crystal of known index which will be practically invisible when immersed in the sample.   Of course, complete invisibility would not necessarily result even if the crystal and the surrounding fluid possessed the same refractive index.   Unless the two also exhibited the same degree of dispersion, the outline of the crystal would be visible.

In order to reduce the number of trials necessary to find a standard which matches the sample, one takes advantage of an interesting phenomenon known as the *Becke line*. The latter is the name applied to the bright border, or "halo," which bounds a thin crystal when surrounded by a liquid of different refractive index. To accentuate this halo, it is necessary to employ axial illumination, with the condenser diaphragm closed down to yield a comparatively narrow cone of light.

The important advantage of the Becke line is not merely the fact that it indicates a difference between the indices of two media, but that it indicates which possesses the higher value. To illustrate this we might consider a crystal of potassium chloride immersed in benzene. At room temperature, the indices of these two substances are respectively 1.490 and 1.495. When observed under the microscope as described above the Becke line should be in evidence. The useful feature, however, would appear upon slightly raising or lowering the focus of the instrument. In the present instance, upon raising the focus, the halo or Becke line should move away from the crystal or toward the benzene. On the other hand, when the objective is lowered a bit the halo should move away from the benzene or toward the interior of the crystal. This demonstrates the general rule. When focusing up, the Becke line moves toward the medium of higher refractive index; when focusing down, the halo is displaced toward the medium of lower index. Those interested in explanations of the cause of this phenomenon will find brief summaries of several theories in Chapter 15 of Johannsen.[2]

With ordinary care the Becke test can be accurate to within ± 0.005. It is important to keep in mind the fact that the index of refraction varies at different temperatures, so that it is not sufficient to assign any single value to a liquid standard unless it is always used at the same proper temperature. The value for liquids decreases about 0.0004 for each degree the temperature is raised.[3] If the index n is known for a given temperature, the approximate value of n', the index at a higher temperature, can be determined from the equation

$$n' = n - 0.0004 \, \Delta t,$$

where Δt represents the increase in temperature.

Crystals employed for these determinations should not be very thick. The accuracy of the method may also suffer if the crystals are bounded by faces which are not perpendicular or nearly so. The condenser diaphragm should be stopped down as far as possible.

Refractive index also varies somewhat with different wave lengths of light. For this reason observations should be made with the same type

[2] Albert Johannsen, *Manual of Petrographic Methods*, McGraw-Hill, 1918.
[3] Larsen: *U. S. Geological Survey Bulletin No. 679*, p. 15.

of light by which the standard liquids or crystals were measured. Commonly the values are determined by sodium light, since this is readily duplicated by several methods.

Obviously, with a set of liquid standards it is possible to determine the refractive indices of crystals, while a set of isotropic crystal standards enables one to ascertain the values for liquids.[4] When working with solid specimens it is not even necessary to have well-developed crystals. In the investigation of minerals the Becke test has been applied successfully even in the case of relatively small grains of material. By resorting to special refinements some workers have claimed an accuracy of ±0.002 and even ±0.001.

A variation of the foregoing immersion method resorts to the use of oblique illumination for estimating refractive index. If an opaque screen or a card is placed over part of the aperture in the diaphragm below the substage condenser, part of the field seen through the microscope will be darkened. If an isotropic crystal is immersed in a liquid and examined by such oblique light, one side of the crystal will appear bright while the other is shaded. Just which side appears bright will depend upon the relative refractive indices of the crystal and the immersion medium. Should the index of the crystal exceed that of the liquid, both will appear bright on the same side. On the other hand, if the crystal has the lower value, its bright edge will appear toward the shaded portion of the immersion liquid.

A condenser should be employed if available, but, if the microscope has none, similar results may be achieved by swinging the substage mirror to one side, with the concave surface in use. After the specimen has been brought into focus, part of the light reflected up to the object slide is gradually screened out by slowly moving a small card across the diaphragm opening. The card is introduced from the side opposite the mirror. The effect should be studied while introducing and withdrawing the card several times. The boundary between the shaded and the bright sides of the liquid medium may be graduated instead of sharp.

Just as in the method using the Becke line, so by this oblique illumination method, the values obtained are influenced by the temperature and by the wave length of light employed. Preferably, the objectives employed should be between 16-mm and 32-mm equivalent focus, since these are of relatively low numerical aperture.

If the microscope used has a graduated fine adjustment, it is possible to

[4] The Eastman Kodak Company puts up a series of liquid standards in uniform glass-stoppered bottles. Although these compounds cover a fairly wide range of values, one may purchase as small a number as desired. On the other hand, in the Shillaber series of liquids there is a definite stepwise increase in refractive index between each liquid and the succeeding member in the series. These carefully standardized liquids are available from R. P. Cargille, of New York.

measure refractive index of liquids by a direct method. It is a familiar fact that an object lying on the bottom of a pool of water appears considerably closer to the surface than it really is. This phenomenon can be employed in measuring the index of refraction. To carry out such determinations under the microscope, the liquid is placed in a stage refractometer, which consists of a circular cell cemented to a glass slide (Figure 6.8). If the 16-mm objective is to be employed, the depth of the cell should not exceed 2 mm. The exact depth of the same should be known; otherwise it must be measured. After filling with sample, the refractometer cell must be

covered with a thin glass slip. The latter must be sufficiently large to project some distance beyond the cell wall on one side. The 16-mm objective is focused (through the cover glass) on the surface of the slide, as at point A in Figure 6.8. After recording the reading of the fine adjustment scale, the refrac-

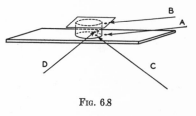

Fig. 6.8

tometer is moved over to bring point C beneath the objective. This will not be in focus until the objective is raised slightly by slowly turning the fine adjustment in the proper direction. The distance CD, which represents the distance through which the image has been displaced by the liquid, is also the height through which the objective has been raised. This distance should be equal to the difference between the two readings of the graduated fine adjustment. By subtracting CD from the actual depth of the liquid sample AB, the apparent depth is obtained. The refractive index can then be calculated from the equation

$$n = \frac{\text{Depth of sample}}{\text{Apparent depth}}.$$

Because of lag in the fine adjustment, it must be turned in only one direction when making any measurements. If one inadvertently turns it too far in one direction, the trial should be repeated. Merely turning the screw in the opposite direction will not give the correct reading. Unfortunately this method is not capable of any great degree of precision. Part of the difficulty lies in the depth of focus of the objective; irregularities in the fine adjustment screw are another source of error. Ordinarily the figures obtained by this method are correct only to the second decimal place.

Wright [5] has suggested a modification of the foregoing "image displacement method" which is capable of much greater accuracy. The same type of cell is required, but it can be somewhat deeper. The actual

[5] See Chamot and Mason, *op. cit.*, p. 379.

depth, however, need not be known. The object in this method is to determine the "image displacement" for several liquids of accurately known indices of refraction. With the data thus obtained it is possible to plot a reference curve for use with any unknown samples.

As in the direct method, the microscope is focused (through the cover glass) on the surface of the refractometer slide, as at A, in Figure 6.8.

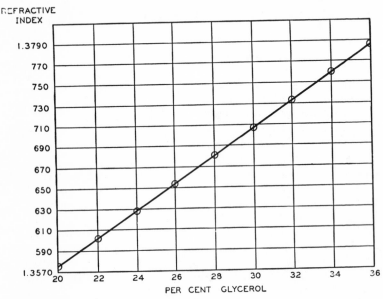

FIG. 6.9. RELATIONSHIP BETWEEN CONCENTRATION AND REFRACTIVE INDEX OF AN AQUEOUS GLYCEROL SOLUTION. This curve serves to illustrate one way in which the microscopic determination of refractive index may be utilized in the quantitative estimation of the concentration of a solution. Since an increase of 1 per cent in the glycerol concentration results in a corresponding change of better than one unit in the third decimal place of the refractive index, the microscopic method can be applied if the accuracy need not be too great. (For more complete numerical data, see L. F. Hoyt, *Ind. & Eng. Chem.* **26, 329** (1943).)

This being accomplished, the cell is brought beneath the objective, so that the instrument can be focused, through the liquid, on point C. From the graduated fine adjustment one obtains the image displacement, CD, for the liquid in the cell. Having determined the displacements for several accurately known liquids, these values are plotted against the corresponding refractive index values on a large sheet of graph paper. A curve similar to Figure 6.9 is drawn through the points thus obtained. The curve should be extrapolated to include displacement = 0, and $n = 1.000$. To find the refractive index of any liquid, the image displacement is measured just as for the reference liquids. The corresponding index can then be read from the curve. This method is more accurate than the direct method for several reasons. An important factor is that any irregularities in the micrometer screw are minimized by selecting reference liquids covering different sections of its utilized range. The use of a

A

B

FIG. 6.10. A. Nichols Refractometer: Macro model. This model requires 2 to 4 drops of sample liquid. B. Nichols Refractometer: Micro model. Only 6–8 cu mm of liquid are required, of which 5–6 cu mm may be recovered.

slightly deeper cell likewise helps to reduce the errors of measurement. With reasonable care an accuracy of ±0.005 is readily obtained, but this can be improved upon by exercising some control over temperature, light, etc.

Even greater accuracy is possible with the Nichols stage refractometer. Essentially this is a metal plate provided with two cylindrical cells. Each cell contains two small glass prisms as shown in Figures 6.10 and 6.11.

In one cell the prisms have a refractive index of 1.52; those in the other cell, 1.72. The former cell is recommended for liquids having indices below 1.40 and above 1.65, while the other is employed for values falling between 1.40 and 1.65 and for those of 1.85 and higher.

To use the Nichols instrument, a cell is filled with sample and covered with a special cover slip. When this assembly is focused under the microscope, two dark lines should be observed (Figure 6.11). The distance between these depends upon the relationship between the refractive

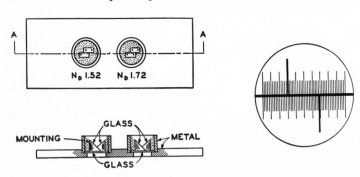

Fig. 6.11 A. Top View of Nichols Refractometer. B. Cross Section A A of Nichols Refractometer. C. View of scale and lines as they appear in an experiment, 19.3 divisions. (*Courtesy Arthur H. Thomas Co.*)

index of the liquid sample and that of the glass prisms. The relative distance is observed by means of an ocular micrometer.

Before actual determination can be found, the cells and the microscope must be calibrated against five standard liquids which are included with the outfit. For each standard the number of divisions observed in the ocular is plotted against the corresponding refractive index (Figure 6.12). This enables one to plot a reference curve for each cell. Subsequently, to determine the value for any liquid, it is merely necessary to fill one of the cells and observe the number of micrometer divisions which separate the two lines which appear in the ocular of the microscope. The actual index is then obtained by reference to the appropriate curve.

One advantage of this method is that it does not depend upon a graduated fine adjustment. Obviously, determinations must be carried out under the conditions for which the calibrations were made. The same tube length, same objective, and the same ocular must be employed. After acquiring some practice, an accuracy of ±0.001 should be obtained under ordinary laboratory conditions. By using monochromatic light, a filar micrometer, and suitable temperature control, an accuracy of ±0.0004 is claimed. Although this may appear far less accurate than a refractometer of the Pulfrich type, it is also true that in many instances the precision of the latter instrument is not required. If the cost must be considered, the Nichols type enjoys the advantage of being less expensive.

To evaluate the methods just described they might be compared with the Fisher refractometer. Although the latter is an independent unit, not to be used with a microscope, it serves as an example of a relatively inex-

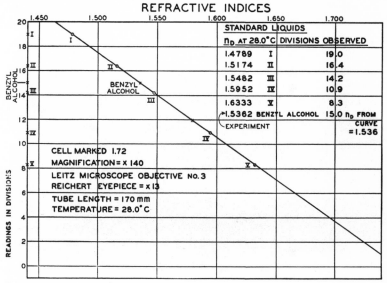

FIG. 6.12. EXAMPLE OF A CALIBRATION CURVE OBTAINED WITH THE 1.72 CELL OF NICHOLS REFRACTOMETER. (*Courtesy Arthur H. Thomas Co.*)

pensive instrument. Its manufacturers claim for it an accuracy of ±0.002.

Determining percentage composition.—Although the microscope is not generally looked upon as an instrument for weighing, a rather unique method for estimating the proportion of certain components in a mixture has been developed by T. E. Wallis.[6] Fundamentally the procedure depends upon the use of reference mixtures containing known amounts of the ingredients to be determined, along with known weights of lycopodium powder. The latter consists of the spores of the fern, *Lycopodium clavatum*, and is regularly sold by various supply houses. From a large number of careful counts Wallis has found that these spores are rather uniform in size, averaging 94,000 per milligram. The appearance of these

[6] Cf. T. E. Wallis, *Quantitative Microscopy*, Arnold & Co., London.

spores is unaffected by triturating in a mortar or by boiling in dilute acids and alkalies. This advantage is important when working on mixtures which require such treatment before the quantitative estimates are made.

Should one desire to find the percentage of starch in a given powdered sample, the first step in the analysis would be the preparation of an appropriate reference mixture. This can be done as follows. Into a glass mortar a convenient weight of a mixture is placed containing a known percentage of the type of starch to be analyzed. For this first trial, a 50 per cent preparation can be used. To this is added a known weight of lycopodium powder. All of the solid particles must then be uniformly suspended in a suitable medium, such as castor oil, by triturating the mixture in a small volume of the oil. More of the latter is added, followed by further trituration. After a third addition of oil the fluid is transferred to a small flask. None of the fluid must be lost.

Since part of the suspension adheres to the pestle and to the inner wall of the mortar, more oil is added to the latter. By further trituration the suspension in the mortar becomes "diluted." This new portion is transferred to the flask containing the first batch. Practically all of the solid particles can be removed from the mortar and pestle by repeating this addition of small portions of oil. The completed mixture should contain about 50 mg of the lycopodium for each 10 ml of oil. A larger proportion of lycopodium tends to result in showing too many spores per field. Finally, the combined suspensions in the flask are rendered as uniform as possible by adequate shaking. A drop is transferred to a slide and covered with a round cover slip. This drop should be of such magnitude that it fills completely the entire area beneath the cover, without oozing beyond its edge.

With the use of an eyepiece equipped with a net micrometer, the number of spores and the number of starch grains in several different fields are counted. It is advisable to make such counts on a number of slides. From these counts, the average number of starch grains per given number of lycopodium spores can be calculated. Naturally, a definite system should be employed. Using a mechanical stage, Wallis recommends counting twenty fields, although 10 fields should prove adequate for many purposes. The 4-mm objective is focused on the center of the cover glass. By moving the slide 2 mm to the right (or left) the first field is brought into view. The suggested loci of the other fields are represented in Figure 6.13.

The next step is to prepare a similar suspension of spores and the sample to be analyzed. Although it may increase the weighing time, the procedure is simplified if the weight ratio of lycopodium powder and sample is the same as the ratio taken in the known mixture. Counts are made, and the average is determined just as previously. Assume that, by way of illustration, with the 50 per cent preparation there were, on an average, 60 starch grains to 8 lycopodium spores. Now, should the unknown yield an average count of 15 starch grains per 8 spores, the mixture apparently contains $15/60 \times 50$ per cent, or $12\frac{1}{2}$ per cent starch. This should represent a fair approximation. For greater accuracy, counts should next be made on a suspension of lycopodium with a sample known to contain $12\frac{1}{2}$ per cent of the same kind of starch.

In general, if there is to be any semblance of accuracy in analyses made by this method, the unknown component must be present in the form of particles which are fairly uniform in size. Obviously, the suspensions must be prepared with adequate care to insure a homogeneous distribution of particles. Even in cases where the error amounts to ± 2 per cent, the results may prove quite valuable. Furthermore, in some instances no more reliable procedure is available. Typical applications are the determination of the percentage of corn starch or potato starch added to more expensive starches or to wheat flour and the testing of the quality of certain insect powders.

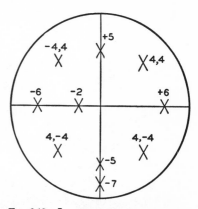

Fig. 6.13. Location of the fields to be counted. The objective is first focused on the center of the cover glass, represented by the circle; then each field is found by moving the slide the appropriate distance from the centered position. The numbers within the circle denote the respective distances in millimeters.

Micro melting point.—An important numerical value which can be determined under the microscope is the melting point or melting range. According to Johns, "The microscopic determination of melting point is so far superior to the usual capillary tube method that it should always be employed wherever the apparatus is available."[7]

The microscopic determination of melting point requires the use of an electrically heated "warm stage," or "hot stage," as it is sometimes called. It should be designed to permit the melting specimen to be observed by transmitted light. The rate of heating should be capable of rather precise control, and the lag between the temperature of the stage and the value indicated by the thermometer should be negligible. When these conditions are met, the microscopic method offers several advantages over the capillary tube method.

[7] I. B. Johns, *Laboratory Manual of Microchemistry*, Burgess Publishing Co., Minneapolis, 1941, p. 53.

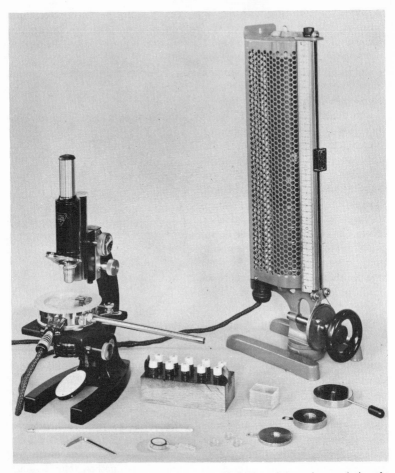

FIG. 6.14. KOFLER HOT STAGE SET UP FOR USE. Variable resistance for regulating the temperature is on the right. (*Courtesy Arthur H. Thomas Co.*)

The melting point apparatus of Kofler (Figure 6.14) has proved very satisfactory. The increase in the temperature of this electrically heated stage is easily controlled by means of a rheostat provided with a graduated scale. The thermometers furnished by the manufacturer are carefully calibrated for the specific stage which they accompany, so that when used under certain prescribed conditions the observed temperatures require no stem corrections. By the microscopic method only a few minute crystals or particles are required for a determination, and the changes occurring in an individual particle are readily followed.

Although it is customary for organic chemists to consider a "sharp" capillary melting point a criterion of purity, the Kofler method has demonstrated that numerous preparations which appear pure by this criterion betray the presence of contaminants when their melting points are determined by the micro method. Typical examples of this discrepancy are "pure" acetanilide, which may have a melting range of 113–115 degrees when determined under the microscope, and phenacetin, which may melt at 132–135 degrees according to the Kofler method, even though it exhibits a sharp capillary melting point.

When investigating the purity of an organic compound, the determination of a eutectic temperature may prove more informative than its melting point. Thus, although β-naphthol may be contaminated with naphthalene, the impurity exerts such a slight depression on the melting point that the presence of less than 5 per cent may be overlooked. However, a mixture of pure β-naphthol and anesthesin has a eutectic temperature of 54 degrees. The presence of naphthalene causes the mixture (ternary) to melt at 45 degrees, so that the presence of as little as 2 per cent naphthalene in the original naphthol is readily detected.

Frequently, during a melting point determination on the warm-stage the observer can note the formation of minute bubbles on a crystal. These may indicate the release of water of hydration or some other form of decomposition. In numerous instances it is possible to observe certain sublimation characteristics while running the melting point determination. With some substances, a tendency to change from one crystalline form to another (polymorphism) may be observed. Ordinarily these phenomena are not evident during melting point determinations performed in capillary tubes.

Analysis of binary mixtures.—An interesting application of the Kofler hot-stage in the quantitative analysis of certain binary mixtures depends upon the determination of refractive index. The temperature at which a molten organic product exhibits a given refractive index is readily determined under the microscope by heating in the presence of a calibrated glass powder. The identity of the components of the sample must be known. Having determined the temperature at which the refractive index of the molten sample matches that of a calibrated glass powder, the percentage of each component is found by consulting a previously prepared reference curve. The latter must be obtained by plotting the composition of several known samples against the temperatures at which they exhibit the required index of refraction. In working with cycloform-anesthesin mixtures, for example, it is convenient to employ a glass powder of index 1.5400. Pure cycloform matches the value at 66 degrees, while pure anesthesin matches it at 120 degrees. (In this temperature range the change in refractive index of glass is negligible.) Molten mix-

tures of cycloform and anesthesin will match this refractive index somewhere between 66 and 120 degrees. Preparation of such a reference curve
is comparatively simple and requires only small amounts of material.
Thereafter the analysis of a mixture can be performed very quickly, using only minute quantities of sample.[8]

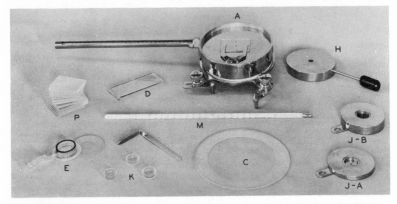

FIG. 6.15. KOFLER HOT STAGE AND VARIOUS ACCESSORIES. (*Courtesy Arthur H. Thomas Co.*)

A. Hot Stage without cover
C. Glass Cover for Hot Stage
M. Thermometer
D. Glass Baffle (Bridge)
H. Cooling Block
P. Micro Slides, 1½ × 1 inches

J–A. Fischer Sublimation Block, Type A
J–B. Fischer Sublimation Block, Type B
E. Vacuum Sublimation Chamber, Kofler-Dernbach
K. Sublimation Dishes, Pyrex

By means of accessories designed for the Kofler apparatus it is possible to study sublimation characteristics under various conditions. In
fact, even high vacuum sublimations can be executed on a microscopic
scale. In these operations, however, the temperatures indicated are
subject to a greater error than in the melting point determinations. Although the Kofler apparatus is, unfortunately, rather expensive, where

[8] Readers who are interested in the quantitative possibilities of the Kofler stage
should consult *Mikromethoden zur Kennzeichnung organischer Stoffe und Stoffgemische,* by Ludwig and Adelheid Kofler, published by Universitätsverlag Wagner,
G.m.b.H., Innsbruck, Austria, 1948. A unique feature of the book consists of identification tables listing approximately a thousand organic compounds. Each of these
is characterized by its melting point, refractive index at some convenient temperature,
and the eutectic temperature of the substance with each of two other compounds.
To illustrate, the melting point of benzylaniline is given as 35.5 degrees (Kofler); its
eutectic temperature with azobenzene, 25 degrees; the eutectic temperature with
benzil, 23 degrees; refractive index at 43–44 degrees equals 1.6010, and at 68–69 degrees
equals 1.5898.

much work of this type is contemplated such an outfit represents a very desirable investment.

Study Problems

1. Describe briefly six devices for the linear measurement of microscopic objects.

2. Discuss the more serious sources of error involved in measurements made by means of the foregoing equipment.

3. Explain how an ocular micrometer is calibrated.

4. Why is it important to record the tube length for which an ocular micrometer is calibrated?

5. With the aid of diagrams show how the observed length of a microscopic object is influenced by the presence or absence of a cover glass.

6. Outline the method of using a haemacytometer slide.

7. In making a count of solid particles in a certain fluid medium there was a total of 114 particles in five of the larger squares of a Neubauer haemacytometer. Calculate the number of particles per milliliter.

8. How can the camera lucida be employed in connection with linear measurements?

9. When certain crystals were placed in a drop of water, they were practically invisible. The same crystals appeared very distinct when observed in glycerol. Explain the reason for the different behavior.

10. Explain how the behavior of an isotropic crystal indicates whether its refractive index is higher or lower than that of the liquid in which it is immersed.

11. Even when an isotropic substance is immersed in a liquid having exactly the same refractive index, it will not necessarily be completely invisible. Explain the reason.

12. In determining the refractive indices of liquids by the immersion method only *isotropic* crystals are used as standards for comparison. Explain why it is not feasible to use anisotropic material.

13. In what manner are refractive index determinations influenced by the color of the light employed?

14. Outline Wright's modification of the image displacement method.

15. By extrapolation of the curve in Figure 6.7 determine the refractive index of a 45 per cent aqueous glycerol solution. How does your value compare with the value reported in Hoyt's original paper?

Chapter VII

POLARIZED LIGHT: PRINCIPLES, SOURCES, AND APPLICATIONS

Double refraction; polarized light.—Thus far our discussion has been concerned only with ordinary light. The student should keep in mind not only the fact that light is propagated by waves, but also that these transverse waves are vibrating at right angles to the direction of propagation. When a breeze sets up small waves or ripples on the surface of a pool of water, a chip of wood which may be present will be seen to bob up and down, while the wave effect travels forward on the surface of the water. The vertical movements of the floating chip are at right angles to the direction in which the wave is being propagated (Figure 7.1). In the case of ordinary light waves, however, the vibrations are not restricted to one single direction; the vibrations can be in all directions which are perpendicular to the direction of propagation.

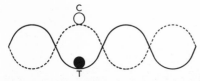

FIG. 7.1. Let the continuous curved line represent a cross-sectional view of waves in water at a given instant. *C* represents a block of wood floating on the crest of a wave. After the wave has traveled forward the distance of one-half wave length, a cross-sectional view of the same region would be represented by the broken line. Instead of having traveled forward with the wave, the block of wood is found in the wave trough at *T*. Although the waves roll constantly forward, the block merely bobs up and down. The direction of these vertical vibrations is perpendicular to the surface of the water.

Some very interesting properties of light can be explained by studying the behavior of a clear crystal of Iceland spar. (Also known as calcite or crystalline calcium carbonate.) If such a crystal is laid on a printed page, the observer sees not *one* but *two* images of each word covered. This phenomenon, known as *double refraction,* is exhibited by various other substances, but only few show it to such a marked degree.

A previous chapter (cf. I) explained how a beam of light may be refracted, or bent, from its original path when passing from one transparent medium into another. This refraction, however, merely causes a displacement of the image, whereas double refraction results in the appearance of two images. It can be demonstrated that when a beam of light enters the crystal of calcite it is divided into two components. This is shown diagrammatically in Figure 7.3. Here CC' represents the cross section of a calcite crystal, with a fine pencil of ordinary light, AB, impinging on the face of the crystal at right angles. At the opposite side one component emerges as the ray DE, while, below it, emerges the other component FG. These rays are parallel with each other and of equal intensity. The ray DE, which is a continuation of AB, is known as the *ordinary ray*, while

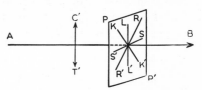

FIG. 7.2. In the sketch the long arrow AB indicates the direction in which the waves are propagated, while the direction of vibration of particles in the wave is represented by the short arrow $C'T'$. Now let AB represent the direction in which a beam of light is traveling, while PP' represents a plane perpendicular to the beam. It will be seen that vibrations in all directions within the plane PP' must be perpendicular to the direction in which the beam AB is being propagated.

FG is the *extraordinary ray*. If the crystal is rotated around BD as an axis, the ordinary ray will remain fixed, whereas the extraordinary ray FG will rotate with the crystal.

Suppose, now, that a clear crystal of calcite is cut into two halves

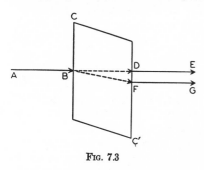

FIG. 7.3

along the diagonal as shown in Figure 7.4. If two such halves are cemented together with Canada balsam, the result will be a *Nicol prism*. Although its geometric form may resemble an ordinary calcite crystal, the optical properties have been changed. The phenomenon of double refraction appears to have been lost. If the end of the cut prism is placed on a page of print, an observer no longer sees double images. The explanation of this peculiar change lies in the fact that in Canada balsam the ordinary ray and the extraordinary ray do not have the same refractive index. For one of the rays the refractive index in calcite is the same as in the balsam, and therefore it passes on through to the other half of the prism just as though this were a single crystal (Figure 7.4). For the other ray, however, the refractive index in balsam is greater than in calcite. Since it strikes the balsam boundary at an angle in excess of the critical angle, total reflection is the result.

A logical question to raise now is: "Which of the two rays travels through the prism to emerge at the opposite end?" It was stated previously that when a calcite crystal is rotated on its axis the extraordinary beam rotates with the crystal while the ordinary ray remains stationary.

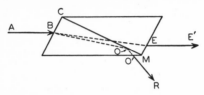

FIG. 7.4. PRINCIPLE OF THE NICOL PRISM

Incident ray, AB.
Path of ordinary ray, BOO'.
Path of extraordinary ray, BE.
CM represents a film of Canada Balsam.

The extraordinary ray EE', as it leaves prism, is plane-polarized. The ordinary ray, $OO'R$, is also polarized, with its vibrations perpendicular to those of EE'. Usually the sides of the Nicol prism are coated with an opaque paint which absorbs the ordinary ray.

In the case of a Nicol prism this property enables one to demonstrate that it is the extraordinary ray which traverses both halves.

If there are available two Nicol prisms another very important characteristic of the extraordinary ray can be demonstrated. One of the prisms should be mounted in a suitable device for holding it stationary. Directly behind this prism should be mounted the second Nicol, in such manner that it can be rotated about its long axis. Since each of these Nicol prisms is quite transparent, one might expect light to penetrate the entire length of both just as readily as through a thick block of clear glass. If, while looking into this system of two Nicol prisms, the movable prism is slowly turned around its axis, the observer will find that eventually no light gets through to the eye. If rotation of the prism is continued, light will penetrate again, but after a time complete extinction is repeated. A careful check will show that in the course of one complete revolution of the Nicol prism total darkness, or *extinction*, occurs twice.

The phenomenon just described could be explained by assuming that a beam of light emerging from the first prism is propagated by waves vibrating in only one plane, instead of all planes which are perpendicular to the line of travel. If this were true, it would appear plausible to consider the second prism capable of transmitting a beam only if its rays are vibrating in one plane perpendicular to the direction of propagation. Under these circumstances light emerging from one Nicol could pass through the second prism only if the two were in similar positions. If the two prisms are not in corresponding positions, then a beam coming from one will be shut out by the other. As a rather prosaic analogy one might consider a coin and the slot of a vending machine. The coin cannot be inserted into the slot cross-wise; both the slot and the coin must be in similar positions.

The kind of light just described is referred to as *plane-polarized* light, or, frequently, merely as *polarized light*. When two Nicol prisms are used as in the foregoing paragraph, the first prism is called the *polarizer* because it holds back all excepting the plane polarized light. The second prism is the *analyzer*. When the analyzer has been rotated to the position in which it excludes passage of the light coming from the polarizer, the prisms are said to be *crossed*. When the analyzer is in the position which yields the maximum intensity of light, the Nicols are *parallel*, relative to each other.

There are several other methods for obtaining polarized light. In certain transparent minerals, notably tourmaline, the ordinary rays are removed by absorption, so that polarized light is the result. Tourmaline, unfortunately, also absorbs a fair proportion of the extraordinary beam. Polarized light may also result from reflection. Sir David Brewster found that light

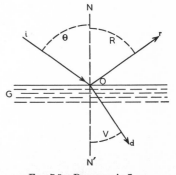

Fig. 7.5. Brewster's Law

θ = Angle of incidence = 56 degrees.
R = Angle of reflection = 56 degrees.
V = Angle of refraction = 34 degrees.
n = Refractive index of this glass,

$$= \frac{\sin O}{\sin R} = \frac{\sin of 56}{\sin of 34} = \frac{0.829}{0.559} = 1.483.$$

Tangent θ = 1.483

reflected from a polished nonmetallic surface is polarized if the tangent of the angle of incidence is numerically equal to the refractive index of the reflecting medium (Figure 7.5). Applying this principle, black glass, opal glass, and piles of clear glass plates have been employed to obtain polarized light. Glossy paper, a sheet of polished black Bakelite, the surface of a pool of water, or wet sidewalks may serve as sources of plane-polarized light by reflection.

In the past the available means for obtaining polarized light were too expensive, too restricted in size, or too inconvenient to manipulate, for certain purposes. At the present time we are fortunate in having an efficient polarizing medium in the form of *Polaroid*. This consists of a plastic film in which are imbedded myriads of microscopic crystals of quinine-iodosulfate. Polaroid is available in fairly large sheets which can be readily cut into any desired shapes. Since the film is easily damaged by abrasion, it is mounted between sheets of optical glass when intended for use in equipment which is subjected to rough handling. In

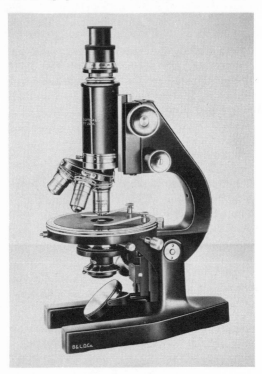

FIG. 7.6. BAUSCH AND LOMB "MODEL M" CHEMICAL MICROSCOPE. Among the refinements of this versatile instrument are the graduated fine adjustment, rotating stage, substage polarizer and condenser, and a cap analyzer.

connection with microscopy one advantage of Polaroid is that appropriate polarizers and analyzers made of this material cost much less than those which employ Nicol prisms. Although Polaroid may not yield exactly correct colors, it will serve very well for most types of chemical work.

The polarizing microscope.—A microscope which has been specifically designed for the utilization of polarized light is referred to as a polarizing microscope. The polarizer, which has generally been of the prism type is located below the stage. In some instruments the polarizer can be inserted in only one position, while others permit of rotation. In the latter case the rim of the mount may be graduated in degrees. As a rule the apparatus is also provided with a notch and pin, so that there is an audible click when the polarizer is turned to its "zero" position.

The analyzer is placed somewhere between the observer and the specimen. In some microscopes the body tube is provided with a slot into which the "slide analyzer" can be inserted when required. This simple slide analyzer is not rotatable. A more elaborate arrangement is to have the analyzer built into the body tube in such manner that a certain limited amount of rotation is possible. The type known as "cap analyzers" are designed to be placed over the eyepiece of the microscope. The better-grade analyzer of this type is provided with a rim graduated in degrees.

When the analyzer is placed in the body tube, it will exert a greater effect on image quality than would be the case with a cap analyzer. Astigmatism and certain other defects will be introduced. To some extent these imperfections are sometimes overcome by providing the analyzer with a special compensating lens. One advantage of the body tube analyzer, if it is rotatable, is the

FIG. 7.7. POLARIZING SUBSTAGE CONDENSER.
(*Courtesy American Optical Co.*)

convenience of manipulation. An objection sometimes raised in connection with a cap analyzer is that it prevents the observer from placing his eye at the eyepoint. This disadvantage is especially undesirable when using high-power objectives. It might be overcome by the use of a special ocular. For taking photomicrographs, the cap analyzer seems preferable.

In many cases a microscope which was not specifically designed as a polarizing instrument can be fitted with appropriate Nicol prisms without any difficulty. Whether or not this can be done with any given instrument can be determined by writing to the manufacturer or his representative. In practically all cases it is possible to equip the microscope with a Polaroid polarizer and analyzer. Polarizing equipment, whether based on Nicol prisms or on Polaroid, considerably extends the field of usefulness of a microscope.

Ordinarily a polarizing microscope is equipped with a rotating stage, which permits the observer to note the effects produced by rotating the specimen while the polarizer and analyzer remain fixed. At least one firm, Zeiss, has offered a device that permits adding this feature to an ordinary instrument. The auxiliary stage, with a built-in polarizer, is merely attached to the regular microscope stage by means of stage clips.

When making observations with polarizing equipment, it is frequently desirable to employ an ocular provided with crosshairs. For convenience, the polarizer should be in such position that the resulting light is vibrating from front to rear of the microscopic field, that is, in a direction to and from the observer. In some microscopes the eyepiece slips into the draw

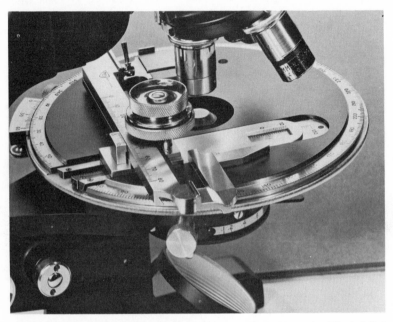

FIG. 7.8. GRADUATED, ROTATING MECHANICAL STAGE. (*Courtesy American Optical Co.*)
This piece of apparatus permits angular measurements as well as linear measurements.
This is of value, for example, in the measurement of extinction angles of crystals.

tube only in such a manner that, relative to the observer, one of the cross-hairs must be directed in a 6 o'clock- 12 o'clock position. The other hair, of course, intersects at right angles. With the polarizer and the cross-hair ocular thus oriented, the Nicol prisms should be in the "crossed" position if the analyzer is rotated until its index mark is opposite the 90-degree notation.

This condition is repeated when the analyzer is turned to 270 degrees. This being true, the prisms will be parallel to each other, and therefore transmit the maximum amount of light, when the index on the analyzer points to 360 degrees (same as zero) or to 180 degrees. Some of the simpler cap analyzers are merely graduated in quadrants of a circle instead of degrees.

Isotropic and anisotropic substances.—If certain crystals, such as sodium chloride or potassium chloride, are examined between crossed Nicols, they will be almost, if not completely, invisible. No matter what positions they assume, their appearance remains unaltered. This is true for all compounds which crystallize according to the cubic system. Substances which behave thus between crossed Nicols are said to be *isotropic*. It should be remembered, of course, that in observing specimens between crossed Nicol prisms it is important that the top of the microscope stage be shaded from any extraneous bright light.

If the crystals are birefringent, that is, if they exhibit double refraction, this property can be detected by an examination between crossed Nicols. With the polarizer and analyzer parallel to each other, assume that a crystal of some birefringent substance is brought into focus lying in the center of the stage. After the analyzer is rotated to the "crossed" position, the microscope stage is slowly revolved. (If the instrument is not equipped with a revolving stage, the slide itself is slowly turned, using care to keep the image of the crystal in view.) It will be found that, instead of remaining practically invisible in all positions, as was true with the cubic crystals above, the image of this specimen fades out in only a few definite positions. All substances which are distinctly visible when they assume certain positions between crossed Nicols are *anisotropic*.

Picric acid could be taken as an example of one type of anisotropic compound. If a very thin crystal is examined at a magnification of 50 or 100 diameters, using ordinary white light (either daylight or tungsten) it will appear practically colorless. If the Nicol prisms are used, the observer will find that, when they are crossed, the image of the picric acid crystal will persist unless the long axis of the crystal is parallel with one of the vibration planes (Figure 7.9). Assuming that the image has been extinguished between the crossed Nicols, when the rotating stage is turned slightly, the image will reappear, becoming brighter as its angle with the original position becomes greater. After passing through a position of maximum brilliance, the image begins to darken as the stage is rotated, until eventually extinction of the image is repeated.

It can be shown that, in passing from the first position of extinction to the next, the crystal has been rotated through an angle of 90 degrees. In other words, if in its first position of extinction the crystal was parallel with the polarizer, in the second position it must be parallel with the analyzer. In rotating the crystal through a complete circle, therefore, extinction should occur four times.

Should extinction result when an anisotropic crystal lies in a position which is parallel with the plane of polarization of one of the crossed Nicols, the compound is said to exhibit *parallel* extinction (Figure 7.9). There are many instances, however, in which crystals undergo extinction when in a position which is not parallel with either the polarizer or analyzer. This is described as *oblique* extinction. Here, again, the angles of extinction are 90 degrees apart. Sometimes students have inferred that a crystal which exhibits oblique extinction does so when its axis makes an angle of 45 degrees with the vibration planes of the crossed prisms.

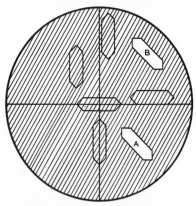

FIG. 7.9. PARALLEL EXTINCTION. Darkened field as seen through eyepiece when the cross-hairs are parallel with the vibration planes of the polarizer and analyzer respectively. A crystal which exhibits parallel extinction is only faintly visible when its long axis lies along a line parallel with the plane of vibration of either the polarizer or the analyzer. Crystal A is oriented in such a position that its axis is parallel to a plane which bisects the angle between the vibration planes of the crossed prisms, i.e., it makes an angle of 45 degrees with each of these planes. The brilliance of the resulting image is at its maximum. The same applies to crystal B, since its position in respect to the Nicol prisms is comparable with the position of crystal A. This could be verified by moving the specimen slide directly forward on the stage until the image of B appears in the rear quarter of the field of view. The student should understand that extinction or maximum brilliance of the crystal image depends not upon the location within the field, but, rather, upon the angle which the axis of the crystal makes with the vibration planes of the Nicols. In the case of many anisotropic compounds viewed between crossed polars, the crystals which are not in extinction position exhibit brilliant polarization color.

Such a position would be represented by crystal A in Figure 7.9, and would correspond with an extinction angle of 45 degrees. Although this is correct for many crystals, it is not true for all. The extinction angle may be less than 45 degrees.

In measuring the angle of extinction, crystals should be selected which are rather thin but not too fine or narrow. If the crystals are small, a number of them may have to be observed before definite conclusions can be justified. Except in the case of mineral crystals, it is advisable to examine those which have been formed on the same slide on which they are to be studied. In this way abnormal results arising from internal strain and other causes are more likely to be avoided. With regard to the size of crystals examined, it might be mentioned that in the study of minerals it is very common to determine optical data even on minute crystals and fragments, but this kind of determination requires the refinements of equipment generally found only on a petrographic microscope. Individual crystals, rather than masses or matted groups, should be observed. When some anisotropic compounds are viewed between crossed Nicols, they appear white or colorless. Many, however, present a brilliant kaleidoscopic display of all the colors of the spectrum, even though they may be colorless by ordinary light.

Selenite plate; gypsum plate.—If a specimen is only feebly birefringent, this phenomenon may escape detection when the substance is ex-

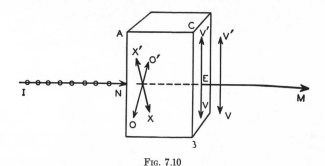

Fig. 7.10

amined between crossed Nicol prisms in the usual way. Before deciding that a given sample is isotropic, it should be studied with the aid of a *selenite plate,* also known as a *gypsum plate* or a *first-order red plate,* which may be in the form of a circular plastic or metal mount, supporting a thin plate of transparent gypsum. When such a plate is placed on the microscope stage and viewed between crossed Nicols, the color will change as the disc is rotated. In making one complete rotation the gypsum plate passes through four positions in which it exhibits its characteristic color with the maximum intensity. The reason will become clear after a discussion of the principle involved.

Using monochromatic light (red, for example) which has passed through a Nicol prism, there is obtained an incident beam of polarized light, *IN* (Figure 7.10). Let it be assumed that these incident rays are vibrating in a plane perpendicular to the paper. As explained earlier (see p. 99), when this beam enters a birefringent substance it is divided into two rays, known respectively as the ordinary and extraordinary rays.

It will be recalled that these two rays will be polarized and that their vibrations are perpendicular to each other. Therefore, when the ray *IN* enters the doubly refracting substance *AB*, the two rays produced in the latter will be vibrating in the directions *XX′* and *OO′*. Since the two rays do not travel through with the same velocity, one will be retarded, or will fall behind the other.

It is conceivable that the substance used here could be of such thickness that when the light emerges from the face *BC* the slower component will be just one-half of a wave length behind the other. In other terms, it has been *retarded* one-half wave length. For reasons beyond the scope of this work, if the two waves are out of phase by one-half wave length at face *BC*, they may emerge as a single wave.[1] This emergent wave will be vibrating in direction *VV′*, which is perpendicular to the direction in which the incident ray *IN* is vibrating. With the Nicol prisms crossed, (that is, in this case, with the analyzer turned to admit vertical vibrations) the emergent ray *EM* can pass through the analyzer. The result of directing the light through this "half-wave plate" has been to change the direction of vibration of the observed light from horizontal to perpendicular.

From the foregoing it might be expected that if the Nicols were in parallel position the emergent ray *EM* could not pass through the analyzer. This would be true only for one wave length. Even when light filters are employed, a considerable number of different wave lengths are transmitted. Because of this and certain other reasons, extinction does not result when the half-wave plate is placed between parallel Nicols.

Actually, the difference in the effect produced when white light is passed through a half-wave plate such as just described is not very great. By selecting a piece of gypsum somewhat thicker it would be possible to obtain a phase difference of 2/2 wave lengths, or of 5/2 wave lengths for certain red rays. So long as the difference would amount to an odd number of half-wave lengths, that particular color would still emerge from the plate as a wave vibrating in a direction perpendicular to the incident ray. The selenite can be made of such thickness that, in traversing the distance *NE*, the wave lengths at the red end of the spectrum are retarded an odd number of half-wave lengths while those at the other extremity are retarded an integral number of wave lengths. Such is the case with a first-order red plate. After passing through the selenite plate, the red rays are vibrating at right angles to their original direction; therefore, they should pass through the analyzer if the latter has been crossed in respect to the polarizer. The color of the plate will appear red. One could, of course, have a plate of such thickness that its sensitive tint

---

[1] See Thomas B. Brown, *Foundations of Modern Physics*, Wiley, 1940, pp. 64 ff.

would be blue or purple. Of recent years manufacturers have favored the last-named color, but many technicians still claim that red is more satisfactory.

Let it be assumed that a selenite plate has been interposed between the crossed Nicol prisms of a microscope. Similar results are obtained, whether the plate is of the "cap" type, which is placed over the eyepiece, or of the type which is inserted in a slot at the lower end of the body tube. If the instrument is then focused on crystals of a birefringent compound, many of them will appear very brilliantly colored. This will be true even with substances which ordinarily do not exhibit very much color between crossed Nicols alone. As the slide is rotated on the stage, some of the crystals seem to disappear from sight. Although their outline may be discernible the color gradually merges with that of the sensitive tint plate. Meanwhile new crystal images have appeared in parts of the field.

Now, with the selenite plate removed, suppose certain crystals, whose properties are known, are arranged in their positions of extinction between crossed Nicols. In this case the field will appear entirely dark. If a selenite plate is introduced, keeping the Nicols crossed, the entire field should appear red. (Naturally, the field will appear violet, if this is the sensitive tint of the plate used.) If the slide containing the crystals is rotated through even a very small arc, the crystals will become visible. When a crystal lies in its extinction position, the rays which represent the sensitive tint of the selenite plate are able to pass just as though no crystal were present, but when it assumes some other position the effects will be more complex.[2] The specimen will appear brightly colored. Crystals for which the birefringence is too feeble to be detected merely by observation between crossed Nicol prisms may readily reveal this property when examined with the aid of a selenite plate.

All crystalline substances which are isotropic, that is, those which do not exhibit the property of double refraction, belong to the cubic system. In the case of crystals which are very minute one may not be able easily to identify them as belonging to the cubic system merely by observing the geometric appearance. By noting their behavior when using crossed Nicols and a selenite plate, the question is answered fairly quickly.

Interference figures; optical crystallography.—Anisotropic crystals embrace those which belong to all systems other than cubic (or regular). Their optical properties divide anisotropic crystals into two main groups, i.e., *uniaxial* and *biaxial*. The former embrace those which belong either to the tetragonal system, or to the hexagonal. The three

---

[2] For a detailed discussion of what happens to polarized light which travels through anisotropic media before reaching an analyzer, the student may refer to Chapter 23 of Albert Johannsen's *Manual of Petrographic Methods*, McGraw-Hill, 1918.

remaining crystal systems, namely the orthorhombic, monoclinic, and triclinic systems, are biaxial.

In a crystal of calcite, for example, there is one certain direction along which a ray of light may be propagated without undergoing double refraction. This is known as the *optic axis*. In all other directions light is subjected to the phenomenon of birefringence. Crystals which have only one optic axis (also known as *axis of isotropy* or *axis of no double refraction*) are referred to as uniaxial. As was discovered by Sir David Brewster, there are many crystals which possess two such axes; that is, in some crystals there are two directions along which a ray of light can be propagated without suffering double refraction. Such crystals are said to be biaxial.

It is quite feasible to determine whether anisotropic crystals are uniaxial or biaxial by examining their *interference figures*. These are beautifully colored patterns formed when the crystals under proper conditions are examined between crossed Nicols, using convergent polarized light. In fact, the identification of minerals by the methods of microscopic petrography leans heavily on the interpretation of interference figures. For this purpose there have been prepared extensive tables which summarize the optical data needed for the identification of crystalline mineral components (cf. Larsen and Berman). Similar information has been compiled for many inorganic solids which do not occur in minerals (cf. Winchell or Fry). Especially during recent years, some investigators have been determining the optical properties of certain alkaloids, sugars, and other groups of crystalline organic compounds. The identification of solids by means of their optical properties requires a polarizing microscope which is equipped with a rotating stage, centerable objectives, a slot for inserting compensators (that is, selenite plate, mica plate, and a quartz wedge) and a Bertrand lens for observing interference figures. Essentially this means that one requires a good petrographic microscope or its equivalent.

Although adequate treatment of optical crystallography lies beyond the scope of this book, a brief outline of the procedure can be given. Let it be assumed that we have access to a petrographic microscope, such as shown in Figure 2.2. After placing the specimen on a slide, the first step is to locate a properly oriented crystal (or grain) between crossed Nicols. Having adjusted the slide so as to place the selected particle in the exact center of the field of view, the observer may next determine whether the substance is uniaxial or biaxial. This is accomplished by observing the interference figure produced. When an appropriate compensator, such as a selenite plate, is inserted into the system, crystals may be further distinguished as uniaxial positive or negative, and biaxial positive or negative (cf. Figure 2.2 in Chapter II). Interference figures can be observed by peering into the eyepiece and adjusting the Amici-Bertrand lens (Figure 7.11). A Maltese cross obtained with the crystal in extinction position would indicate the presence of a uniaxial substance. If a selenite plate is used, the relative location of patches of yellow will indicate whether the specimen is optically positive or negative. When examined by polarized light, a uniaxial substance exhibits not *one* but

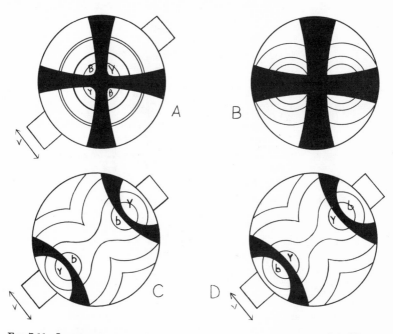

Fig. 7.11. INTERFERENCE FIGURES OBTAINED BETWEEN CROSSED POLARS (Nicol Prisms or Polaroid Filters). Under appropriate conditions a thin uniaxial crystal in extinction position between crossed polars may yield a dark cross with colored rings, as in A. The number of rings depends upon several factors, including the thickness of the crystal and its orientation on the slide. By inserting a selenite plate, in which the vibrational direction of its slow component is indicated by the arrow v, the interference figure will exhibit patches, or fringes, of color in diagonally opposite quadrants. If the specimen is uniaxial positive, yellow appears in the quadrants Y,Y; the other quadrants may exhibit blue. For a uniaxial crystal with negative birefringence, the yellow color appears in quadrants B,B. Properly oriented, a biaxial crystal in extinction position between crossed polars may yield an interference figure in the form of a dark Maltese cross and bands of color, as shown in diagram B. When the specimen is rotated, the cross gives way to *isogyres*, moving away from the center, as in C; if rotation is continued through 90 degrees the cross reappears. With a selenite plate in the optical system, fringes of color appear along, or beside, the isogyres. In the case of a biaxial positive crystal, yellow appears outside the boundary, as represented by Y,Y, in C, while the interference figure of a biaxially negative crystal exhibits the yellow color along the inner boundary Y,Y, as shown in D. Unless the specimen is well centered, the interference figures will be distorted.

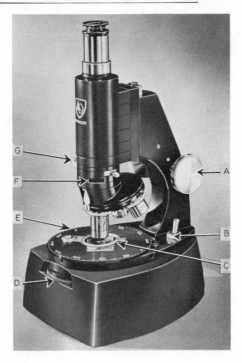

Fɪɢ. 7.12. Recent model of inexpensive polarizing microscope with built-in light source. A, one knob serves in place of the conventional coarse and fine adjustments; B, on-off switch for substage lamp; C, new type stage clip to hold slide in place; D, rotating diaphragm disc, which takes the place of adjustable iris diaphragm; E, simplified graduated, rotating stage; F, slot for insertion of sensitive tint plate, etc.; G, Polaroid analyzer in sliding metal frame. The polarizer is permanently mounted in the base of the microscope. (*Courtesy of American Optical Co.*)

two different refractive indices, representing respectively the *ordinary* ray and the *extraordinary* ray. These indices can be determined by the Becke line method, using appropriate immersion media and polarized light. From these observations sufficient data have now been obtained to enable the analyst to characterize the substance, or to identify it if its optical properties have already been catalogued.

*B*iaxial substances are recognized by interference figures which are characteristic of the group. To secure the optical data needed for ultimate identification, the procedure followed is in general similar to that employed with uniaxial material, but more complex. Instead of *two* refractive indices, for example, there are *three*. To give the student a general idea of the nature of interference figures one experiment in the laboratory manual explains how to obtain figures without the use of expensive accessories.[3]

Study Problems

1. Explain how the Nicol prism serves as a source of plane-polarized light.

2. Tell why the ordinary ray does not travel through both halves of a Nicol prism.

3. Is it possible to have the incident ray strike one face of a Nicol prism at such an angle that the ordinary beam is able to pass through both halves of the Nicol? Explain your answer.

4. Assume that Canada balsam were unobtainable. Name the properties required by any medium used as a substitute in cementing together the components of a Nicol prism.

5. Draw up a list of other means for obtaining polarized light.

6. How could you determine whether light reflected from a wet sidewalk is polarized?

7. One means for obtaining polarized light is by reflection of incident light from a pile of glass plates. Would the angles of incidence and reflection be the same for different kinds of glass? Explain.

8. State Brewster's Law regarding polarization by reflection.

9. Briefly explain each of the following terms:
   a. Crossed Nicols.
   b. Parallel extinction.
   c. Anisotropic.
   d. Birefringence.
   e. Extinction angle.

10. If examined between crossed Nicols, how many times does an anisotropic crystal exhibit the phenomenon of extinction when rotated through 360 degrees?

11. Briefly describe the use of a selenite plate.

12. With the aid of a diagram explain the principle on which the selenite plate is based.

[3] A very brief discussion of the use of interference figures is included in W. H. Fry, "Petrographic Methods for Soil Laboratories," *U. S. Department of Agriculture Bulletin 344* (January 1933). Probably the most concise working directions in this field are those offered a few years ago by Philip W. West in *The Chemist Analyst* **34**, 76–81 (1945) and in **35**, 4–8, 28–35 (1946). However, since it is generally true that the blind following of directions in "cook book" fashion may offer many pitfalls, those who plan to do serious work in optical crystallography should learn some of the theory on which the procedures are based. More comprehensive treatment is given in Albert Johannsen's *Manual of Petrographic Methods*, McGraw-Hill, and in Alexander Winchell's *Elements of Optical Mineralogy*, Volume I, Wiley.

Chapter VIII

CHEMICAL PROCEDURES ON MICROSCOPIC SCALE: GENERAL

Advantages of chemical microscopy.—In a large measure the methods applied in chemical microscopy ultimately involve the formation of characteristic crystals which can be identified when studied with the aid of the microscope. Although George Denigés appears to regard Teichmann's haemin test (developed 1853–1857) as the real forerunner of this fascinating means of analysis, it must be admitted that not a few workers had been conversant with microscopic tests for several decades. In part this is evidenced by certain features embodied in Chevalier's "microscope universal," which was brought out in 1834. Among the advantages claimed for this instrument was the ease with which it could be converted into a chemical microscope. The latter was of the inverted type, and was originally claimed an excellent instrument for chemical experiments and for studies in crystallization. Later workers, however, considered its images inferior.

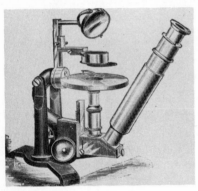

FIG. 8.1. AN EARLY BAUSCH & LOMB LABORATORY MICROSCOPE, ARRANGED FOR CHEMICAL WORK. Since the objective here is below the specimen, one can examine crystals in their natural position regardless of the depth of liquid in which they lie. The objective is protected from any corrosive chemicals and their fumes, "and the observer's head is sufficiently distant from the stage to avoid any noxious fumes." This plan may have been suggested by J. Lawrence Smith, about 1851.

It might be argued that if a qualitative reaction takes place on a microscopic scale it should be just as conclusive as the same reaction performed on a macro scale. Actually, the micro reaction may frequently

114

prove the more satisfactory. Whereas certain reactants may merely produce a white precipitate when the procedure takes place in test tubes, when the same test is performed under the microscope the resulting white precipitate may be seen to exhibit certain important characteristics. The latter may prove to be a conclusive specific test, while the macro precipitate may require some further confirmatory test. Since the tests so frequently depend upon the formation of characteristic crystals, the chemical microscopist must learn to carry out the slide reactions under controlled conditions. In view of the minute quantities involved it behooves him to acquire a few special techniques in connection with such processes as evaporation, boiling, filtration, sublimation, and others. Furthermore, the importance of cleanliness cannot be overemphasized.

Special equipment required.—Before undertaking that phase of microscopy which involves chemical reactions on slides, certain special equipment should be procured. The usual 3×1 slides are taken for granted, and they should be of good quality. Certain of the cheaper grades exhibit flaws which may at times lead to a misinterpretation of the observed results. There is no real economy in selecting low-grade slides. Furthermore, slides which have acquired any abrasion should not be used. Fine scratches may well lead to erroneous conclusions, especially when searching for certain very slender crystal forms. For convenience some workers keep on hand a small supply of slides which are etched at one end. This etched square is very desirable when it is necessary to label temporary specimens, because the required identification numbers can be quickly written on with an ordinary pencil. Their added cost is nominal.

Certain reactions require a hanging drop slide. The latter differs from the usual microscope slide in being made of much heavier glass and in having a concavity in the center. This concavity should be 0.7 or 0.8 mm in depth.

In general it is not advisable to stock large volumes of reagent solutions. It is better to prepare small amounts when required, and to dispose of unused portions at the end of the day's work. This procedure reduces the risk of contamination which may result when a solution remains in contact with glass for long periods. Very serviceable solution vessels are made from homeopathic vials. By means of a hot-wire, these should be cut off about 15 mm from the bottom. The rough-cut edge may be ground in the usual way. It is possible, of course, to obtain the Griffin form of Pyrex beakers in micro sizes.

Some of the biological supply houses offer a type of containers known as recovery dishes, measuring about 25 by 15 mm. For solutions which are too costly to throw out, and reagents which must be kept in closed vessels because of fumes, there are available very neat glass-stoppered

Pyrex bottles with a capacity of about 5 ml. Solid reagents may be kept in small vials provided with plastic screw caps. In certain cases the inner walls of the bottles or vials should be coated with ceresin wax or some other inert substance. Small, hard rubber bottles are obtainable if needed.

Quite naturally the novice will raise the question concerning the number of reagents which should be available. Behrens found it convenient to have a box containing 60 small bottles of solid reagents. A number of authors recommend 60, but some suggest as many as 80 or even 150. Unless the individual worker feels he must be prepared for all eventualities, it appears more reasonable to restrict the number to those reagents which are most likely to be required in the type of work generally undertaken. The bottles may be kept in a wooden block which has been drilled with the requisite number of holes, or in a small case provided with an appropriate cover or hinged lid. Generally the base contains a drawer for small accessories, such as tweezers, platinum wires, needles, etc. According to common practice the bottles bear only numbers. The identity of the contents of any vial is determined by reference to a chart. A very inexpensive arrangement is to purchase a wool block which is drilled to receive 60 test tubes of the $2 \times \frac{1}{4}$ inch size. Two-ml vials provided with Bakelite screw caps are very satisfactory, and they can be arranged so that the labels are visible.

FIG. 8.2. REAGENT SET FOR CHEMICAL MICROSCOPY, AS SUPPLIED BY ARTHUR H. THOMAS CO. ·This block contains 60 vials, size 35×12 mm.

For handling small quantities of solid reagents, when these are called for in slide reactions, there should be several spatulas. One of them should be of platinum. The latter is easily made from a short length of number 18 or 20 wire. About 6 or 8 mm of one end of the wire is flattened by striking it with a hammer on an anvil or other hard, polished surface. The other end of the wire may be sealed into a length of glass tubing, which will serve as the handle. The spatula also may be attached to a needle holder, such as employed with dissecting needles or inoculating needles. Because of lower heat conductivity, a bone handle is preferable to one of metal. One type, known as the Rosenberger-Greenman needle holder, has a handle covered with vulcanized fiber.

A type of spatula frequently used is Hayman's micro spatulas illustrated in Figure 8.3. Although all three are desirable, style C may prove most in demand. In addition, a few glass spatulas will prove useful on occasion. These are easily made by sealing and flattening the ends of a 12- or 15-cm length of glass tubing which has been drawn out to a diame-

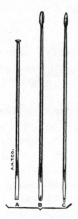

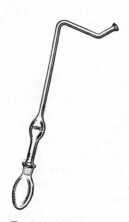

FIG. 8.3. HAYMAN MICRO SPATULAS. These are made of stainless steel and measure 5½ to 6½ inches in length. (*Courtesy Arthur H. Thomas Co.*)

FIG. 8.4A. BENEDETTI-PICHLER-SCHNEIDER MICRO DISTILLING FLASK. (*Courtesy Fisher Scientific Co.*)

FIG. 8.4B. CAPILLARY PIPET.

ter of 2 or 2.5 mm. Such sections are often obtained when drawing out tubing for cutting the micropipets described below.

Micropipets will be required for so many operations that at least a score should be available. Several times this number would be better. They will have to be made in the laboratory, since the type required is not available commercially. Although some variation is permissible, a satisfactory size can be drawn from 6- or 7-mm soft glass tubing. The tubing from which the pipets are to be made should be thoroughly cleaned inside by immersing in chromic acid cleaning solution for some time, followed by several rinsings with distilled water. Using a Bunsen burner with a wing top, the glass is drawn out to such dimensions that one can obtain pipets on which the tips have an outside diameter of about 1.5 mm (Figure 8.4B). Some workers may find it more convenient to manipulate the pipets if the wide portion is longer than indicated in the figure. From practical considerations it is desirable that all of them have about the same total length. Although the author has found the 1.5-mm size most generally useful, there are occasions when it is advantageous to have several pipets of slightly larger bore, and a few which are finer. Different sizes should, of course, be kept in separate containers.

In use the micropipets depend upon capillary rise. They serve not only for adding reagents to slides but also for the removal of liquids. When inclined at a suitable angle, they will drain away any desired amount of liquid found on a slide.

There should be available, also, a number of fine glass needles. These are made by drawing out appropriate lengths of 3- or 4-mm glass rod. The slender portion should measure several centimeters in length. It is desirable to have several different diameters on hand.

For filtering just a few drops of material, such as mixtures resulting from slide reaction, various devices have been suggested. For filtration from a slide when the filtrate is to be saved, the following filter tube has proved useful. The tube is similar to a micropipet, with the capillary portion measuring 1.5 or 2 mm in outside diameter. The edges of the tip should then be ground to remove irregularities. The tube is held upright by the thumb and first two fingers, and the grinding is done by applying a circular motion to the tube while it is held against a fine abrasive. The latter may be fine emory cloth, valve-grinding compound, or a fine stone. Care should be taken to have the ground edge at right angles to the axis of the tube. The wide end of the filter tube is fitted with a small rubber bulb, as used on medicine droppers.

When filtration involves volumes of 0.5 ml or more, certain suction devices may be used. Micro Buechner funnels have proved very serviceable. They may be employed with small suction flasks or with side-arm tubes. Appropriate filters are easily cut from larger sheets of filter paper by means of a cork drill. Small Hirsch funnels, which are also available, have not been found to be very practicable. For certain work micro Gooch crucibles may be used to advantage.

The equipment required for carrying out sublimations varies, depending to some extent upon the type of material involved, and the amount. The sublimation may be from a micro crucible to a slide, in which case a special clamp should be used for holding the slide on the crucible while the latter is being heated. For sublimation from watch glass to micro slide, the former should measure only 25 mm in diameter. Occasionally it may prove desirable to perform a slide-to-slide sublimation with the aid of a glass ring measuring 2.5 or 3 mm in depth. Such rings are regularly sold by the scientific supply houses. There are available, too, small glass squares through which a circular opening has been drilled.

These may be used in place of glass rings, especially when a more shallow cell is required.[1]

In some types of organic investigations there are occasions when the substance actually tested under the microscope is obtained as a distillate from the original sample. If the available sample comprises only a small volume, the distillation may require special glassware. A very efficient micro distillation apparatus is the Benedetti-Pichler-Schneider distilling flask. In its earlier forms the entire apparatus was made in one single piece. Although this is still listed by certain dealers, it will prove far more convenient to work with the later two-piece design which has the fractionating tube ground to fit into the separable boiling flask. For

Fig. 8.5. Two satisfactory types of microburners. (*Courtesy Fisher Scientific Co.*) The simple burner on the left is quite adequate for most micro requirements. The burner on the right is provided with four interchangeable tips, and is therefore more versatile. A much finer flame is possible with this burner.

handling mere fractions of a milliliter of sample the Emich type of micro flasks may be required.

As to a source of heat, where a microflame is required the comparatively simple burner shown in Figure 8.5A is satisfactory. One serious fault, however, is its lack of a sufficiently heavy base. For this reason it tilts over rather easily unless it is attached to some other base or clamped. Another type of burner which has proved quite satisfactory is the Fisher microburner shown in Figure 8.5B. This one is readily adaptable to a variety of conditions because it is provided with interchangeable burner tips of different sizes. The type of burner so commonly recommended for student work in semi-microqualitative analysis has not been very adequate for microscopy.

Various procedures and techniques.—Slides which are to be employed in the various chemical tests must be unusually clean. The ordi-

---

[1] An ingenious apparatus for fractional sublimation on a removable transparent film is described by A. O. Gettler, C. J. Umberger, and L. Goldbaum in *Analytical Chemistry* **22,** 600 (1950). Microscopic examination of different fractions of sublimate can be carried out without removing from the film.

nary cleaning methods are not entirely satisfactory. For some of the work even a brand-new slide may not be acceptably clean. The following method of cleaning will ensure a properly cleaned slide.

After ordinary washing in water to remove adhering solids, the slides are placed in a chromic acid cleaning solution. This solution requires, first, a saturated aqueous solution of potassium dichromate. Eight volumes of concentrated sulfuric acid are then **cautiously** added to 5 volumes of the saturated dichromate solution. *Warning:* It should be remembered that considerable heat is evolved when these two liquids are mixed.

To keep the slides from adhering to each other, thus preventing contact with the solution, several slide-staining dishes can be employed. The opposite walls of these dishes are grooved, so that the slides are kept separated. They are regularly stocked by scientific supply houses.

After sufficient soaking in the chromic acid mixture, the slides are thoroughly rinsed in several changes of tap water, followed by two rinsings in distilled water. The cleaned slides may be kept in a jar of distilled water until required for use. The final step in the cleaning process is to immerse the slide in ethyl alcohol, and then to hold it to the flame of a burner so that any adhering alcohol will be ignited. After the alcohol has been consumed, the slide is ready for use.

The micropipets must be clean and dry to give the required service. The cleaning process is similar to that suggested for slides, but the alcohol rinse can be omitted. The rinsing with distilled water must be quite thorough, after which the pipets should be inverted in a jar or beaker and stored in a cabinet free from dust and fumes. If necessary, this drying time can be reduced by dipping the pipets into alcohol before they are inverted to drain. It should be noted that it is not generally desirable to hasten drying by using compressed air. The air may contain sufficient oil (from the compressor) to deposit a film which will impede capillary rise. It is likewise inadvisable to blow one's breath through the capillary pipets. By having a large supply of dry micropipets available, waiting for the wet ones to dry can be avoided.

When a precipitation reaction is to be carried out on a slide, the reagent usually is not added directly to the sample being tested. If both the sample and reagent are in solution, one drop of each is transferred to a clean slide. The two should be close together but should not touch. In order to mix the drops, a fine glass needle is touched to the surface of one drop and carefully drawn over until both liquids merge. This procedure permits of two variations: the reagent may flow into the sample or the latter may flow into the reagent. It is not the intention to bring about a rapid, intimate mixing of sample and reagent. Instead, there should be only a gradual mixing of the two, with different zones representing a gradation in concentrations.

When there is any need to concentrate the sample solution by partial evaporation or by evaporation to dryness, the heating must be controlled. If a microburner is the heat source, only a small flame should be used. The slide is held so that the far end is tilted upward. In order to heat the sample, the inclined slide is passed over the flame several times in such manner that the flame, in effect, passes from the lower end to the raised end. After the slide has been passed over the flame, evaporation can be hastened by blowing one's breath across the drop of liquid. Ordinarily it is not necessary to cause the latter to boil, even when evaporating to dryness. Excessive heating must be avoided. Generally the slide should not be heated by holding it over the flame for an uninterrupted period but should be kept in motion. If too much heat is employed in evaporating to dryness, the resulting solid may fail to adhere firmly to the slide. In some cases the residue may be so flaky as to blow away. We repeat: *At no time* is evaporation carried out by holding the stationary slide directly over the flame; *the heating should be intermittent.* Just as in other phases of chemistry, there are occasions when it is advantageous to heat materials on some form of steam bath. For slides and micro crucibles a very serviceable bath consists of a lid from a metal can placed over a beaker of water. The water may be heated over a Bunsen burner or on a small electric hot plate.

When a solid reagent is to be added to the test drop, the platinum spatula can be used. The spatula should be cleaned immediately after use. Following a rinse in distilled water, the spatula is dipped into concentrated nitric acid and again rinsed in distilled water. The process is repeated several times, until the spatula imparts no color when heated in the gas flame. Naturally, the usual precautions concerning platinum must be observed. In particular, it must not be heated in contact with alkalies. In many cases, of course, the transfer of solid reagent can be made by means of a glass, aluminum, or stainless steel spatula. To avoid too great a loss of time, a number of spatulas are required.

After a precipitation reaction, it may be desirable to separate the filtrate for further investigation. Some precipitates are of such nature that the separation can be effected by decantation. On a microslide the decantation is conveniently accomplished with the aid of a capillary pipet. When the tip of the pipet is applied to the edge of the drop of clear liquid, capillary rise should take place. Practically all of the liquid can be drained away if the tube is sufficiently inclined toward the horizontal.

When decantation does not prove feasible, several methods of filtration are available. The tube described on page 118 is used with a bit of filter paper slightly larger than the cross-sectional area of the tip. The paper is placed on the slide, close to the medium to be filtered. With the fingers of one hand the tip of the filter tube is brought down on the paper. The tube must be held vertically, so that the ground tip makes good contact all around. Part of the air is expelled by exerting slight pressure on the bulb. Meanwhile, the tube and paper are moved to the drop which is to be filtered. When the filter paper has become moistened, the pressure on the rubber bulb is released, whereupon the filtrate moves up into the tube. Since this method of filtration requires the use of both hands part of the time, it is somewhat awkward. However, with practice this method is efficient, especially if both filtrate and precipitate are to be saved. During the actual filtration, it is important that the filter tube be held firmly against the paper. If it is not held in proper position, air will leak in around the exposed edge of the tip, thus decreasing the efficiency.

If the volume of material amounts to more than just a few drops, a Gooch crucible or a micro Buechner funnel may be used. With the former the asbestos fibers used for the filter mat should not be too long or too coarse. The filter is prepared in the usual way. Frequently it is quite feasible to use a good grade of filter paper instead of the asbestos. As mentioned previously, circles of appropriate size are readily cut by means of a sharp cork drill. Since the micro filter flask is very light in weight it either should be supported in a clamp or should be attached to a special base to avoid any mishap. Generally the micro Buechner funnel will prove more convenient to manipulate.

If a microcentrifuge is available, many of the separations can be effected in tubes of $\frac{1}{2}$-ml to 2-ml capacity. Although small test tubes may serve the purpose, the regulation tapered centrifuge tubes make for a more effective concentration of the precipitate. After centrifuging, the clear filtrate is removed by a capillary pipet. In cases where a minute quantity of precipitate is suspended in a relatively large volume of liquid, the use of a filter may practically mean the loss of the precipitate, since the fibers of the latter may firmly adsorb the few solid particles. The centrifuge eliminates loss by adsorption. In certain other instances what might mean a very tedious separation if carried out by suction filtration may require merely 3 or 4 minutes if a centrifuge is available. If the centrifuge has a capacity of two tubes, both must be in place when the motor is turned on. In those which accommodate a larger number of tubes there must always be enough of them to balance properly the centrifuge head. Tubes which are diagonally opposite each other should contain approximately equal volumes of liquid. Failure to distribute the load properly will prevent the smooth operation of the centrifuge. Eventually this results in serious damage.

Occasionally it may be desirable to subject to sublimation the small quantity of material which is formed during a slide reaction. To do this some workers suggest collecting the sublimate on a second slide. One end of the upper slide is separated from the lower slide by a small piece of thin glass rod. A convenient variation is to rest the upper slide on a glass ring of appropriate height. Such rings are sold by biological supply houses for constructing special mounting cells. They are available in various depths, but for this purpose 2.5 or 3 mm would be most suitable. To obtain more efficient cooling a small beaker of water can be placed on the upper slide. Should one desire a sublimation chamber of less depth, the glass ring may be substituted by a thin glass plate provided with a circular opening. Such plates may be obtained as thin as 0.5 mm.[2] Another simple method is to place a 25-mm watch glass over the sample which is to be sublimed. In this case additional cooling can be achieved by placing a small wad of wet absorbent cotton on the watch

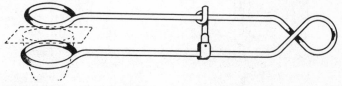

FIG. 8.6. Sublimation clamp for subliming from microcrucible to microslide. (Clamp available from *Will Corporation*)

glass. An objection to the use of a watch glass for collecting the sublimate is the fact that the curved surface may prove a handicap if the material is to be examined under the microscope. Sublimation from a microcrucible to the slide is very conveniently accomplished by the aid of a special clamp (Figure 8.6). The previous statement concerning the heating of substances on a slide applies to micro sublimations. Ordinarily the slide should not be held steadily in a fixed position above the burner.

Certain tests depend upon the identification of a gas. Such identification sometimes involves the formation of characteristic crystals when the gas reacts with a solution of the reagent. On a microscopic scale this may be performed by the hanging-drop method. The reactants which bring about the evolution of gas are placed in an appropriate vessel, such as a microcrucible or a microbeaker. A slide containing a drop of the reagent is carefully inverted and then laid on the crucible so that any gas formed by the reactants must impinge on the "hanging drop." After sufficient time has elapsed, the slide is turned right side up, and the reagent drop can be examined under the microscope. At times it may prove convenient to employ a Feigl gas absorption tube (Figure 8.7). When this is done, the solution must be transferred to a slide for examination after the reaction is completed.

[2] Microchemical Service, Douglaston, N. Y.

Although the boiling point is not determined by methods of microscopy, it is such a valuable constant that those who do much work with organic compounds should master the technique for determining the boiling point of a drop of liquid. The method of Siwoloboff is easily mastered. The actual procedure to be followed is described in the laboratory manual (cf. Experiment 20), but since corrections have been completely ignored in so many instances, it has appeared desirable to include a brief discussion of these corrections.

When boiling points are measured by means of an ordinary laboratory thermometer, not all of the mercury column is subjected to the same tem-

A   B   C

FIG. 8.7. FEIGL GAS ABSORP-
TION TUBES, CAPACITY 1.5 ML.
(*Arthur H. Thomas Co.*)
A. Tube with rubber stopper
and solid glass drop rod. B.
Tube with loosely fitting hol-
low glass stopper provided
with capillary openings. C.
Tube with solid standard taper
ground glass stopper.

FIG. 8.8. FEIGL
MICRO DISTILLING
APPARATUS. (*Arthur
H. Thomas Co.*)
This consists of
boiling chamber,
1.5 ml. capacity,
and ground-in dis-
tilling head with
interchangeable
standard taper
joint. A micro-
crucible or centri-
fuge tube serves as
a receiver.

perature. In the micro method, which requires the use of a heating bath or of a metal heating block, only the lower portion of the thermometer is immersed in the heating medium; the upper portion may be subjected to lower temperatures. If the length of mercury column above the level of the heating bath extends over only a few scale divisions, the correction may be insignificant. For high-boiling liquids, however, the length of mercury column which is not immersed in the bath may extend over many divisions, so that the correction may amount to 2 or more degrees. There are occasions when an error of this magnitude is a decided disadvantage.

The following equation for *stem correction* has given good results.

$$X = N(t_1 - t_2)0.000154,$$

where X = correction, in degrees, *which must be added* to the actual reading on the thermometer;

N = portion of mercury column in degrees which projects above the
bath liquid or the heating block;

t_1 = temperature actually registered by the thermometer;

t_2 = average temperature of N, the exposed mercury column.

This may be determined by means of an auxiliary thermometer hung
beside the other one.   The bulb should be placed about midway between
the top of the heating bath and the top of the exposed mercury column.

0.000154 = apparent coefficient of expansion of mercury in normal
glass.

When there is an appreciable difference between the barometric pressure of the laboratory and the normal pressure, or 760 mm, an appropriate
correction for this factor must be made.   For associated liquids, such as
water, organic acids, alcohols, and hydroxy compounds in general, the
boiling point, corrected to standard pressure, may be obtained by adding
to the observed boiling point (after applying stem correction), the following value.

$$\frac{273 + \text{observed b.p.}}{1020} \times \frac{760 - \text{prevailing pressure}}{10}.$$

The "prevailing pressure" refers to the correct barometric pressure, in
millimeters.   For non-associated liquids, the number 1020 in the denomi-
nator of the foregoing fraction is replaced by 850.

The following illustration should clarify the application of the correction formulas.

The boiling point of an amyl alcohol was being determined in a bath
which left the mercury column of the thermometer exposed above the 70°
mark.   At the boiling point the thermometer registered 130.5°, and the
auxiliary thermometer indicated that the average temperature of the
exposed mercury column was 55°.   The correct barometric pressure was
748 mm.   The exposed portion of the mercury column is equal to
130.5 − 70, or 60.5.   Applying the "stem correction" formula, we get the
value

$$60.5(130.5 - 55)0.000154 = 0.7034.$$

Rounding off to the nearest tenth gives the correct observed boiling temperature as 130.5 + 0.7 = 131.2°.   However, since the determination was
carried out below normal pressure, the standard boiling point would be

somewhat higher than 131.2. Applying the Smith--Menzies formula, we get the value

$$\frac{273 + 131.2}{850} \times \frac{760 - 748}{10} = 0.571, \text{ or } 0.6°.$$

That is, at the normal pressure of 760 mm the boiling point would be 0.6° higher than at the barometric pressure which prevailed during the experiment. The normal boiling point, therefore, would be 131.2 + 0.6 = 131.8°. This is 1.3° higher than the value obtained by merely reading the thermometer and making no corrections.

Chapter IX

CHEMICAL PROCEDURES ON A MICROSCOPIC SCALE: INORGANIC REACTIONS

Detecting several components with a single reagent.—As mentioned previously, the tests in chemical microscopy usually depend upon the formation of characteristic crystals when certain reagents are applied under controlled conditions. This obviously means that the compound which represents a positive test must be relatively insoluble. Quite frequently, however, a given reagent is capable of yielding insoluble crystals in the presence of any one of several different radicals or compounds. As an example one may cite potassium mercuric thiocyanate (or ammonium mercuric thiocyanate). Among the metallic radicals which may yield characteristic crystals with this reagent are lead, gold, copper, zinc, and cadmium. When the test is performed on the solution of a pure salt of one of these metals, the resulting crystal will be typical for that metal. A zinc compound causes the separation of colorless, feathery crosses while cadmium results in the formation of orthorhombic prisms.

When potassium mercuric thiocyanate is applied to a solution containing both zinc and cadmium ions, the resulting crystals are neither feathery crosses nor orthorhombic prisms. Instead, under favorable conditions, there results a new type of crystal which is characteristic of a mixture containing both zinc and cadmium ions. Thus the potassium mercuric thiocyanate reagent can be applied for the detection of zinc ions, cadmium ions, or a mixture of the two. This principle, however, cannot be applied generally. Ordinarily, if certain ions are individually capable of yielding characteristic crystals with a certain reagent, mixtures of these ions will not result in a product which can be used for identification purposes. In other words, certain interfering ions must be removed in order to obtain decisive tests.

In specimens which are presented to the analyst for investigation it is not necessary to test for the presence of every known ion. A comprehensive analytical scheme would not only require a rather unwieldy series of procedures but would entail in most instances an inordinate waste of time. In many instances the source of a given specimen limits the number and variety of possible components. One analyst may be interested solely in the metals generally associated with zinc ores, while another may be concerned with only the precious metals. With a view to efficiency, therefore, a procedure should be devised which is especially adapted to the type of work concerned. Examples of several typical procedures follow.

Identification of metallic protective coatings.—The metals most generally employed as protective coatings for those which are less resistant to corrosion may be arranged in the following categories.

A. Inexpensive metals
   1. Zinc
   2. Cadmium
   3. Tin
   4. Lead
   5. Copper (alone, or as a constituent of brass)
B. High quality metals
   (These are more resistant to wear and corrosion.)
   1. Nickel
   2. Chromium
C. Precious metals
   1. Gold
   2. Silver
   3. Platinum
   4. Palladium

With the exception of copper and brass, which possess distinctive colors, in dealing with the inexpensive metals it is not generally feasible to identify the coating by mere visual inspection, even when circumstances limit the number of possibilities to one or two. This is true, for example, of certain types of hardware and kitchen utensils. Application of the methods of chemical microscopy may provide the answer to such questions in a comparatively short time and without damaging the object being tested. One example which came to the author's attention was an Oriental copper tea kettle, which was claimed to be lined with tin. A simple chemical test proved that the interior was not tin but lead, which was not appropriate for the intended use.

Some tests suitable for the individual metals are outlined below. It should be remembered, however, that numerous other microscopic tests are available for these same metals.[1] Not infrequently the specific test chosen depends upon personal preference.

---

[1] Many of these may be found in Volume II of Chamot and Mason, *the Analytical Edition of Industrial and Engineering Chemistry* (recently changed to *Analytical Chemistry*) and *Mikrochemie*.

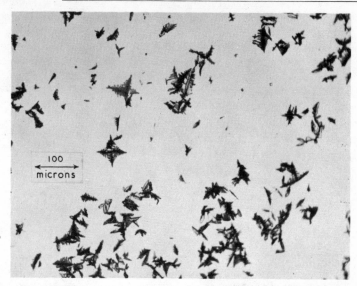

FIG. 9.1. TEST FOR ZINC ION, USING POTASSIUM MERCURIC THIOCYANATE.
(approx. 150-×)

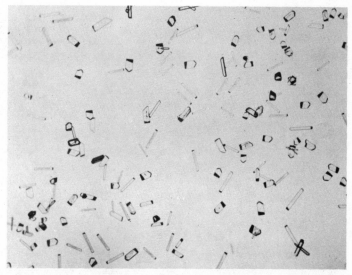

FIG. 9.2. TEST FOR CADMIUM ION BY MEANS OF POTASSIUM MERCURIC THIOCYANATE
REAGENT. (approx. 115-×)

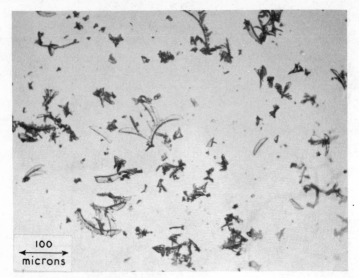

FIG. 9.3. ZINC-CADMIUM MIXTURE, AS INDICATED BY POTASSIUM-MERCURIC THIOCYANATE REAGENT (approx. 115-×).

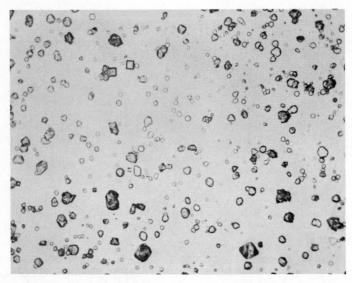

FIG. 9.4. DETECTION OF TIN BY RUBIDIUM CHLORIDE (approx. 115-×).

Potassium mercuric thiocyanate, which corresponds to the formula $K_2Hg(SCN)_4$, under favorable conditions reacts with zinc ions to form very interesting crystals of zinc mercuric thiocyanate—$Zn(SCN)_2 \cdot Hg(SCN)_2$. The crystals of the latter separate in the form of opaque, feathery crosses (Figure 9.1). When the reagent is used on the solution of a pure cadmium salt, there will separate orthorhombic crystals of cadmium mercuric thiocyanate—$Cd(SCN)_2Hg(SCN)_2$. These crystals differ from those of the corresponding zinc compound, and they are characteristic (Figure 9.2). If the zinc compound which is being tested also

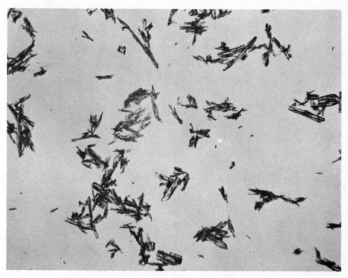

Fig. 9.5. Detection of lead by means of thiourea.

contains cadmium, even in only small amounts, the characteristic feathery crosses formed by zinc ions alone will not be found. Instead, the analyst may observe dark crosses devoid of any feathery appearance, elongated arrowheads (Figure 9.3), or even thin plates, depending upon the proportion of cadmium ion present. In the absence of interfering ions, the potassium mercuric thiocyanate may serve to detect the presence of zinc ions, cadmium ions, or a mixture of the two, provided the amount of cadmium in the mixture is not too great.

Tin, in the form of stannic chloride, may be detected by means of cesium chloride or rubidium chloride (Figure 9.4), forming cesium chlorostannate ($CsSnCl_6$) or rubidium chlorostannate respectively. The latter may be preferred because the crystals formed are not quite so small as those formed with cesium chloride reagent.

A very sensitive test for lead employs thiourea as the reagent (Figure 9.5). It is claimed that only thallium and certain of the platinum metals give a similar test, but an *excess* of silver, copper, or bismuth ions will interfere.

Copper may be detected by means of the triple nitrite reaction which derives its name from the characteristic crystals formed by potassium copper lead nitrite, having the formula $2KNO_2 \cdot Cu(NO_2)_2 \cdot Pb(NO_2)_2$ (Figure 9.6). The crystals usually appear as opaque cubes or rectangular prisms, having a very dark brown (almost black) color by reflected light.

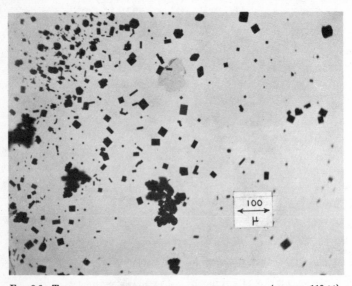

FIG. 9.6. TEST FOR COPPER VIA THE TRIPLE NITRITE REACTION (approx. 110-×).

However, some of the crystals may separate as thin plates, which are isotropic and exhibit a brown or orange color when viewed by transmitted light. Even if this preparation is allowed to stand until all the moisture has evaporated, characteristic opaque crystals may still be observed.

The appearance of either chromium or nickel, on the one hand, is sufficiently characteristic to distinguish this pair of metals from the group of inexpensive metals. However, mere visual inspection does not always suffice for distinguishing between chromium and nickel or for positively identifying either of them. In our simplified scheme, nickel, in ammoniacal solution, is identified by the well-established dimethylglyoxime reagent,

$$H_3C-C=NOH$$
$$H_3C-C=NOH$$

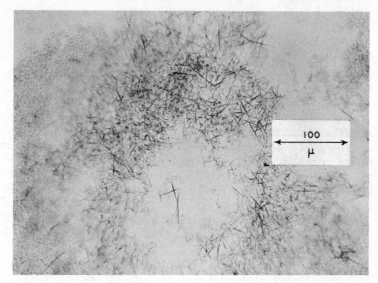

FIG. 9.7. DIMETHYLGLYOXIME TEST FOR NICKEL (240-×).

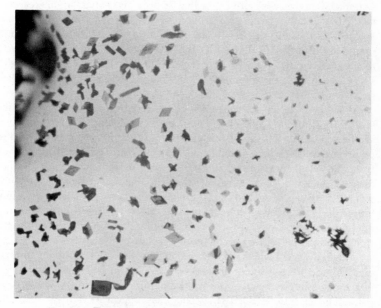

FIG. 9.8. TEST FOR DICHROMATE ION BY MEANS OF SILVER NITRATE.

which yields typical pink or magenta crystals of nickel dimethylglyoxime,

$$Ni(C_4H_7N_2O_2)_2 \text{ (Figure 9.7).}$$

Chromium, if present as chromate or dichromate ion is readily detected by conversion to the corresponding silver compounds (Ag_2CrO_4 and $Ag_2Cr_2O_7$), which yield characteristic crystals (Figure 9.8).

Silver may be detected by precipitating as the chloride. Palladium is detected as a potassium salt by adding potassium chloride to the prepared sample in aqua regia.

When gold is present as chlorauric acid, its presence can be demonstrated by the addition of pyridine hydrobromide reagent, which causes the separation of the complex, $C_5H_5N \cdot HBr \cdot AuBr_3$ (Figure 9.9). The latter appears in the form of characteristic crystals, and the test is specific for gold.

Platinum, when present as chloroplatinic acid, can be converted into yellow octahedral crystals of potassium chloroplatinate, K_2PtCl_6, by the addition of KCl (Figure 9.10).

Detection of sodium, potassium, and ammonium ions.—In most laboratories there are numerous occasions on which the problem in hand can be solved by merely determining which one of three metallic ions is present, viz., sodium, potassium, or ammonium. This represents an ideal example of an everyday problem which is promptly solved by microscopic methods. Sodium ion, if present, is readily detected by applying uranyl acetate—$UO_2(C_2H_3O_2)_2 \cdot 2H_2O$—to precipitate the double salt, sodium uranyl acetate—$Na(C_2H_3O_2) \cdot UO_2(C_2H_3O_2)_2$—which appears in the form of characteristic tetrahedra or triangular plates (Figure 9.11). Under certain conditions, because of total internal reflection, these pale yellow crystals may actually appear black.

If the positive ion in the sample being tested should be potassium instead of sodium, crystals of the corresponding double salt of potassium should separate. These crystals assume the form of long slender needles or prisms tipped with pyramids, so that they are readily distinguished from the tetrahedra formed in the presence of sodium. Since the potassium double salt is more soluble than the sodium compound it requires more time to separate out. This test may also serve to detect potassium ion as a contaminant in a sodium salt. However, the reverse does not apply, because a large excess of potassium ion interferes with the formation of the characteristic sodium uranyl acetate crystals.

Another reagent which may be employed to detect potassium is tartaric acid (Figure 9.12). Under proper conditions tartaric acid in the presence of the potassium ion causes the separation of anisotropic crystals of acid potassium tartrate, $HKC_4H_4O_6$. They may appear as short prisms, thin

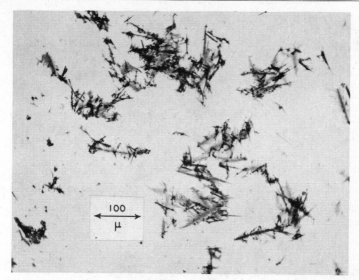

FIG. 9.9.   TEST FOR GOLD, USING PYRIDINE AND HYDROBROMIC ACID (approx. 115-×).

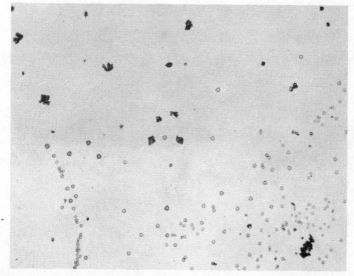

FIG. 9.10.   TEST FOR PLATINUM AS POTASSIUM CHLOROPLATINATE, USING KCl AS REAGENT.

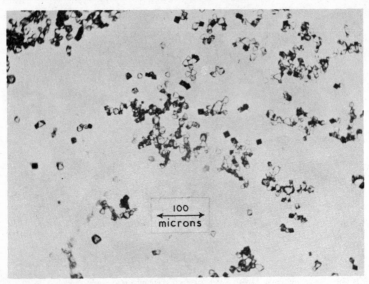

FIG. 9.11. DETECTION OF AMMONIA BY MEANS OF URANYL ACETATE (approx. 115-×).

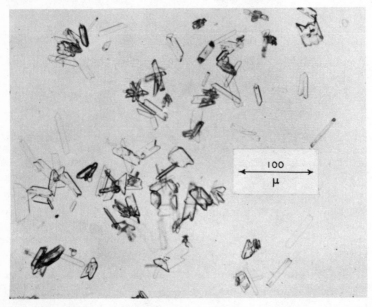

FIG. 9.12. POTASSIUM, BY MEANS OF TARTARIC ACID AND SODIUM TARTRATE (240-×).

plates, etc. The ammonium ion should not be present when using this reagent to detect potassium.

Chloroplatinic acid is of interest here since it may serve to detect both the potassium and the ammonium ion. Since the presence of either cation would mask the test for the other, the ammonium ion must first be eliminated by expelling it as ammonia. This is easily accomplished by treating the sample with NaOH. Any ammonia evolved is taken up in dilute HCl to form ammonium chloride, which may then react with chloroplatinic acid to form characteristic octahedra of ammonium chloroplatinate, $(NH_4)_2PtCl_6$. When this reagent is applied to solutions of potassium salts, similar crystals of K_2PtCl_6 are formed.

Tests for common anions.—If the addition of silver nitrate solution to a sample causes the separation of a white precipitate which is insoluble in nitric acid, the presence of chloride, bromide, or iodide is indicated. (The fluoride ion is not precipitated by silver nitrate.) The test is not a satisfactory means for distinguishing among these three anions. The following reactions provide a convenient basis for determining which of the halide ions are present.

The presence of chloride ion is based on the "chromyl chloride" test. The sample must first be prepared by adding potassium dichromate and evaporating to dryness to form an intimate mixture of chloride and dichromate. If concentrated sulfuric acid is added to the mixture, chromyl chloride, CrO_2Cl_2, will be gradually evolved. When the chromyl chloride is taken up by water, hydrolysis occurs, thus forming chromic acid, H_2CrO_4, and hydrochloric acid. Evaporation of the latter solution to dryness will leave only chromic acid. When this residue is dissolved in water, its presence can be demonstrated by the addition of silver nitrate, which will yield the red precipitate of silver chromate. If the original sample was free from chloride ion, there could be no chromyl chloride from which to obtain chromic acid by hydrolysis. Neither the bromide ion nor iodide ion yields corresponding volatile chromyl compounds. However, the fluoride ion should be absent.

In order to detect bromide ion the halogen may be caused to yield a crystalline bromine derivative of either m-phenylene diamine or aniline. The bromine is released by treating the sample with sulfuric acid and potassium dichromate. In the presence of a hanging drop of m-phenylene diamine sulfate (or the hydrochloride) the released halogen reacts to form the symmetrical tribromo derivative, which separates from solution in the form of characteristic crystals. Similar results can be obtained with aniline hydrochloride. This test can be employed in the presence of chlorides and iodides, since the former will not be oxidized by the chromic acid reagent, and iodide ion will not react with the amine reagent.

Iodides are readily detected by the familiar starch test for iodine.

The anion is converted into the elementary form by one of the milder oxidizing agents, such as potassium nitrite, whereupon the free iodine is conveniently identified by the blue color imparted to starch grains.

As is well known, fluorine differs in many ways from the other members of the halogen family. The fluoride ion, for example, is not precipitated as an insoluble silver salt when silver nitrate is added to a fluoride solution; calcium fluoride, on the other hand is almost insoluble, in contrast with the other calcium halides. Because of its deviation from many

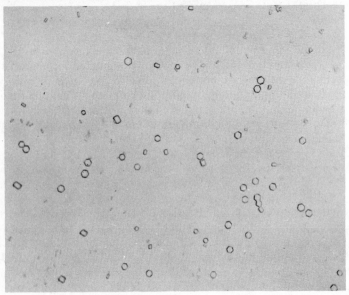

Fig. 9.13. FLUORINE, AS SODIUM FLUOSILICATE (115-×).

of the other halogen characteristics, the analyst must resort to different reactions when required to detect the fluoride ion.

When concentrated sulfuric acid is made to react with a mixture of silica and a fluoride, silicon tetrafluoride is formed, as summarized in the following equation.

$$4KF + 2H_2SO_4 + SiO_2 \longrightarrow SiF_4 + 2K_2SO_4 + 2H_2O.$$

Although the silicon tetrafluoride is a colorless gas, when it is absorbed in water hydrolysis occurs, thereby producing the insoluble silicic acid and soluble fluosilicic acid.

$$3SiF_4 + 4H_2O \longrightarrow H_4SiO_4 + 2H_2SiF_6.$$

The precipitate of silicic acid indicates the presence of fluorine in the original mixture, but if a confirmatory test is deemed advisable the fluo-

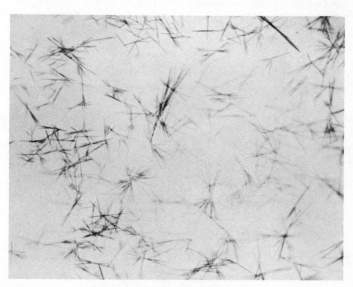

FIG. 9.14. DETECTION OF NITRATE RADICAL BY MEANS OF NITRON IN 30% ACETIC ACID. Two different fields from the same preparation. (Approx. 115-×.)

silicic acid is easily converted into characteristic crystals of its insoluble sodium salt by the addition of sodium chloride (Figure 9.13).

Sulfides may be detected by the release of hydrogen sulfide gas when the sulfide reacts with an acid. Even very small amounts of hydrogen sulfide will impart a noticeable coloration to lead acetate. Sensitivity is increased by using a lead acetate solution which has been saturated with ammonia.

While it is true that frequently silver nitrate solution is employed to establish the presence of dichromates, it is likewise true that a similar precipitate may be formed by the interaction of silver nitrate and chromates. However, the analyst can distinguish between chromates and dichromates by the use of manganese acetate which yields needle-like crystals with the former.

For the detection of nitrates under the microscope an acetic acid solution of nitron (diphenyleneanilodihydrotriazol) is employed to advantage (Figure 9.14). With this reagent nitrates yield characteristic bundles of fine needles. It is true that crystals may be precipitated when nitron is added to certain other anions (nitrite, chlorate, iodide, oxalate, salicylate, etc.), but the needles formed by nitrate ion are characteristic.[2]

[2] The analyst who requires methods for detecting ions not included in this brief discussion should refer to Volume II of Chamot and Mason's *Handbook of Chemical Microscopy,* 2nd ed., Wiley, 1938.

Chapter X

CHEMICAL PROCEDURES ON A MICROSCOPIC SCALE: ORGANIC REACTIONS

The place of chemical microscopy in organic chemistry.—Although chemical microscopy can be adapted to a systematic analytical scheme for the detection of nearly all the ions to be found among the inorganic compounds, numerous limitations are encountered when the microscope is applied to organic chemistry. The methods of chemical microscopy alone are not sufficient for detecting or identifying all types of organic compounds. In the present state of our knowledge, therefore, a qualitative organic analytical scheme based solely on chemical microscopy is out of the question. In spite of this limitation the organic chemist will find that the microscope may serve as an invaluable instrument. Although it is true that in numerous instances the organic problem under consideration cannot be solved by the exclusive application of chemical microscopy, it is likewise true that generally even such a problem can be substantially aided by the judicious utilization of a microscope. The material which follows is an attempt to present a representative group of reactions which can be employed in the study of organic compounds. Some of the tests are of a general type, but others are specific.

In order to confine the work within the scope of the present small volume any given field must be treated rather briefly, and only a few can be included. The question of which subjects to include becomes rather difficult to answer. The author feels, however, that mastery of the material here presented should enable the chemist to readily apply in his own work such microscopic methods as are described in the literature dealing with specialized fields, or frequently, when the need arises, to devise his own adaptations from well-known macro procedures. The latter practice becomes necessary at times because in certain divisions of chemistry the microscopists have not yet devised or published satisfactory ready-made methods.

141

Alcohols.—In general, alcohols are not directly converted into derivatives which are readily identified by their microcrystalline characteristics. In spite of this the microscope can be employed to advantage in dealing with some of the members of this group of compounds. One of the useful reactions which is easily adapted to the microslide is the iodoform test. Most compounds which contain either the H_3C—C=O or the

$$H_3C—\overset{\overset{\displaystyle H}{|}}{\underset{|}{C}}—OH$$ group will yield iodoform when subjected to appropriate

treatment. Thus, a positive iodoform test can be produced by ethanol, isopropyl alcohol, acetone, methyl ethyl ketone, etc. It should be recalled that the reaction mixture contains the hypoiodite radical. When the test is applied to a solution containing ethanol, the reaction proceeds in three stages, as shown below.

$$\text{I.} \qquad \underset{\text{Ethanol}}{H_3CCH_2OH} \xrightarrow{\overline{OI}} \underset{\text{Acetaldehyde}}{H_3CCHO} + H_2O + \overline{I}$$

$$\text{II. } H_3C \cdot CHO + 3\overline{OI} \longrightarrow \underset{\text{Tri-iodoaldehyde}}{I_3CCHO} + 3\overline{OH}$$

$$\text{III. } I_3C \cdot CHO + \overline{OH} \longrightarrow I_3CH + \underset{\text{Formate ion}}{\overline{COOH}}$$

When methyl alcohol is subjected to this test, the oxidation product is formaldehyde, which cannot yield iodoform. Therefore this test may serve to distinguish between ethyl and methyl alcohol.

When oxidized by sodium hypoiodite secondary alcohols are converted into ketones. Those which yield methyl ketones, as in the case of isopropyl alcohol, eventually result in the formation of iodoform.

$$\underset{\text{iso-Propyl alcohol}}{H_3CCHOH \cdot CH_3} \xrightarrow{NaOI} \underset{\text{Acetone}}{H_3C \cdot CO \cdot CH_3} \xrightarrow{NaOI} \underset{\text{Tri-iodoacetone}}{H_3C \cdot CO \cdot Cl_3} \xrightarrow{NaOH}$$
$$\underset{\text{Iodoform}}{I_3CH} + \underset{\text{Sodium acetate}}{H_3COONa}$$

When performed on the microslide the iodoform reaction constitutes a fairly rapid test which gives positive results even when the concentration of the organic component amounts to only a few per cent. If the concentration equals only a fraction of one per cent, appropriate compounds will give a positive test if performed on two droplets obtained by subjecting several drops of the original sample to a micro fractional distillation.

Aldehydes and ketones.—Reagents which have proven useful in the analysis of materials containing aldehydes or ketones are fairly numerous.

Many of the tests originally devised for macro methods have been modified to yield excellent results in the hands of the microscopist. One of these is the silver mirror test of Tollens. On the microscopic scale the reactants are brought together on the edge of a bit of filter paper. Instead of forming the well-known silver mirror, a positive test appears in the form of very finely divided black particles of the reduced silver. The result is readily observed under the microscope even when an appropriate carbonyl compound is present in a very low concentration. Even when there is an abundance of sample for testing, the micro procedure appears preferable. It is quite sensitive, fairly rapid, and does not result in the formation of a dangerous quantity of explosive silver compounds. The analyst must remember, however, that Tollens' reagent is not specific for aldehydes; positive tests may be obtained with various phenols and other reducing agents.

Various other tests depending upon the reducing action of the aldehyde group can be adapted to the same technique suggested above. Fehling's reagent and Benedict's reagent are representative of those involving the reduction of cupric to cuprous ions.

When dealing with mixtures there are occasions when the analyst may find it desirable to isolate in pure form any component aldehyde or ketone before the actual identification. In many instances such isolation may be accomplished by utilizing the tendency which many of these compounds have to form addition products with sodium bisulfite. After having isolated and purified the bisulfite addition product, the original aldehyde or ketone can be regenerated by the addition of a little acid or alkali. The regenerated compound can be extracted by an appropriate volatile organic solvent. When the latter finally evaporates, it leaves the pure aldehyde or ketone.

In the study of aldehydes and ketones, the phenyl hydrazones have for a long time played an important role. For micro purposes p-nitrophenylhydrazine has proved itself a most satisfactory reagent, although the ortho and meta isomers have also shown merit. As developed by Fisher and Moor [1] the nitrophenylhydrazones can be obtained even from a single drop of very dilute solution. However, the crystals of nitrophenylhydrazone formed by a specific aldehyde or ketone are not sufficiently characteristic in appearance positively to identify the substance. Fisher and Moor solve the problem by comparing the micro melting point of the hydrazone with the values of known hydrazones. (Cf. Experiment 26 on page 237.)

The hydrazone formation is represented by the equation

[1] *Mikrochemie* 15, 74–86 (1934).

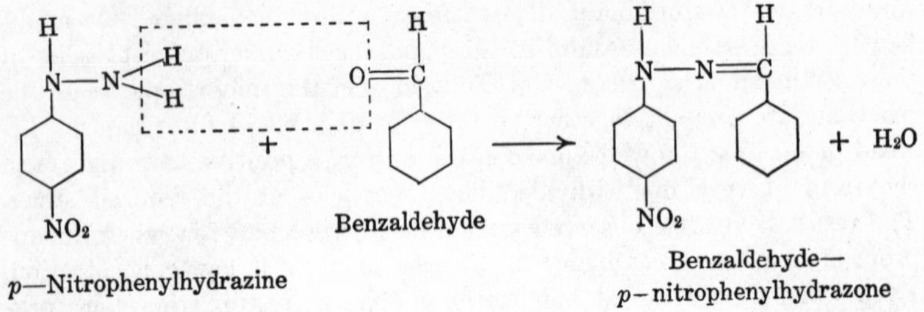

p—Nitrophenylhydrazine

Benzaldehyde

Benzaldehyde—
p—nitrophenylhydrazone

Since the reducing sugars are either aldoses or ketoses, they are frequently detected by reactions which are due to their aldehydic or ketonic structure. Among the most important of these reactions is the formation of phenylosazones, which are really dihydrazones. The action of the phenylhydrazine reagent may be represented by the following equations.

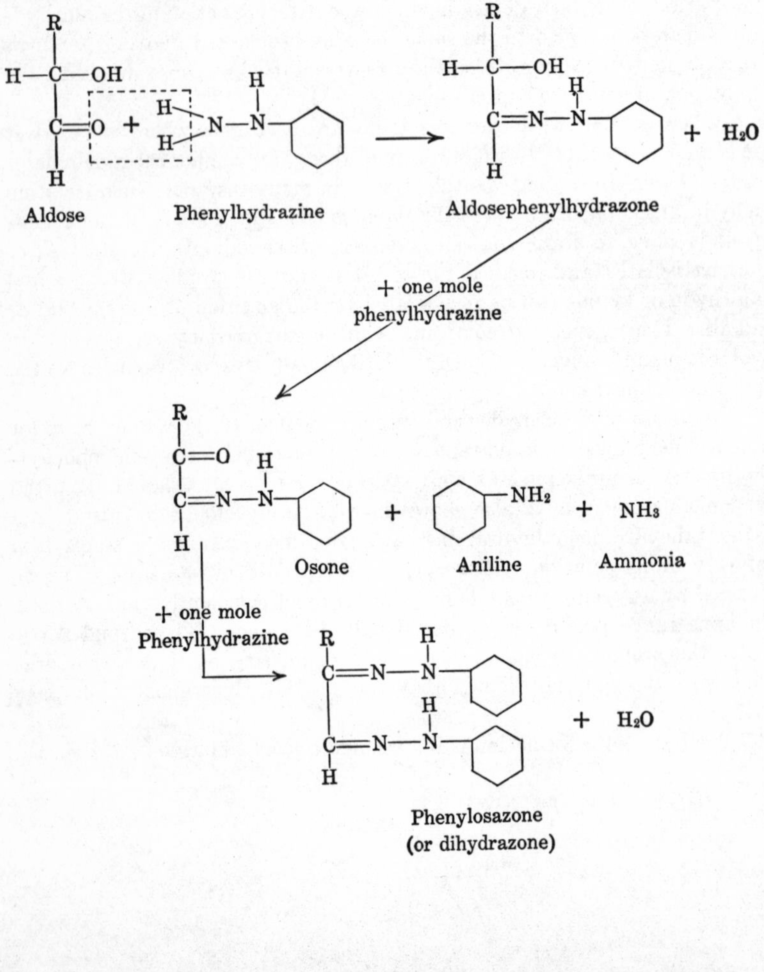

Aldose

Phenylhydrazine

Aldosephenylhydrazone

+ one mole
phenylhydrazine

Osone

Aniline

Ammonia

+ one mole
Phenylhydrazine

Phenylosazone
(or dihydrazone)

Observe that three moles of phenylhydrazine are required to transform the carbonyl compound into an osazone.

SACCHARIDES

In spite of the importance of the phenylosazone test it has not been generally applied as a slide reaction in the past because of evaporation which results when such small volumes of reaction mixture are subjected to prolonged heating. It is true, of course, that in the study of plant material Molisch [2] and others have applied the osazone reaction to thin sections of tissue. According to this procedure, however, the tests are carried out in glycerol solution.

Since such long delays usually are disadvantageous, the present author has devised a simple technique (cf. Experiment 26) which enables one to carry out the ordinary osazone reaction with minute droplets on a microslide. The success of the procedure depends upon fixing the cover glass so that water vapor cannot escape while the preparation is being heated. This technique has been made practicable by the use of Dow-Corning silicone stopcock lubricant as the heat-resistant sealing medium. One advantage of this procedure is that a tiny fragment of solid sample or a mere droplet of test solution is sufficient for a test. If desired, the osazone crystals may be recovered for a micro melting point determination.

Phenolic compounds.—A reagent which is very frequently employed in the testing of phenols is dilute ferric chloride solution. Although no crystals are formed there is no reason why the test should be ignored by the microscopist. Many phenolic compounds yield colored solutions when treated with dilute ferric chloride, and it is quite feasible to adapt the test to the microslide. Ordinary phenol, for example, imparts a violet color to the ferric chloride reagent, while all of the cresols (hydroxytoluenes) yield a bluish color. Catechol (o-dihydroxybenzene) produces a green color, and its meta isomer, resorcinol, colors the reagent a dark violet. Hydroquinone (also called quinol or p-dihydroxybenzene) is oxidized to quinone by ferric chloride and also by other mild oxidizing reagents. Bluish crystals may be formed in this case.

In addition to the green color which results when dilute ferric chloride solution reacts with catechol, a violet color is formed if the green solution is subsequently treated with sodium bicarbonate. The violet color is eventually superseded by red. Similar color changes result when ferric chloride and sodium bicarbonate are applied to a number of other dihydric phenols.

[2] Hans Molisch, "Mikrochemie der Pflanze," Gustav Fischer, Jena 1923, p. 132.

A number of phenols readily form crystalline derivatives with bromine water. Thus, phenol yields small prisms of 2,4,6-tribromophenol, m.p. 92°. Resorcinol likewise forms a tribromo compound, and phloroglucinol yields fine, hairlike crystals which are characteristic of the compound.

To some extent the salts of gold, silver, platinum, palladium, and mercury can be employed in the study of phenols. To illustrate, α-naphthol may be distinguished from its β-isomer by the effect of palladium chloride solution. With this reagent a water solution of α-naphthol forms small characteristic crystals, some of which are burr-like and may appear in clusters or rosettes. These are not formed by β-naphthol.

French and Wirtel [3] discovered that some phenols readily yield crystalline derivatives with α-naphthylisocyanate. The present author has found that in a small tube good results can be obtained by mixing a single drop of the suspected phenol with 1 or 2 drops of the reagent, and heating just at the boiling point over a microburner for about one minute.

α-Naphthyl-isocyanate + Phenol → An α-naphthylurethane

If the product fails to solidify upon cooling to room temperature, the mixture may be reheated. The urethanes are removed by extracting the reaction mixture with boiling ligroin. Evaporation of the latter leaves crystalline urethanes which may be characterized by their melting points.

TABLE I

Compound	M.P. of Urethane (°C)
Phenol	132–133
o-Cresol	141–142
m-Cresol	127–128
p-Cresol	146
o-Aminophenol*	201
o-Nitrophenol*	112–113
m-Nitrophenol	167
p-Nitrophenol	150–151
α-Naphthol	152
β-Naphthol	156–157

* Ligroin solution of trimethylamine or of triethylamine is required to catalyze reaction with this compound.

[3] J. Amer. Chem. Soc. 48, 1736 (1926).

Polyhydric phenols do not react with the naphthylisocyanate. The melting points of several a-naphthylurethanes reported by French and Wirtel are given in Table I.

Amino compounds.—Under favorable conditions many amino compounds react to form well crystallized picrates. Although the analyst cannot generally characterize these substances merely by crystalline appearance, some of the picrates possess characteristic melting points. Picrates having definite melting points are also formed by some amino acids. Among common tertiary amines the following may be cited.

ter-Amines	M.P. of Picrate (°C)
Diethyl aniline	142
Dimethyl aniline	163
Pyridine	167
Quinoline	203
iso-Quinoline	222

Many amino compounds react readily with chlorauric acid and chloroplatinic acid, although the products are not necessarily crystalline. A number of the addition compounds with chloroplatinic acid possess definite melting points. Several examples follow.

Amine	M.P. of Addition Compound (°C)
Dimethyl aniline	173 (decomp.)
a-Picoline	195 (decomp.)
Quinoline	218
Quinaldine	226
iso-Quinoline	263 (decomp.)

In the study of amines it is frequently the custom to employ a solution in dilute acid, as hydrochloric or acetic. In the results given in Table II the respective amines were dissolved in a 25 per cent (approx.) aqueous solution of acetic acid. The picric acid was a saturated solution in 95 per cent alcohol while the chloroplatinic and chlorauric acids were 5 per cent solutions in water.

A reagent which may assist the analyst when working with aliphatic amines is a-naphthylisocyanate, which was also mentioned in connection with the phenols.[4] Many primary and secondary aliphatic amines react with a-naphthylisocyanate, without heating, to form crystalline urethanes. Although the crystals of the latter are not readily identified merely by their appearance under the microscope, their respective melting points may prove useful. Benzylamine, acetamide, and acetanilide also react. Those amines which fail to form their respective urethanes at room temperatures will do so in the presence of a catalyst in the form of a solution

[4] Cf. H. E. French and A. F. Wirtel, *J. Amer. Chem. Soc.* **48**, 1736 (1926).

TABLE II—REACTIONS OF AMINES

Amine	Picric Acid	Chloroplatinic Acid	Chlorauric Acid
n-Butylamine		Hexagonal plates in many sizes.	—
Diethylamine			+
Triethanolamine	+	+	
Aniline	Fine, long, hairlike crystals.	Needles and lath-like crystals.	Amorphous red-brown to deep blue ppt.
Diethyl aniline	+	—	Red to orange globules; eventually minute crystals may appear within globules.
o-Toluidine	+		Amorphous green ppt.
p-Aminophenol	+		+ (may appear violet).
a-Naphthylamine	+	Some rectangular prisms.	Intense blue-violet.
o-Amino diphenyl	Oily globules	—	Blue-violet.
Pyridine	Fine, hairlike crystals; short, rectangular tablets.	Few short, rectangular prisms.	Branched crosses, etc.
Quinoline	Very short needles; singly and in clusters.	Yellow prisms.	Branched crosses and X's.

of trimethylamine or triethylamine in dry ether. The melting points of several common amines are given below.

Urethane of:	M.P. (°C)
Methylamine	196–197
Ethylamine	199–200
Dimethylamine	158–159
Diethylamine	127–128
iso-Amylamine	131–132
Di-isoamylamine	94–95
Benzylamine	200–203
Acetamide	211–212
Acetanilide	116–117

Another reagent which readily yields crystalline derivatives with many amines is 3,5-dinitrobenzoic acid. The reaction is carried out very simply by merely mixing an alcoholic solution of the amine with an alcoholic solution of the dinitrobenzoic acid. Although the crystals alone are not sufficient for identifying amine compounds, they may serve as a valuable aid. Should the problem merely require one to distinguish between the isomeric naphthylamines, for example, the test serves very well. Whereas α-naphthylamine yields reddish-orange crystals with 3,5-dinitrobenzoic acid, the β-isomer forms bright yellow crystals. The dinitrobenzoates are formed not only with amines but also with certain other compounds, as acetamide, thioacetamide, acetanilide, urea, etc. The capillary melting points of a number of the derivatives are shown in the following table.

CAPILLARY MELTING POINTS OF 3,5-DINITROBENZOATES

Compound	M.P. (Corr.) (°C)
Aniline	134.7
o-Toluidine	134.9
m-Toluidine [a]	139–144
p-Toluidine	145–147.4
o-Chloroaniline	152.7
m-Chloroaniline	121.8
p-Chloroaniline	133
p-Aminophenol	178.2–178.8
m-Nitroaniline [b]	112–114.4
p-Nitroaniline [b]	126.6–128.6
o-Aminobenzoic acid	205.2–205.6 (dec.)
m-Aminobenzoic acid	167–172.2
p-Aminobenzoic acid	192–196.7
Methyl aniline [a]	121.8
Dimethyl aniline	113.2–114
Acetanilide	129.1–130.1
α-Naphthylamine	200.5
β-Naphthylamine	156.5–157.2
Benzidine	205.7 (dec.)
Pyridine	171.3
Quinoline [c]	151.4–152.2
Ammonia	246.7
Urea [d]	120.5
Acetamide	93.9–103.9
Benzamide	138.6–140.4
p-Phenylenediamine [d]	177.3–178 (dec.)
o-Phenylenediamine [d]	177.3 (dec.)
m-Phenylenediamine	158.7

[a] Decomposition on redissolving.
[b] Recrystallized from cold benzene.
[c] Recrystallized from mixture of alcohol and benzene.
[d] Recrystallized from hot benzene.

Note: The above melting points are taken from Buehler, Currier, and Lawrence, *Industrial & Engineering Chemistry, Analytical Edition* 5, 277 (1933)

Amides.—An interesting reagent for the preparation of crystalline derivatives of urea and other amides is xanthydrol. As shown by Phillips and Pitt [5] there are many acid amides which, under favorable conditions, yield insoluble crystalline condensation products with this reagent. With urea the reaction takes place according to the equation

[5] *J. Amer. Chem. Soc.* **65**, 1355 (1943).

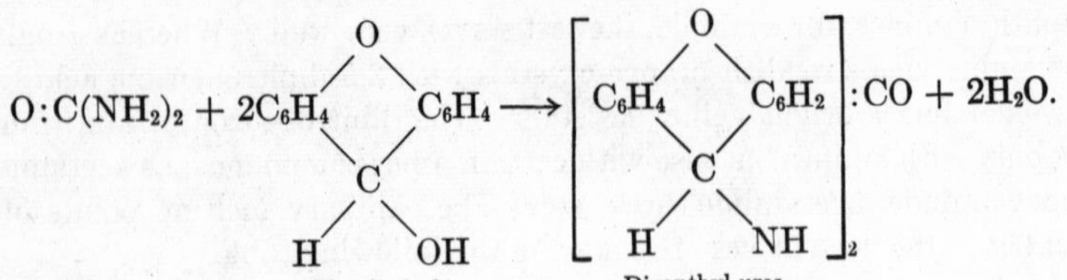

$$O:C(NH_2)_2 + 2C_6H_4 \overset{O}{\underset{C}{\diamond}} C_6H_4 \longrightarrow \left[C_6H_4 \overset{O}{\underset{C}{\diamond}} C_6H_2 \right]_2 :CO + 2H_2O.$$

Urea   Xanthydrol   Dixanthyl urea

In the presence of acetic acid this reaction applies to amides in general. On the microscale the reaction requires less time than indicated by Phillips and Pitt, many of the crystalline derivatives appearing within two or three minutes even at room temperatures. The melting points (*uncorr.*) for a number of the derivatives were determined by these authors, using a copper block and a standard 360° thermometer. Several of their values follow.

Amide	*M.P. of Xanthyl Derivative (°C)*
Acetamide	238–240
Propionamide	210–211
m-Butyramide	185–187
iso-Butyramide	210–211
Phenylacetamide	194–195
Benzamide	222.5–223.5
Succinimide	245–247
Phthalimide	176–177

Note: Of more than a score of derivatives investigated by Phillips and Pitt the one formed by phthalimide was the only instance of a derivative melting lower than the original. (Phthalimide melts at 220°.)

Xanthyl derivatives are also formed by such compounds as urea, ethyl urea, butyl urea, thiourea, etc.

Sulfa drugs.—Potent drugs are in the category of substances which the analyst may be called upon to identify when only limited amounts of suspected material are available. The various sulfa drugs fall within this classification. Only a few can be considered here, and even these must be treated very briefly.

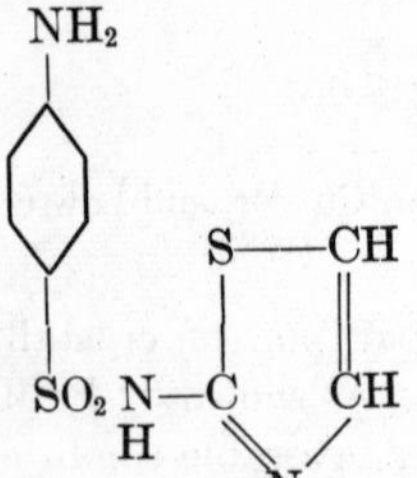

Sulfathiazole

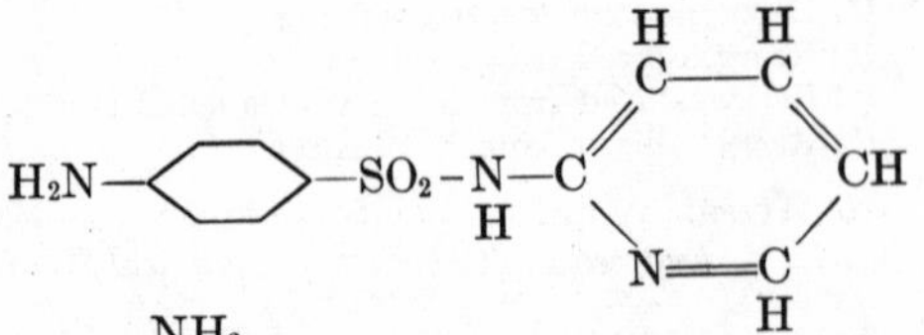

Sulfapyridine

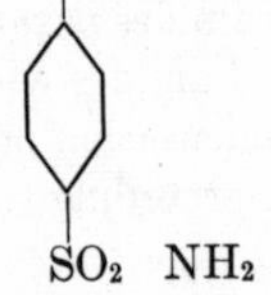

Sulfanilamide

FIG. 10.1. SULFANILAMIDE: BEHAVIOR TOWARD PICRIC ACID REAGENT.

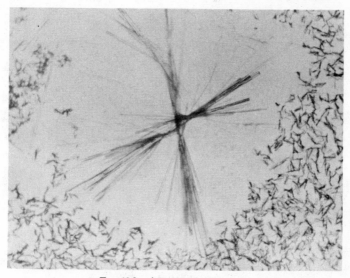

FIG. 10.2. ACETYLSULFANILAMIDE.

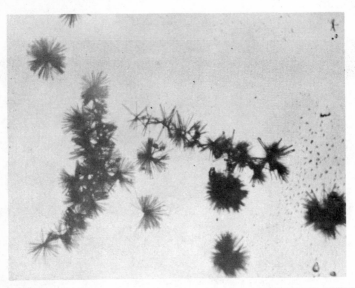

Fig. 10.3. Types of crystals formed by treating sulfapyridine with alcoholic picrolonic acid reagent.

FIG. 10.4. SULFATHIAZOLE: BEHAVIOR TOWARD ALCOHOLIC PICROLONIC ACID.

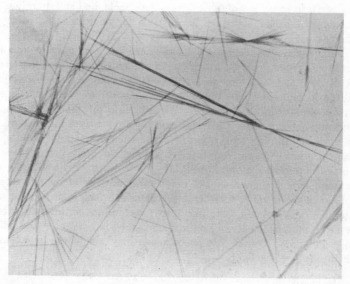

FIG. 10.5. SULFATHIAZOLE PICRATE.

Since picrolonic acid forms derivatives with many of the organic nitrogen bases, it is not surprising to find that it reacts with some of the

Picrolonic acid

sulfa drugs. Sulfathiazole, sulfapyridine, and the sodium salt of the latter form beautiful crystalline derivatives of low solubility when treated with an alcoholic solution of this reagent, whereas sulfanilamide does not.[6] Crystals which are useful in microscopic tests are formed by the reaction of picric acid with alcohol solutions of sulfathiazole, sulfanilamide, and the sodium salt of sulfapyridine (Figure 10.1). The sulfapyridine itself does not yield crystals in this picric acid test, but an aqueous solution of the drug does react with chlorauric acid.[7] With acetic anhydride, sulfanilamide also forms an acetyl derivative which is well adapted to the needs of the microscopist (Figure 10.2).[8]

Under certain conditions, therefore, the few reagents just mentioned may serve to identify sulfanilamide, sulfathiazole, and sulfapyridine, especially if a Kofler hot stage is available for micro melting point determinations.

Fluorescence microscopy.—Possibly one branch of microscopy which chemists have not given the attention it deserves is fluorescence microscopy (cf. Radley and Grant or de Ment). This technique, which has been utilized in biological investigations for a number of years, should also prove a useful tool for chemists. When certain substances are exposed to ultraviolet radiation, which is invisible, they may emit part of the energy in the form of longer, visible, wave lengths. Quinine sulfate, for example, when exposed to ultraviolet rays in a darkened room gives off a blue fluorescence, quinine salicylate fluoresces a bright violet, while anthraquinone appears orange colored. The intensity of the fluorescence of different solids varies considerably. Some substances, such as caffeine, fluoresce feebly, while others, like uranyl acetate and anthracene, exhibit a very bright fluorescence. Textile fibers exhibit fluorescence under ultraviolet radiation, so that this phenomenon may aid in the detection of substitutes in woven cloth.

[6] G. L. Keenan, *J. Assoc. Official Agr. Chem.* **25**, 830 (1942).

[7] *Ibid.* **24**, 830 (1941).

[8] John V. Scudi, *Ind. Eng. Chem., Anal. Ed.* **10**, 346 (1938).

Some investigations based on fluorescence microscopy can be carried out without acquiring any additional equipment other than a suitable light source and filters. One appropriate source of ultraviolet is the quartz-tube mercury arc lamp, such as supplied by the Hanovia Company. Since the radiation emitted by the mercury arc extends far into the visible spectrum this type of lamp must be used with a filter, such as a Corning glass filter no. 5840, or its equivalent. Another appropriate source is the carbon arc lamp, which is available in some laboratories. Such a lamp generates considerable heat, hence the ordinary filter (which is not heat resistant) must be protected by means of a cell containing copper sulfate solution.

After adjusting the lamp so as to direct its rays on the microscope stage, the fluorescence of small crystalline specimens, fibers, etc., can be observed through the ocular. A preliminary check on adjustments can be made by placing a known fluorescent specimen on the stage. For this purpose crystals of anthracene, uranyl acetate, or quinine sulfate will serve quite well. After the microscope has been focused on a slide containing one of these compounds (i.e., under ultraviolet radiation) it is a simple procedure to examine the specimen to be investigated. To avoid confusion it is important to select slides which are free from abrasions and which show no marked fluorescence. For a given substance the nature of the fluorescence will be influenced by the intensity of the ultraviolet illumination and by the actual wave lengths present. Some observations recorded in the literature are at variance with each other because the type of ultraviolet radiation has not been specified. Fluorescence may also be influenced by minute amounts of impurities.

When working with ultraviolet it is important to avoid exposing the eyes directly to the radiation, especially when using an intense source. Painful effects, sometimes permanent injury, may result.

Note: Some interesting suggestions on the possibility of applying fluorescence to the study of emulsions, penetration of leather by dyes, behavior of flotation agents, etc., are mentioned by C. J. Frosch and E. A. Hauser, Industrial & Engineering Chemistry, Analytical Edition 8, 423 (1936).

Isoquinoline as a reagent for metals.—A large number of organic compounds can be employed for the identification of various metal ions because they serve as complexing agents which yield characteristic crystals. An example of a heterocyclic nitrogen compound recently adapted for this purpose is isoquinoline. In the presence of thiocyanate ion, isoquinoline hydrochloride can be employed for the quantitative precipitation of zinc and copper, although the latter does not yield ideal crystals for microscopic identification. While the reagent can form precipitates

0.2 mm.

Figure a. Crystals Formed by Reaction of Isoquinoline-Ammonium Thiocyanate Reagent with Zinc Chloride

0.1mm.

Figure b. Typical Crystals Formed by Reaction of Isoquinoline-Ammonium Thiocyanate Reagent with Cadmium Chloride

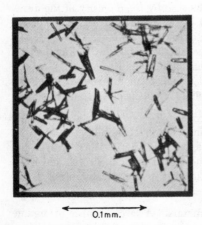

0.1mm.

Figure c. Deep Blue Crystals. Developed When Reagent Combines with Cobalt Chloride Solution

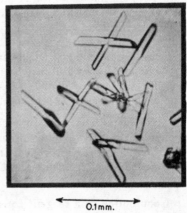

0.1mm.

Figure d. Pale Green Crystals. Occasionally Resulting from Interaction of Isoquinoline-Ammonium Thiocyanate Reagent and Nickel Chloride Solution

FIG. 10.6

with a number of other metals, in the absence of certain interfering ions it can serve for the identification of zinc, cadmium, cobalt, and copper. Of these the first two form characteristic colorless microcrystals (Figures 10.6A and B).

The presence of cupric ion causes the prompt separation of a copious precipitate having a characteristic yellow-green color. These crystals, which appear to be very thin leaves with a tendency to stand on edge, are so small that they may resemble an amorphous mass. Their color, however, is sufficient indication of cupric ion, since no other metal appears to yield a similar precipitate under the conditions of the test. Unless the concentration is very low (i.e., less than 1 part Cu in 2500), the green precipitate can be distinguished by the unaided eye. Under the microscope a positive test can be observed when the copper content of the sample is as low as 1 part in 15,000, whether the metal be present as acetate, chloride, or sulfate.

A very useful property of the isoquinoline-ammonium thiocyanate reagent is that it permits the detection of cobalt and copper in the presence of each other and in the presence of nickel. Cobalt causes the separation of interesting crystals of a beautiful deep blue color (Figure 10.6C). The latter can be identified even if the original solution contained a considerable excess of copper. For example, when the reagent is added to a test drop containing 1 part cobalt and 5 parts copper per thousand, the result is the formation of a green precipitate which, to the unaided eye, resembles the one obtained when cupric ion is the only cation present. Under the microscope, however, the observer will see the gradual separation of a pale green liquid along the edges of the preparation, followed by the appearance of a blue liquid. Eventually the deep blue crystals of the cobalt compound develop.

Under favorable conditions, i.e., with the metal concentration equal to 1 or more parts in 500, nickel can be identified by the formation of characteristic, highly refractive crystals, faintly tinged with green (Figure 10.6D).

For the derivatives which the isoquinoline-thiocyanate reagent forms with zinc, cadmium, and copper, it has been shown that the composition corresponds with the formula $M(C_9H_7N)_2 \cdot (CNS)_2$. Nitrogen determinations indicate a similar formula for the cobalt complex.

Among the common metals which may interfere with the tests just described are silver, lead, mercury, iron, bismuth, and antimony. The noble metals, gold, platinum, and palladium, should also be absent. In the presence of ferric ion the test for cadmium, zinc, nickel, or cobalt may be obscured by the formation of practically opaque cubic crystals and a red solution. However, if the iron is present in very low concentrations (1 part in 10,000) the tests will not generally be obscured.

PART II

LABORATORY EXPERIMENTS

FOREWORD

Regardless of the type of work for which the instrument is to be employed, the desk or table on which the microscope is to be used should have certain articles readily accessible at all times. These include the following.

A hardwood slide support.
A clean, sharp safety razor blade.
One pair of slide forceps.
One dissecting needle with handle.
Several 6-inch squares of well-laundered (unstarched) muslin.
Small camel's-hair brush.
Supply of good quality lens tissue.
Small drop-bottle of xylene (same as xylol).
Supply of clean slides in a protective container.
Supply of circular cover slips, No. 1, 18-mm diameter.
Box of slide labels or Dennison's gummed labels, #223.

The hardwood slide support is merely a hardwood block about 1½ inches square and 8 inches long. Slide preparations which are laid on this support can be picked up much more conveniently than when they are laid on the table. By placing numbers on the block, identification of the slides is simplified.

The muslin squares are very convenient for wiping slides and cover glasses. When there is need for cleaning the metal parts of the microscope or for quickly wiping away material which has been spilled on the stage, such squares of cloth are quite desirable. Obviously, these cloths should not be used repeatedly for an indefinite period. To be useful they must be clean.

The brush, xylene, and lens tissue are intended for cleaning microscope lenses, as explained in Experiment 1.

In addition to the standard 3×1 inch slides of clear glass, there are available slides which are etched at one end, that is, one end has a ground-glass surface. This surface is very convenient for labeling or numbering with an ordinary pencil. Since the extra cost of etched slides is very small, it is a good plan to include a supply of them.

The slides should be clean. They should be kept in a receptacle which

FIG. 1. NEW TYPE BAKELITE SLIDE BOX (*Clay-Adams Co., New York*). Made of Bakelite, with cover designed for a snap fit, this compact box represents an improvement over the former wooden boxes for storing prepared slides.

protects them from dust and fumes. Many slides can be cleaned and used a number of times. However, it is poor economy to continue the use of slides which have become scratched, corroded, or fogged. Use of such

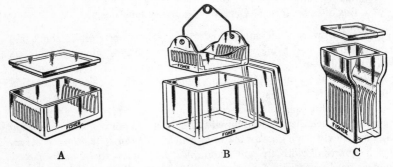

A   B   C

FIG. 2. STAINING DISHES (*Fisher Scientific Co.*). Although these vessels were designed for the use of biologists for staining bacteria and tissue sections on slides, these 'dishes' will be found convenient for soaking slides in various cleaning media. Type B offers the advantage of a tray which permits the transfer of a dozen slides from one solution to another without requiring handling.

inferior slides may lead to erroneous conclusions. The method of cleaning slides depends, in part, upon the nature of the substances to be removed. In many instances washing in water, followed by a rinse and a "wipe," will prove adequate. An improvement is to wash the slide quickly in water containing Calgonite [1] and then rinse thoroughly. Even when left to dry by evaporation, such slides appear clear and sparkling. In fact, this method has been found satisfactory for cleaning many types of laboratory glassware.

However, good judgment should be used so that time spent in cleaning slides does not become excessive. Organic solvents are comparatively expensive; large-scale cleaning methods, such as soaking a few score slides in several successive cleaning baths, have a tendency to scratch many. The best slides cost about one cent each, and a student's time is worth something.

Frequently, however, it may be necessary to clean even brand-new slides. In the earlier experiments it will be sufficient merely to remove dust and lint. For more exacting work specific directions will be given later.

[1] Calgonite is sold by supply houses, such as the Fisher Scientific Co., of Pittsburgh, Pa.

EXPERIMENT 1

GETTING ACQUAINTED WITH THE MICROSCOPE

(Reference: Chapter II)

Referring to Figure 3 in this manual, the student should familiarize himself with the various parts of his microscope. Beginning with the eyepiece, or ocular, it will be found that this can be lifted from the draw tube very easily. Dust and fingerprints should be removed from the lenses before using. To do this put a drop or two of xylene on a piece of folded lens tissue and gently wipe each lens surface. It is not necessary to flood the lens with xylene.

After replacing the ocular in the draw tube, gently pull upward on the latter until the 160-mm graduation coincides with the upper rim of the body tube. (Some instruments are not equipped with adjustable draw tubes.)

It is quite probable that the objectives of your microscope are mounted in a double or triple revolving nosepiece. In this event, turn the coarse adjustment (16 in Figure 3) until the objective directly beneath the body tube is about one-half inch above the stage. To bring a different objective into position, apply the thumb and forefinger to two of the objectives and exert a slight pressure so as to revolve the nosepiece around its axis. A faint click is heard when the new objective snaps into proper position. The lower lens of each objective should be cleaned by wiping lightly with lens tissue and toluene.

If the instrument has a substage condenser (6 in Figure 3) it is preferable that it be removed for the first work of the novice. In some models the condenser is removed simply by pushing it down to pass the mount through a snugly fitting sleeve. One hand should be placed below the condenser to receive it as released. In many models the condenser is held in a semicircular support by means of two small lugs backed by springs. Such a condenser must first be racked down somewhat by means of an adjustment knob; it is then snapped out of its support by pulling forward on it.

For the present purpose the substage mirror should be adjusted so that the plane surface will reflect light up into the objective. Before using, the surface of the mirror should be cleaned with lens tissue. Until the principles of illumination are discussed it will be sufficient to employ almost any convenient light source which is not too brilliant. An ordinary 25-watt frosted bulb placed a short distance from the substage mirror will serve the present needs. Any of the simpler types of microscope lamps may be employed. In daytime one may use the light coming from a

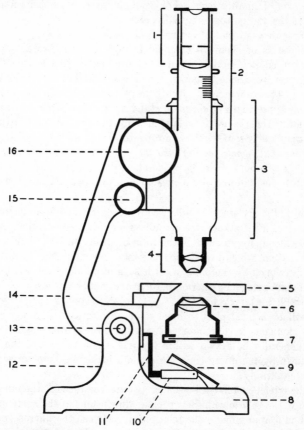

Fig. 3. Parts of the Microscope. (See Fig. 2.1 on page 17 for designation of parts.)

window. It is inadvisable to incline the substage mirror directly toward the sun, as this may have a blinding effect.

Unless instructed otherwise, in the experiments which follow, the draw tube, if adjustable, should be extended to the 160-mm mark. Following the procedure outlined in Chapter II (pages 19 to 22), about ten different specimens should be examined. Even if no prepared slides are available, there will be no difficulty in finding an abundance of satisfactory specimens to study. The following list is merely suggestive:

1. Fibers of wool, cotton, rayon, silk. Use only isolated, fine fibers. If they do not lie flat on the slide, a cover glass will help.

2. Hair taken from various animals or even from different parts of the same animal.

3. Parts of small insects. For example, parts of wings, antennae, or legs of moths, mosquitoes, houseflies, etc.

4. Specimens of mold from bread or cheese.

5. Crystals of chemical compounds such as borax, cream of tartar, oxalic acid, copper acetate, alum, photographer's hypo, Epsom salt. In general, prepare a small quantity of a warm or hot saturated aqueous solution of the compound. Place 1 drop of solution on a clean slide and attach an appropriate label; upon standing for some time crystallization will occur. The precise form assumed by the crystals of a given compound may vary somewhat according to the conditions which prevail. *Remember that, when peering into the eyepiece, focusing should always be* **UP**. *Keep both eyes open; don't squint.* If necessary, employ a shield until you can keep both eyes open. (See page 21 and Figure 2.7.)

Admittedly, the study of microscopy is not a course in freehand drawing; but in many instances we actually see much more when we endeavor to represent our impressions in the form of a sketch. The habit of careful observation, which necessarily plays an important role in microscopy, can be developed by sketching what is seen in a number of representative types of specimens. Furthermore, there are instances where such sketches are desirable for later reference.

It will be a good plan to have some uniformity. In order that the various sketches in your notebook can be more readily compared, they should generally be drawn within a circle which represents the field of view shown by the microscope. A circle 3 inches in diameter serves the purpose admirably.

In the circle, sketch the specimen as observed through the microscope. Naturally, the relationship between the dimensions of the sketch and the circle should approximate the relationship between the microscope image and its field of view. That is, if a crystal viewed through the microscope has one edge equivalent in length to two-thirds the diameter of the field of view, then the sketch in your notebook should represent that particular edge as being two-thirds as long as the diameter of the circle within which it is drawn.

Obviously, the drawings should be on unruled paper.

Prepare sketches for as many specimens as the instructor directs.

When the day's laboratory work has been completed, all equipment should be returned to its proper place in **good condition.** This also means **clean.**

The microscope should be returned to its case. An individual worker using his own instrument in a private laboratory may prefer to keep his microscope beneath a glass bell-jar or under a transparent plastic shield; the important point is to make certain that the instrument is clean before putting it away, and then to store it in such a way that it is protected from dust and from tampering by individuals. It is always advisable to ascertain whether any drops of liquids or particles of solids have adhered to any of the objectives. If such foreign bodies are permitted to remain until the next laboratory period, serious damage may result. Liquids may attack the cement which holds the various lens components in intimate contact. Both liquids and solids may exert chemical action on the metal parts. Even if no actual damage occurs, it generally is more difficult to remove substances which have been permitted to remain for an extended period.

In college and university classes the instructors in charge will do well to inspect the instruments at the end of each laboratory period until every individual has acquired proper habits.

EXPERIMENT 2

DETERMINATION OF THE EYEPOINT, OR RAMSDEN DISC

(Reference: Chapter II)

The microscope should be provided with the 16-mm objective and a 5-× or 6-× ocular, and the draw tube should be raised to the 160-mm mark. If yours is one of the older instruments, use the ⅔-inch objective and the number 1 ocular. For this experiment the illumination should come from an artificial light source.

First focus the microscope on a slide containing a very thin specimen covered by a cover slip. An appropriate specimen may be prepared by allowing a drop of ink to evaporate on a slide. After focusing on the specimen, remove the slide, but leave the adjustment of the microscope unchanged.

By means of a ring clamped to a ringstand, or by any other convenient means, support a sheet of ground glass a few centimeters above the eyepiece. The ground surface of the glass should face down. Arrange the light source and the substage mirror so that a bright spot is projected on the ground glass. Adjust the latter to various heights until you have found the position at which the projected disc is of the minimum diameter. This small disc is the Ramsden disc, or the eyepoint. The diameter of the disc may be measured by means of dividers or, preferably, by means of vernier calipers. The measurement should be made carefully since the value will be used in a later experiment (No. 4). The diameter of the disc can be checked by means of a pair of dividers or compasses.

When the correct position has been found, carefully measure the distance between the top of the ocular and the lower surface of the glass screen. Here, too, dividers may be the most convenient device for measuring the distance. Record your data in a table similar to Table I.

TABLE I. POSITION OF EYEPOINT

Name of microscope manufacturer: ....

Serial number of microscope: ....

Ocular	Objective	Position	Diameter
5-×	16-mm	No. of mm above ocular	

In the same table include your findings for the 10-× or 12-× ocular when used with the 16-mm objective, and for different oculars used with your other objectives.

Although it is not imperative to place the eye exactly at the eyepoint when making observations, the eye should be rather close to it.

According to your measurements, does the distance from ocular to eyepoint vary when different oculars are employed with the same objective?

Is there any change in the position of the eyepoint when the same ocular is employed with different objectives?

Clamp a piece of stiff wire or a ruler to mark the height of the eyepoint. With a specimen in focus beneath the microscope, determine the effect of placing the eye above the eyepoint and below the eyepoint.

EXPERIMENT 3

FIELD OF VIEW, DEPTH OF FOCUS

(Reference: Chapter II)

A. DIAMETER OF THE FIELD OF VIEW

For this experiment a stage micrometer will be required. Essentially, this is a glass slide which has a ruled scale in the center. The slide is somewhat heavier than standard microscope slides (object slides) but it conforms with them in length and width, viz., 3 × 1 inches. A small black circle around the center of the slide marks the location of the ruled scale. The latter is not easily seen by the unaided eye, hence the use of the black circle.

The stage micrometer should be stored in its original box or case when not in actual use, in order to protect it from harmful liquids and fumes. The micrometer scale is ruled on a small plate of very thin glass which has been cemented to the slide. Friction, solvents, and dust particles may damage it. Fingers should never be permitted to touch the central portion of the slide. Should cleaning become necessary, use a camel's-hair brush.

Because of the likelihood of damaging the micrometer, do not place any specimens on it for direct measurement. Generally the stage micrometer is merely employed for calibrating an ocular micrometer. This procedure will be described in a later experiment.

Using the 5-× or 6-× ocular and 16-mm objective, focus your microscope on the micrometer scale. Observe that the total length of the graduated portion is 2.2 mm. In the closely ruled section to the left, two of the 0.1-mm divisions have been subdivided into ten parts each, so that one of the smallest subdivisions represents 0.01 mm. In the remainder of the micrometer scale each of the small divisions is equivalent to 0.1 mm.

Adjust the micrometer so that the scale extends across the center of the field of view. Observe the diameter of the circular field. Make similar measurements for other combinations of objectives and oculars, and record your data in a form similar to Table II.

B. DEPTH OF FOCUS

Place under the microscope a slide containing some very fine crystalline substance such as crystallized dextrose, cupric-chloride, hydroquinone, etc., and examine with various objective and ocular combinations. Can all planes or levels (that is, from the top of specimen down to the

TABLE II.   VARIATION OF DIAMETER OF FIELD AT DIFFERENT MAGNIFICATIONS

Ocular	Objective	Approximate Magnification	Diameter of field in mm

slide surface) be brought into distinct focus at one time?   Observe how the depth of focus varies with the degree of magnification.

If the microscope is equipped with a graduated fine adjustment, it will be possible to make a more nearly quantitative estimate of the depth of focus.   For this purpose a 10-× ocular and a 16-mm or 8-mm objective may be employed.   The zero line of the graduated drum should be directly opposite the stationary index line.   An appropriate slide is brought into focus, using only the coarse adjustment.   Having selected some prominent feature, for example, one sharp edge of a thin crystal, raise the objective very, very slowly, as long as the edge remains in focus.   If it has become slightly blurred, cautiously lower the objective until sharp focus is re-established.   Now, using the graduated fine adjustment, carefully lower the objective as long as the crystal edge remains in sharp focus.   The distance through which the objective has passed by means of the fine adjustment represents, approximately, the depth of focus.   Naturally, several trials should be made.

In order to determine the distance covered by turning the fine adjustment, it is necessary to know how many divisions the drum has been turned beyond the original position.   Knowing the value of one division, you can calculate the distance.   The values of the graduations are not the same on all instruments, but for a given microscope the value is usually engraved on the movable collar.   On one of the popular Spencer models, for example, one complete turn of the fine adjustment screw is equivalent to 1000 microns.   Since the collar is divided into 100 equal portions, each division represents 10 microns.   In the more precise instruments provided with a more expensive fine adjustment, a complete turn of the screw is equivalent to a smaller number of microns.   Certain Zeiss instruments, for example, are provided with fine adjustments so geared that one of the divisions of the drum corresponds to a vertical movement of one micron.

EXPERIMENT 4

MEASUREMENT OF WORKING DISTANCE

(Reference: Chapter III)

For this experiment there should be available a specimen which is very thin. Satisfactory specimens can be prepared by several different methods. Some organic compounds which are occasionally referred to as amorphous powders are really microcrystalline in structure. This is true of fine grades of pyrogallic acid. If a glass rod is thrust into a mass of this compound, many microcrystals adhere to the rod when it is withdrawn. If the rod is given a sharp rap with the finger, many of the larger crystals are dislodged. By tapping the tip of the rod on the surface of a clean glass slide some of the fine crystals will be transferred. The aim is to have a relatively small number of very small crystals. Various other organic compounds, such as m-nitrobenzoic acid, p-nitrobenzoic acid, cystine, finely crystallized glucose, some grades of phenolphthalein, etc., may seem to be amorphous powders, but actually they consist of microcrystals.

Some substances yield very thin crystalline forms when a drop of dilute solution undergoes spontaneous evaporation on a clean microscope slide. Cupric chloride, picric acid, cream of tartar, and ordinary borax are a few common examples. The solutions should be very dilute. A mere pinch of the solute is required for 100 ml of solution. Another method employed in some laboratories is to obtain "ink crystals." By means of a pen, two or three ink marks are placed near the center of a clean slide. After the ink has thoroughly dried, it is examined for minute crystals. Several trials may be required.

With the 5-× or 6-× ocular and the 16-mm objective in position, carefully turn the coarse adjustment knob until the front element of the objective *just* touches the slide. Now, while peering into the ocular, slowly turn the coarse adjustment to raise the objective until the specimen is in critical focus. By means of dividers measure the distance from the slide to the front of the objective. Record the mean of several such trials as the working distance. Measure the working distance for the same objective, using a different ocular. Is there an appreciable difference?

Determine the working distance for each objective on your instrument, recording the results in tabular form. The instructor may include several other objectives for measurement.

TABLE III. WORKING DISTANCE

Name of microscope manufacturer: ....

Serial number of microscope: ....

Ocular	Objective	Working Distance

Objectives having the same focal length need not have the same working distance. If objectives of different manufacturers are available, it may prove interesting to determine the variations in the working distances of lenses having the same equivalent focus.

In general, how does the working distance vary with the focal length of the objective?

EXPERIMENT 5

DETERMINATION OF NUMERICAL APERTURE

(Reference: Chapter III)

For the accurate measurement of numerical aperture an Abbe type of apertometer is employed. Considering the rare need for determining the N.A. in the average laboratory, most individuals and institutions find this a rather expensive piece of equipment. Where a high degree of precision is not a requisite, the numerical aperture of an objective can be determined with an inexpensive device known as "Cheshire's Apertometer." This device consists of three parts, as follows: [1]

1. A calibrated chart, as shown in Figure 4.
2. A cube of wood, measuring 25 mm on edge.
3. A metal disc or diaphragm, pierced by a minute hole in the center.

[1] This outfit may be purchased from C. Baker Company, 244 High Holborn, London.

Of several possible methods for carrying out a determination with the Cheshire apertometer, the following combines simplicity with a fair degree of accuracy. With the chart lying on the stage of the microscope, place the 25-mm wood cube beneath the objective to be tested. Drop the metal diaphragm into the upper half of a low-power ocular, which is inserted in the draw tube after replacing the eyelens. Should the metal stop or diaphragm furnished with the outfit prove too large to slip into the eyepiece, a smaller one must be prepared. This is easily accomplished by cutting an appropriate disc of oak tag or heavy paper; the

Fig. 4. Cheshire's Apertometer.

aperture of proper size can be made by piercing the center with a large needle. After focusing the system on the top of the wood block, the latter is removed. If, now, a hand lens is held at the proper distance above the eyepiece, the observer can see the circles of the apertometer chart. After the latter has been centered beneath the objective, the N.A. is obtained by counting the number of circles which lie in the field of view. Each circle corresponds to a value of one-tenth; thus, if five of the concentric circles can be seen, the objective has a numerical aperture of 0.50.

After acquiring practice by determining the N.A. of several objectives of known values, apply the method to several lenses of which the numerical apertures are unknown. It may prove interesting to determine the numerical apertures of old, unmarked objectives and compare them with modern objectives.

Record your findings in Table IV.

TABLE IV.   N.A. OF VARIOUS OBJECTIVES

Objective (Identification Number)	N.A. Designated by Maker	N.A. Determined by Cheshire Method
16-mm		
8-mm		
-mm		
	(Unknown)	
	(Unknown)	

Knowing the N.A. of an objective, how could its angular aperture be calculated?   (Refer to the definition of numerical aperture.)

Calculate the angular aperture for two of your objectives.

Assume that two objectives have the same equivalent focus but different numerical apertures.   Explain why the objective with the higher N.A. justifies the use of a higher-power ocular.

EXPERIMENT 6

EFFECT OF A COVER GLASS

(Reference: Chapter III)

For this procedure there should be available a preparation which is so very thin that its height above the slide is negligible.   An appropriate specimen may be prepared according to one of the methods suggested in Experiment 4.

Without using a cover glass, focus this specimen under the microscope, using the 8-mm or 16-mm objective with either the 10-× or 12-× ocular. When you are certain that sharp focus has been attained, cover the object with a No. 1 cover glass.   It will be observed that the crystals are no longer in focus.   Slowly turn the fine adjustment, first upward, then down.   Which movement re-established sharp focus?

Having focused the specimen beneath a No. 1 cover glass, without moving the slide replace the cover with a No. 3 cover slip.   If there is no supply of No. 3 covers, it may be possible to use one which belongs to a haemacytometer (cf. Chapter VI).   Since the latter type is rather expensive, handle it very carefully. Determine what movement of the fine adjustment is required to return the specimen to sharp focus.

Once more focus on the crystals covered by a No. 1 cover glass. After replacing the thin cover with a No. 3 cover, try the effect of varying the length of the draw tube. Ordinarily the tube is adjusted to a length of 160-mm. In this instance determine the effect produced by moving the draw tube above or below the 160-mm mark. (Obviously, this cannot be carried out on a microscope which is not equipped with an adjustable draw tube.)

By means of a diagram explain why it is necessary to alter the position of an objective when a heavier cover glass is employed.

EXPERIMENT 7

OBJECTIVES AND OCULARS; CERTAIN COMPARISONS

(Reference: Chapter III)

A. OBJECTIVES

Place on a slide a small square of gauze, such as is sold for bandages, beneath a cover glass. Examine it through the 32-mm objective, then, in turn, through the 16-mm, 8-mm, and 4-mm objectives. Which objective yields the most satisfactory result? Draw a sketch of what is seen.

Isolate an individual thread from the gauze and place it in a drop of water on a slide. While holding the thread in place with tweezers or a glass rod, use a fine needle to fray the end of the thread and separate a few individual fibers. After covering the fibers with a slip, again observe the specimen through the four objectives mentioned above. Which objective appears best suited for this specimen? Give the reasons for your answer. Sketch the specimen as seen through the preferred objective.

B. OCULARS

Using the same slide, focus on the fibers with the 16-mm objective and a 5-× or 6-× eyepiece. Next observe the specimen through the same objective but with a 10-× or 12-× eyepiece. Apart from giving a higher degree of magnification, how does the ocular of higher power affect the image?

If a widefield, hyperplane, or telaugic ocular is available, compare its performance with that of the usual 10-× Huygenian ocular. For optimum results with the widefield ocular, have you found that the eye should be placed in the same relative position as that required when using the Huygens eyepiece? If time permits, it should prove interesting to determine the position of the eyepoint for a widefield ocular. (See Experiment 2.)

Can you conceive of any practical advantages in using widefield oculars?

A 25-× ocular with a 16-mm objective (N.A. = 0.25) gives approximately the same degree of magnification as a 5-× ocular combined with a 4-mm objective (N.A. = 0.85). State which of these combinations would be the more satisfactory in observing the form of fine structures, and explain why.

EXPERIMENT 8

SYMMETRICAL ILLUMINATION

(Reference: Chapter IV)

A. AXIAL ILLUMINATION

For this experiment the light source may be daylight, preferably from a north or east window, or artificial light which passes through a sheet of opal glass or ground glass. Remove the substage condenser, so that the substage plane mirror reflects the light directly into the objective. Prepare a test object by placing on a clean slide one drop of mucilage or glycerine into which air has been beaten by means of a thin glass or metal rod.

Examine the slide with the 16-mm objective and either a 5-× or 10-× ocular. Having located a bubble which measures about 0.5 mm in diameter, observe its exact form. If the illumination is axial, the outer boundary of the bubble should be a perfect circle. Inside the dark border there should be a highly luminous disc. If any of the boundaries are not circular, the lighting is not truly axial. To obtain axial lighting, the mirror must be so adjusted that the boundaries of the different regions of the air bubble appear circular.

Try the effects of focusing up and focusing down very slightly. Under axial lighting the image of the air bubble should not be displaced from its position when there is a slight change in focus.

Draw a sketch to represent the appearance of the air bubble as you see it when axial lighting prevails.

After completing the foregoing sketch, tilt the mirror slightly while peering into the microscope. How does this change from axial lighting affect the appearance of the bubble? Sketch the appearance of the bubble as you now see it.

Slightly raise and lower the focus of the microscope while looking into the ocular. Record the effect produced on the image.

B. SYMMETRICAL CONVERGENT ILLUMINATION

1. By means of the mirror. With the concave substage mirror in position, focus on the same slide used with the plane mirror. Whereas the rays were substantially parallel before, those provided by the concave mirror are convergent. However, by properly adjusting the mirror it should be possible to find a position where it illuminates the specimen symmetrically. In other words, the rays converge on the specimen in the form of a cone, the axis of which coincides with the optic axis of the microscope. When this condition is attained, the air bubble is bounded by a perfect circle. Compare the appearance of this image with your sketch of the bubble as it appeared under axial lighting. How is the image affected by a slight change of focus?

2. By means of the condenser. As will be shown later, the substage mirror will not always prove an adequate means of illumination. For this reason a condenser should be available.

For the present experiment, attach the condenser to the substage of the microscope and, if the substage is provided with a rack and pinion movement, raise the condenser to its highest possible position. Light is reflected up into the condenser with the plane mirror. By focusing on an air bubble, once more adjust the mirror until a symmetrical image results. Observe that the condenser yields a much brighter image than that obtained when the mirror is used alone. This of course, is an important function of the condenser.

EXPERIMENT 9

CRITICAL ILLUMINATION

(Reference: Chapter IV)

Thus far the method of illumination required in the experiments has been rather crude. If the microscope is to be a really efficient instrument, a more careful method of lighting is imperative. *The importance of proper illumination cannot be overstressed.* Since, fortunately, the work of the chemist does not demand the utmost in resolution of fine structures his problem of illumination can usually be solved without very elaborate equipment, provided he makes the most of what is available. Naturally there are certain minimum essentials without which it is difficult or impossible to attain the desired results.

When transparent specimens are observed, the image is formed by the light which passes through the specimen and into the objective. The light must be of adequate intensity if the image is not to suffer from being too dim.

If the entire area embraced in the field of view of a given objective is to be visible, it is necessary to have the entire field supplied with light. In other words, the illuminated area must be of adequate dimensions.

However, it is likewise important that the illuminated area be confined within the required dimensions. If this is not done, glare will result and image quality will suffer.

An objective of a certain given numerical aperture collects rays in the form of a cone, the sides of which subtend an angle of definite value. Stated another way, an objective of a given N.A. possesses a corresponding angular aperture. Ideally, the cone of light supplied to the specimen should subtend an angle equal to the angle of the cone of rays collected by the objective; or the condenser aperture should equal the N.A. of the objective. When the condenser aperture is larger, various reflections are set up which result in glare.

The illumination should be of uniform intensity over the entire field. When this condition is not met, misinterpretations may result.

A. LUMINOSITY

Control of the intensity of illumination is effected by various means, depending upon the type of lamp employed.

Most microscope lamps are not provided with any special arrangement for varying the intensity of the light. One method for control in such cases is to vary the distance from lamp to microscope.

Another method is to employ appropriate neutral density filters in the slot usually found beneath the substage condenser. On the other hand, if the lamp is provided with a filter holder it may prove more convenient to use it instead of the slot beneath the substage condenser.

Some microscope lamps are furnished with a variable resistance or rheostat. By reducing the voltage at which the current is supplied to the bulb, the brilliance is decreased. If such a voltage control is not furnished as an integral part of the lighting unit, a suitable rheostat can be obtained and connected into the circuit. Reducing luminosity by operating a bulb below its rated voltage is not always desirable because color values may be altered.

Definitely, luminosity is not to be controlled by means of the sub-

*stage condenser diaphragm or by the iris diaphragm attached to the micro-
scope lamp.*

The student should try out the effects of all his available means for
controlling luminosity.

Ordinarily the illumination should be of such intensity as to give a
clear image when the objective is employed with a condenser cone of about
nine-tenths. (See p. 50.)

B. LIMITATIONS OF THE SUBSTAGE MIRROR

Use a low-power ocular and the 16-mm objective. Having removed
the substage condenser, arrange to provide axial illumination as in part
A of Experiment 8. Remove the ocular and peer down the tube of the
microscope. The back lens of the objective should be illuminated over its
entire area. In fact, the illuminated portion on the object slide may be
even larger than the field of view of the objective. Such a condition may
cause glare. If the lamp has an iris diaphragm, this should be closed
down until the illuminated area on the slide is equal to the field covered
by the objective.

Swing the 8-mm objective into position and examine the back lens.
(If the lamp condenser was closed down when using the 16-mm objective,
it should be opened as far as possible now.) Estimate the relationship
between the diameter of the illuminated area and that of the entire back
lens. How does this condition affect the resolving power of the objective?

Try the same test with the 4-mm objective. Can you estimate the
effective N.A. of the objective when used with this lighting arrangement?

With the 16-mm objective in position, arrange for symmetrical convergent illumination as in part B-1 of Experiment 8. Again swing the
8-mm and the 4-mm objectives into position and estimate the relative
proportion of the back lens illuminated in each instance.

Is the degree of magnification decreased when the objective is not
employed at its maximum aperture, that is, when only part of the back
lens of the objective is illuminated?

Is there any decrease in resolution when an objective is not used at its
rated N.A.?

What can you say concerning the merits of providing microscopes
with 4-mm objectives when the stands are not equipped with substage
condensers?

C. SECURING ADEQUATE CONE WITH CONDENSER

With the substage condenser in position, arrange for symmetrical convergent illumination of the 16-mm objective as directed in part B-2 of
Experiment 8. With the condenser diaphragm wide open, focus on a slide
containing one of the very thin transparent specimens mentioned in

Experiment 4. Very gradually close the diaphragm until the specimen appears distinct. Remove the eyepiece and note whether the entire back lens of the objective is filled with light. The probability is that about three-fourths of the area is illuminated, in which case a three-fourths condenser cone is being employed.

While observing the back lens, slowly open the substage diaphragm until it just permits the entire back lens area to be illuminated. (This assumes that the condenser is properly centered with respect to the objective. If it is slightly off center, compromise by the largest possible illuminated disc within the perimeter of the lens.) The objective is now being used at its full aperture. When the ocular is replaced, does the specimen appear distinct? (Keep in mind the statements mentioned in part A of this experiment, and endeavor to adjust the luminosity properly.)

Without altering the condenser diaphragm, swing the 8-mm objective into position. Is a distinct image of the specimen formed?

Remove the ocular and examine the back lens of the objective. Explain why only a fraction of the lens is illuminated.

Slowly open the condenser diaphragm until the disc of light practically coincides with the lens. If the eyepiece is replaced in the tube, the image produced will be brighter than it was with the smaller light cone. Furthermore, since the objective is being used at full aperture, resolution is increased.

Carry out similar tests with the 4-mm objective.

Explain the importance of using a condenser with an objective having a N.A. in excess of 0.25.

D. CRITICAL ILLUMINATION

1. **With diffused light.** Thus far Experiment 9 has been performed with illumination provided by daylight or by a lamp equipped with a ground glass. Both of these sources are sometimes incorrectly given as examples of parallel lighting. Actually, diffused daylight entering a window and light passing through ground glass contain many rays which are not parallel. However, at some distance away from the window or ground glass the rays coming from a given area will be more nearly parallel. For this reason better results may be secured if the microscope is not placed too close to this type of light source. When using rays which have been rendered parallel by means of a condenser, the only effect resulting from changing the distance from lamp to microscope is the variation in brilliance. However, since such parallel rays are in the form of a bundle of limited diameter, axial lighting requires that the bundle fall on the central portion of the substage mirror.

The most common (and the least expensive) microscope lamps are the type which are merely provided with ground glass instead of a condensing lens. Since they yield diffused light, strictly critical illumination cannot be attained, although one can secure a good approximation.

With the 16-mm objective in place, adjust the lamp and the substage mirror to obtain symmetrical convergent lighting with the condenser, as explained earlier. Having focused the microscope on some convenient specimen bring the condenser to the appropriate position with respect to the object slide. Hold some thin object, such as a needle, directly in front of the ground glass of the lamp; now, while observing the object slide through the microscope, rack the condenser up or down until the image of the needle appears to lie in the same field with the object. The condenser may now be said to image the light source in the plane of the object, that is, on the surface of the slide. If the condenser diaphragm is stopped down to the appropriate aperture, for example, to a nine-tenths light cone, approximately critical illumination results. (It is understood, of course, that light intensity has been regulated by one of the means already suggested.) Unless certain special effects are sought, this method of illumination should be generally employed when best results are desired with diffused light.

If the 8-mm or 4-mm objective is to be used, the position of the condenser need not be changed, but the diaphragm must be adjusted to give the proper light cone.

When using light coming from a window, the procedure is similar to the foregoing. If the window has small panes, the image of the frame may interfere with the image being studied. When this condition applies, the interfering image is eliminated by lowering the condenser just sufficiently for the purpose.

After obtaining approximately critical illumination with the 16-mm objective in place, move the lamp farther away. Determine whether this change in distance requires any change in the position of the substage condenser if critical lighting is to be retained.

2. With a condenser. With the 16-mm objective in position, arrange the substage mirror and condenser to secure symmetrical convergent illumination, according to the method given earlier. If the illumination is of proper brilliance, the remaining steps which must be taken to render the lighting critical are:

(a) Adjusting the substage condenser to the proper height.
(b) Restriction of the area illuminated by the lamp.
(c) Securing the appropriate condenser cone.

To accomplish the first of these steps raise or lower the condenser until an image of the light source (that is, incandescent filament, carbon arc, Argand flame, etc.) appears in focus when you peer into the microscope. Since this image may interfere with the observation of specimens being studied, throw it just out of focus by lowering (or raising) the substage condenser very slightly.

With the diaphragm of the Abbe condenser wide open, gradually close the iris diaphragm of the lamp until it is seen to cut into the field of view. At this point, open it just sufficiently to move its image outside the field of view.

The remaining step is to provide the proper condenser cone as done in part C of this experiment.

Having secured critical lighting, you should observe the effect of lamp diaphragm. To do this, focus some convenient specimen by critical illumination. Next observe the effect produced when the lamp diaphragm is gradually opened.

Return the diaphragm setting until critical lighting is restored. Now swing the 8-mm or the 4-mm objective into position. What changes must be made in order to retain critical illumination when objectives are changed? First try to predict whether the Abbe condenser must be refocused, whether its diaphragm must be opened, and whether the lamp diaphragm must be changed. State the reasons on which you base your prediction, then check by actual trial.

EXPERIMENT 10

OTHER FORMS OF TRANSMITTED ILLUMINATION

(Reference: Chapter IV)

Although critical illumination or an approximation thereof may be the most satisfactory for general work, there are occasions when certain special effects are best secured by other lighting methods.

A. OBLIQUE ILLUMINATION

1. **Without a substage condenser.** Adjust the microscope for parallel axial illumination, using the air bubble test, as given in Experiment 8. Now swing the mirror out to one side and adjust it to secure the maximum light. (This cannot be done on all microscopes. The mirror must be mounted on an "arm.")

Does the bubble image retain its former circular shape? Draw a sketch to show the image produced by illumination.

Adjust the mirror to restore axial illumination, and examine some freshly prepared crystals of a substance such as borax, cream of tartar, or oxalic acid. These are easily obtained by preparing a warm, saturated solution of the compound and placing one drop on a slide. After sketching the appearance of one or two typical crystals as seen by axial illumination, adjust the mirror for oblique lighting. Sketch the same crystals as they appear now.

Suggest an advantage of oblique illumination. Are there any disadvantages?

2. By means of a substage condenser. There are several methods for securing oblique illumination when using the Abbe condenser. Undoubtedly the simplest is to hold a card between the mirror and the condenser so as to obstruct some of the rays along one side.

Prepare a crystal specimen as suggested under paragraph 1, and focus it under the 16-mm objective by symmetrical convergent illumination as directed in Experiment 9. After drawing a sketch to represent a few typical crystals as they appear when thus lighted, study the same crystals as they appear when an opaque card is held beneath the condenser to cut off light coming from the right side. Sketch the crystals as you see them now. How do their images differ from those seen by symmetrical convergent illumination? How are the images affected if the card is used to shut off light from the left side?

Suggest advantages of using oblique illumination.

In what way is it necessary to be cautious in interpreting images observed by oblique illumination?

When using a substage condenser a convenient means for securing oblique illumination is by the use of appropriate stops. Most condensers are now provided with a slot which permits the insertion of a thin glass filter disc just below the iris diaphragm. An appropriate stop can be made from a black paper disc having the same diameter as that of the filter disc, which is about 32 mm. Part of the disc is cut off along a line parallel to a diameter. It may be desirable to prepare several stops to obtain different effects.

When one of these opaque stops is attached to a thin glass disc, it can be inserted in the filter slot of the substage condenser. All that remains to be done to have oblique illumination is the closing of the iris diaphragm to its proper aperture.

Using the 8- or 16-mm objective, compare the following as seen by critical illumination and by unilateral oblique illumination.

1. Starch grains.
2. Freshly prepared crystals of cream of tartar, borax, oxalic acid.
3. Prepared slides of diatoms, if available.

B. DARK-FIELD ILLUMINATION

For this exercise, use a slide containing various kinds of starch grains or freshly prepared crystals of such substances as oxalic acid, borax, or cream of tartar. First examine the specimen by symmetrical convergent illumination, using the 16-mm or 8-mm objective and adjusting the condenser and diaphragm to secure critical conditions.

Measure the diameter of the diaphragm opening after critical illumination has been secured. Next open the diaphragm and examine the specimen as it appears with the various dark-field stops inserted beneath the condenser. How does the diameter of the most satisfactory dark-field stop compare with the recorded diaphragm opening during critical illumination?

If conventional metal dark-field stops are not available, similar results can be secured by inserting a glass disc which has an opaque paper disc fixed to its center by means of some adhesive. The paper discs of various diameters are easily cut by means of sharp cork drills. If opaque paper is not convenient, tin or aluminum foil may be substituted.

C. RHEINBERG ILLUMINATION

By using dark-field stops with colored filters, it is possible to have the image of a specimen appear in any chosen color. If, however, the dark-field stop were replaced by a transparent colored disc, the image would be seen against a colored field instead of a dark background. This condition is achieved by the use of Rheinberg discs. An inexpensive substitute for these discs can be made by cutting 32-mm discs of colored gelatin or cellophane, using a large cork drill. By means of another drill a smaller disc (approximately 8 mm) is removed from the center. By fixing a red ring and a small green disc to a clear glass disc, for example, one may obtain red images on a green background.

It should be noted that in dark-field illumination there is no central cone of rays which pass directly through the specimen and to the objective, whereas in the Rheinberg method rays passing through the central colored disc also pass through the specimen. Hence the color of the specimen image is influenced by both the outer ring and the central disc.

If time permits, the student should examine a few specimens by Rheinberg illumination.

EXPERIMENT 11

ILLUMINATING OPAQUE OBJECTS

(Reference: Chapter IV)

During the examination of an opaque object the image observed by the eye is formed by rays which are reflected from the specimen. Generally a considerable proportion of the rays from the light source are absorbed by the opaque body. For this reason the illumination of an opaque specimen must be more intense than in the case of a transparent object if the final image is to be of comparable brilliance.

Preferably you should employ a lamp which is equipped with a condensing lens and iris diaphragm, so that it serves as a miniature spotlight. The iris diaphragm is used to control the area of the illuminated field. This control is important whether the observations are being made on transparent objects or opaque specimens. Again, it is important to have some means for regulating the intensity of the illumination. The means may be the same as employed with transparent material.

The lamp should be provided with some arrangement whereby it can be adjusted to illuminate the specimen from a variety of angles ranging from nearly horizontal to nearly perpendicular. This feature aids in revealing contours to the best advantage. When the specimen is illuminated by a beam directed from above, the method is sometimes referred to as "top lighting." When top lighting is employed, precautions should be taken to prevent the admission of any light from below the stage.

A number of lamps known as "universal" microscope illuminators are so designed as to provide most of the features ordinarily required for the examination of specimens by either transmitted or reflected light.

If the laboratory has several different types of illuminators for opaque specimens, you should endeavor to acquaint yourself with each in order to determine their respective merits. A list of those available may be secured from the instructor in charge, who should also provide special operating directions where required. Bristles, fibers, textiles, paper, leather, plated metals, and painted surfaces are examples of materials which may be examined by reflected light.

A. Place on a slide a small square of finely woven cloth. Without using a cover glass, examine the cloth with the 16-mm objective. (If available, the student should employ an objective which is corrected for use without a cover glass.) Try the effect of using the lamp in three different positions, as follows.

(1) With the beam of rays striking the slide at an angle of about 45 degrees.

(2) With the beam at an angle as close to 90 degrees as feasible.

(3) With the beam as nearly horizontal as possible.

How do the results of these three different arrangements compare with each other?

B. For this exercise secure a small piece of tin plate. One square centimeter will be more than ample. It may add interest to employ an etched specimen cut from a can which served as a container for peas or fruit juice.

Compare the results observed with the lamp arranged at several different angles, as done in part A of this experiment.

Note whether there is any difference in the features revealed when the light comes from different points of the compass.

Explain why, in the examination of opaque specimens, it is important to make the observation with light coming from several different angles.

C. Examine the glazed surface of a small piece of porcelain ware, using the same lighting arrangements suggested in parts A and B.   (The specimen may be a small piece taken from a broken Coors crucible.)

Next examine the same area of the porcelain with the aid of a vertical illuminator.   The latter, together with the appropriate instruction sheet, should be obtained from the laboratory instructor unless other arrangements have been made.

Describe any additional features which are revealed by the vertical illuminator.

Examine the porcelain through a 4-mm objective by vertical illumination.   At this magnification can a similar result be obtained by the oblique lighting method given in part A?

If time permits, the student should study various other opaque specimens by vertical illumination.   Appropriate examples would be enameled, painted, or plated surfaces, plastics, rubberized cloth, opaque powders, etc.

EXPERIMENT 12

DRAWING

(Reference: Chapter V)

A. WITH THE AID OF A NET MICROMETER

The specimen selected for this exercise may consist of crystals which have just been prepared by the cooling or evaporation of a solution, or by the interaction of two reagents which form a suitable precipitate. Preferably the field selected should contain crystals which exhibit clear-cut boundaries and which are not obscured by amorphous debris.

With a net micrometer in the eyepiece, adjust the slide to present the most desirable field, then secure it firmly in place by means of the stage clips.   After the instructor has approved the field selected, proceed to sketch the specimen on cross-section paper. The micrometer rulings should be indicated on the corresponding rulings of the graph paper. The graph paper should be drawn to such a scale that the diameter of the circle representing the field of view will equal not less than about 3 inches. After you have completed the pencil sketch, go over it with black drawing ink and label it properly.

B. USE OF THE CAMERA LUCIDA

The specimen may be similar to one of those suggested for part A. The mirror of the camera lucida should be inclined at an angle of 45 degrees and the drawing paper should lie flat on the table. By means of appropriate filters supplied with the camera, and by controlling the intensity of the light source, conditions should be so adjusted that the point of the drawing pencil and the microscope image appear equally distinct.

It may be well to have the instructor check on the arrangement when you feel that you have established proper conditions.

Trace the drawing on a separate sheet of white paper. Finally, ink the pencil sketch and label it appropriately. The legend should include a statement of the objective and ocular employed, as well as the kind of camera lucida.

EXPERIMENT 13

PHOTOMICROGRAPHS

(Reference: Chapter V)

It is imperative to keep in mind the fact that, for the student of microscopy, the taking of micrographs is only one of many procedures which can be employed in the investigation of chemical problems. Because of its fascination there is a temptation to spend a disproportionate amount of time on the subject of photomicrography. For this reason it is advisable to plan in advance the approximate amount of time which is to be devoted to this work. First of all, the novice should thoroughly familiarize himself with the subject as outlined in Chapter V of the text.

For his initial attempts the student should select a simple subject which can be observed by transmitted light. The specimen chosen should be rather thin and should be sufficiently large to yield a pleasing image with a 16-mm objective and a 5-× or 10-× ocular. Freshly prepared crystals of borax, cream of tartar, or similar material may be employed. Many commercially available organic chemicals can be used without any special treatment. The latter should be thinly scattered on a clean slide so that a fair portion of the crystals are separated from each other. The selected field should contain several crystals which are sufficiently perfect to give a good conception of their characteristic form.

The specific set-up employed will depend upon the equipment available in any given laboratory, and the type of apparatus will necessarily decide some of the details of the procedure. Regardless of the type of apparatus used in taking a photomicrograph, it is important to observe the following.

1. Have the camera and the microscope in proper alignment. The picture plane of the camera must be parallel with the specimen (or perpendicular to the optic axis of the microscope.)
2. Have the camera-microscope assembly mounted so rigidly as to prevent vibration.
3. Prevent any stray light from striking the specimen from above the stage.
4. Prevent stray light from entering the camera. Only those rays which come through the optical system of the microscope should be permitted to enter the camera.
5. Have the object slide secured to the stage by spring clips.

After the apparatus has been arranged and the specimen has been focused, the question of exposure time must be settled. This time is dependent upon several factors, including the following.

1. Transparency of the specimen.
2. Intensity of the light source.
3. Magnitude of the light cone.
4. Sensitivity of the plate or film.
5. Type of light filters, when used.

Determination of the proper exposure time requires some experience. However, when using a plate camera or a filmpack camera, it is very simple to expose a test film (or plate) which subsequently will serve as a useful exposure guide whenever similar conditions prevail.

When you are ready for an exposure, withdraw the dark slide, open the shutter, and turn on the microscope lamp for, let us say, 5 seconds. With the light turned off, insert the slide to cover part of the exposed film. (Remember, unless the camera has a long bellows extension, the image is that of the circular field and does not extend to the edge of the film.) Turn on the light for another 5-second exposure. Insert the slide farther. The third exposure is made for 10 seconds. The total exposure times on the four different sections of the film correspond with the following.

1. 5 seconds.
2. $5 + 5 = 10$ seconds.
3. $5 + 5 + 10 = 20$ seconds.
4. $5 + 5 + 10 + 20 = 40$ seconds.

Thus for each succeeding strip the exposure time is doubled.

Inspection of the developed film will reveal which of the four exposures is the most nearly correct. It is quite possible, of course, that the entire film is under-exposed, so that another test is in order. On the other hand, it is conceivable that two adjacent tests are respectively under- and over-exposed. A 20-second exposure may be too brief, while a 40-second exposure may prove too long. In such a case you may decide to give the micrograph a 30-second exposure. However, if the subject warrants the expenditure of more time, it may be worth while to use another film for a series of three test exposures, giving 25, 30, and 35 seconds respectively.

As mentioned in Chapter V of the text, it is desirable to keep a record of the data which apply to each negative. In subsequent work reference to such accumulated data may eliminate the need for test exposures, thereby saving considerable time.

EXPERIMENT 14

LINEAR MEASUREMENTS

(Reference: Chapter VI)

A. THE MECHANICAL STAGE

There should be no difficulty in manipulating the mechanical stage if the directions given in the text are followed. To become familiar with this accessory and in order to check his technique, the student should first measure several objects of known dimensions. Rods, wires, tubes, cover slips, needles are a few readily accessible objects which may serve the purpose.

After the technique has been mastered, the dimensions of several unknowns furnished by the instructor should be determined.

Place a small swatch of muslin or broadcloth on a slide and, using incident light, count the number of threads of warp per centimeter. On the basis of several trials, calculate the number per inch. Do the same for the filling. This is referred to as the "thread count" of the cloth.

B. CALIBRATION OF AN OCULAR MICROMETER

This exercise requires a stage micrometer, as well as an ocular micrometer disc. Since the stage micrometer is intended as a standard for use in calibration, it should be protected from dust, grease, fumes, and friction. The slide on which the micrometer is mounted should be handled by the edges. Fingers should be kept away from the area inside the black circle, because the micrometer rulings are mounted there. To remove any dust from the micrometer, a camel's-hair brush should be applied very lightly. Under no circumstances should the student take it upon himself to apply water or other solvents in cleaning the stage micrometer.

The ocular micrometer should be given similar care. If you plan to do much work which requires an ocular micrometer, it will be decidedly worth while to acquire a micrometer ocular which is provided with a focusing eyelens. Thus handling of the micrometer disc is avoided, and frequent cleaning is rendered unnecessary. Furthermore, the adjustable eyelens insures a sharp image of the micrometer graduations regardless of the nature of the user's eye.

Following the procedure described in Chapter 6, calibrate the micrometer for use with the 16-mm objective and either the 8- or the 4-mm objective. (If part D is to be performed, it is suggested that only the 16-mm objective be used in part B.) In the following table indicate whether an ordinary 5-× or 6-× ocular or a special micrometer ocular was employed. Be sure to check on the tube length (if adjustable). Express the value represented by one division in terms of microns. (See sample calculations, page 78, Chapter VI.)

TABLE V–A. CALIBRATION OF OCULAR MICROMETER

Ocular	Objective	Tube Length	Microns per Division
	16-mm		

C. APPLICATIONS OF THE OCULAR MICROMETER

1. Cover-glass thickness. By embedding in a bit of wax or modeling clay, mount a cover glass on a slide so that it sets on edge. The sides of the cover should be quite perpendicular to the slide. Now when the microscope is focused on the edge of the cover glass, it will be very simple to measure the thickness. Actually, to obtain a more representative value, measure the thickness at three or more points on the circumference of the glass. Report the mean value to the instructor for confirmation. (A small error is involved because the specimen is not viewed through a cover glass.)

2. Specific gravity. For this determination, obtain from the instructor one of the numbered "unknowns." This may be some solid of some simple geometric form sufficiently small to come within the compass of the ocular micrometer. The material may be a short section of glass thread, metal wire, or a rectangular portion of sheet metal or plastic. After carefully weighing the specimen, use the ocular micrometer to determine the dimensions which are required for calculating the volume. In the case of a spherical bead, of course, only the diameter is required, whereas in the case of a cylinder both diameter and length must be found. It is always advisable to make several determinations of each dimension. Having found the volume of the sample, you can now calculate the weight per cubic centimeter.

As in all work involving the analytical balance, the specimens should be handled with appropriate tweezers or tongs.

Thickness of a protective coating. Obtain a small piece of painted wood. With a sharp razor blade cut through the sample along a plane perpendicular to the painted surface. By means of wax or modeling clay, mount the wood on a slide. Measure the thickness of the paint in at least three places.

D. CALIBRATION OF FILAR MICROMETER

Calibrate the filar micrometer for use with the 16-mm objective and either the 8- or 4-mm objective. As in part B, find the number of microns represented by one division of the ruled disc in the eyepiece. Record the results in a table similar to the following.

TABLE V–B. CALIBRATION OF FILAR MICROMETER

Objective	Tube Length	Microns per Division
16-mm		

E. APPLICATION OF THE FILAR MICROMETER

Carry out the same measurements suggested under part C. If the latter measurements were previously made with an ordinary ocular micrometer, it will be worth while to determine the increase in precision when employing the filar micrometer.

F. MEASUREMENTS BY A GRAPHIC METHOD

(*By means of the camera lucida*)

Referring to the method explained on page 81 of the text, provide the microscope with an 8- or 16-mm objective, and 8-×, 10-×, or 12-× ocular and a camera lucida. Using a well-pointed, hard drawing pencil, trace the image of the stage micrometer on a sheet of paper. Preferably use graph paper with millimeter divisions. In an appropriate table show the number of microns represented by one millimeter as drawn on the paper, together with the other essential data.

TABLE V–C. MEASUREMENTS WITH A CAMERA LUCIDA

Objective	Ocular	Tube Length	Microns per Millimeter

G. APPLICATION OF THE GRAPHIC METHOD

Using the data secured in part F, measure the diameters of two of the following.

1. "Silk" from a spider's web.
2. A thread of glass wool.
3. Human hair.
4. Pollen grains. (Any convenient variety.)

In each case the specimen being measured should be protected by a cover slip.

H. THE GHOST MICROMETER AND ITS USE

1. Calibration. The use of a ghost micrometer requires that the microscope be provided with a substage condenser. To obviate the need for recalibrating, there must be some convenient means for quickly placing the micrometer in the correct position every time it is to be employed. This can readily be accomplished by the use of a baseboard provided with wood blocks in appropriate positions. The arrangement of these blocks will depend upon size and shape of the base of the microscope. Such blocks enable you to slide the microscope and the ghost micrometer into proper position without the loss of any time. Preferably, the base should be of sufficient length to include the microscope lamp.

To calibrate the ghost micrometer, first focus the microscope on a stage micrometer. Then place the ghost micrometer in front of the microscope with a ruled area parallel with the surface of the substage mirror. Raise or lower the condenser sufficiently to bring its squares into clear focus when the microscope is focused on the stage micrometer. It may be necessary to adjust the angle of the ghost micrometer slightly in order to have all of the squares form equal images. After measuring several squares in the center of the field and four or more along the rim, calculate the average value.

Since the squares are bounded by walls of appreciable thickness, proper allowance must be made. This is conveniently accomplished by considering the horizontal edge of a square equivalent to length of the illuminated square plus the width of the black boundary line along the right side. Measuring vertically, the height is taken as the thickness of the black boundary along the base plus the height of the illuminated square.

Using the 16-mm objective and one of the low-power oculars, determine the number of microns represented by the edge of a square of the ghost micrometer. Measure at least five squares in different sections of the field.

2. Diameters of starch grains. Suspend about 0.1 gram of potato starch in 10 ml of a 1:1 solution of glycerol and water. Place a drop of this suspension on a slide and cover with a cover glass. Since these starch grains tend toward an ovoid shape, the usual outline, as seen from above, appears as an elipse (or nearly so). Measure the length and the greatest width for ten typical grains in scattered portions of the field. What are the average values?

Carry out a similar experiment using corn starch, rice starch, or oat starch.

3. Percentage of one component. Potato starch has been used at times as an adulterant in certain more expensive materials. Such adulteration cannot always be demonstrated by ordinary chemical methods. When the latter methods fail, the microscope may offer the means for detecting the fraud, even to the extent of measuring the percentage of adulterant. In the present exercise we shall endeavor to determine the percentage of potato starch in a mixture of potato and rice starches.

First of all it will be necessary to prepare standards for comparison. As stock solutions there should be available freshly prepared suspensions of the individual starches in a 1:1 water-glycerol solution. If you are required to prepare the suspensions, carefully weigh out 0.500 gram of potato starch and transfer it to a small beaker. Add about 5 ml of the water-glycerol solution and disperse the starch by stirring the mixture with a glass rod. Now add another portion of water-glycerol solution to the suspension, and follow by more stirring.

Continue making additions of solution and subsequent stirrings until about 20 ml of liquid have been added. Transfer this suspension to a 50-ml volumetric flask (preferably one with a ground glass stopper), taking precautions to guard against the loss of any of the material. All starch suspension adhering to the stirring rod and to the inner walls of the beaker must be transferred to the flask by rinsing several times with additional water-glycerol solution. Obviously, the volumetric flask must not be filled beyond the graduation. Finally, stopper the flask and invert repeatedly until the starch has been uniformly suspended. A suspension of rice starch is prepared by a similar procedure.

A mixture in which the suspended material consists of 10 per cent potato starch and 90 per cent rice starch can now be prepared by combining 1 volume of the standard potato starch suspension with 9 volumes of the standard rice starch. Naturally, careful analytical technique must be observed.

The present procedure requires counting the number of grains suspended in a definite volume of fluid. This can be accomplished by the use of a Howard counting cell. The latter is actually a special type of slide provided with a circular well. In the center of the well there is a stage, or platform, which is 0.100 mm lower than the surface of the slide. When any liquid is placed on the surface of this central platform and covered with a plane cover glass, the depth of the liquid will be exactly 0.100 mm. Any excess liquid will overflow into the moat which surrounds the stage. The cover glass used with this cell is rather heavy and is polished so that its surfaces are free from irregularities; hence the height from the stage of the counting cell to the cover glass is the same at all points.

After thoroughly mixing the ingredients of the 10 per cent potato starch suspension, transfer a small drop to the center of the Howard counting cell. The size of the drop should be so chosen that the excess is kept at a minimum. Then apply the optically plane cover glass in such manner as to avoid the introduction of air bubbles.

With the ghost micrometer in place, bring the specimen into focus beneath the 16-mm objective. Now count the number of grains of potato starch within the confines of a definite number of micrometer squares. (For those who plan much work involving the counting of particles it will prove desirable to purchase some form of a mechanical "tally.") Sixteen or twenty-five squares, depending upon size, may be a convenient number to count. In order to avoid duplication and yet to be certain no grains are omitted, follow a definite system. (See method of counting suggested in the discussion of the haemacytometer, page 84.) To be more certain of getting a representative value, make a count on three different drops of the 10 per cent suspension. In each trial the area of the field counted should consist of the same number of micrometer squares. Record the data in Table VI. By similar methods you can

PER CENT STARCH

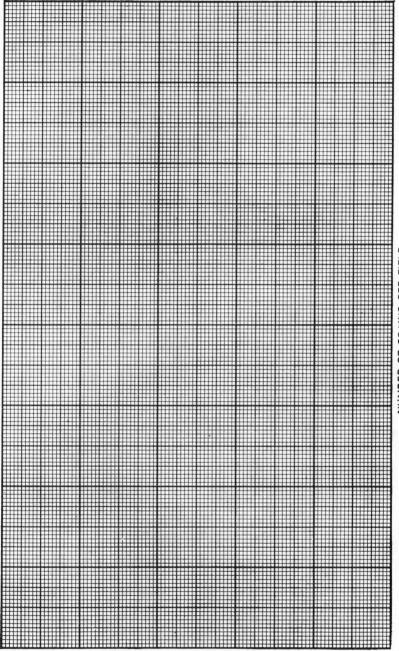

NUMBER OF GRAINS PER FIELD

Fig. 5. Percentage Composition Curve Based on Table VI.

find the number of grains per field for suspensions in which potato starch comprises 20 and 30 per cent of the solid component. Finally, execute a similar count on a mixture of the two starches for which the ratio is unknown.

TABLE VI

% Potato	No. of Squares in Field	Av. No. of Potato-starch Grains
10		
20		
30		
Unknown		

Having assembled the data, plot the percentages against the respective counts. When the count for the "unknown" is entered, its position on the curve should indicate the percentage of potato starch in the original dry starch mixture.

Observe that here it is not necessary to know the actual volume examined; the essential requisite is that all of the counts are made on equal volumes. For this reason, provided the ghost micrometer is always used in the same position in respect to the substage mirror and condenser, an actual calibration is not required.

Instead of a ghost micrometer it would be quite satisfactory to employ a coordinate-ruled ocular micrometer.

EXPERIMENT 15

USING A HAEMACYTOMETER: ESTIMATING THE WEIGHT OF A STARCH GRAIN

(Reference: Chapter VI)

Although the haemacytometer cell was designed for counting the number of corpuscles in blood, this special slide is readily applied in many other analyses which depend upon a determination of the number of particles suspended in a unit volume of liquid. The present exercise will be concerned with determining the number of grains in one gram of starch, from which may be found the weight of an individual grain.

For counting, suspend the starch in a 1:1 solution of water and glycerol. Transfer a sample of potato starch weighing 0.100 gram to a 10-ml graduated test tube, to which add a few milliliters of the water-glycerol. Disperse the starch in the solution by triturating with a glass rod. After raising the rod from the suspension, allow most of the adhering material to drain into the tube, after which carefully pour 1 or 2 ml of glycerol solution down the rod and into the tube. Allow the rod to drain as before. Several repetitions of this procedure should wash practically all of the starch from the glass rod. By means of a pipet add sufficient water-glycerol solution to fill the tube to the 10-ml graduation. With a clean dry rod, stir the mixture until the starch is suspended uniformly. The result should be a suspension containing 10 mg of starch per milliliter.

Transfer a small drop of this suspension to the haemacytometer cell and carefully cover with the special cover glass. By following the procedure described in the text (cf. page 83) you can now count the number of grains in 0.1 cu ml, and then calculate the number per cubic centimeter (which, for our purposes, is the practical equivalent of a milliliter). Knowing the weight originally suspended in this volume, you can calculate the number of starch grains in 1 gram of dry potato starch.

Express the average number of grains per gram, based on three counts.

Calculate the average weight of a single starch grain in terms of grams, milligrams, and micrograms.

Note: It is important that the haemacytometer and its cover glass be cleaned immediately after use. If the sample is permitted to dry in the cell, a more drastic cleaning method will be required, and this may have a damaging effect.

EXPERIMENT 16

REFRACTIVE INDEX

(Reference: Chapter VI)

A. IMMERSION METHODS

Immersion methods offer the simplest means for the microscopic determination of refractive indices. One advantage is that no expensive accessories are required. Even when the figure in the third decimal place is only approximate, the information obtained may be quite valuable.

1. **The Becke line test.** Place a few very small, well-formed crystals of potassium chloride on a microscope slide, or prepare the crystals *in situ* by the spontaneous evaporation of a drop of the salt solution. In the latter instance, when satisfactory crystals appear, the excess liquid can be drained from the slide by touching with the tip of a triangular bit of filter paper. When no more moisture remains, add a drop of benzene to the crystals and protect with a cover glass. Bring the preparation into the focus of a 16-mm or, better, an 8-mm objective, using parallel axial illumination. Observe the bright border, or "halo," which bounds one of the larger crystals. If the halo seems indistinct, it may be made to appear more pronounced by adjusting the substage diaphragm. In general, the N.A. of the system should be kept to the minimum value which permits adequate definition of the specimen under observation.

Slowly focus upward, so that the selected crystal is slightly out of focus. Observe whether the bright line moves away from the crystal (toward the benzene) or toward the crystal. Next, slowly lower the objective and note the direction in which the Becke line moves. This simple procedure enables you to determine whether the liquid surrounding an isotropic crystal has a higher or a lower index of refraction than the crystal. Draw sketches to represent the Becke line around the crystal when the microscope is focused down and when it is focused up.

Now repeat the foregoing test using sodium chlorate, which has a refractive index of 1.515.

State the rule regarding the movement of the Becke line.

As a practical application of the Becke line test, you might consider a procedure for distinguishing among the chlorides of sodium, potassium and rubidium. Reference to Table VII shows that their refractive indices are as follows:

Sodium chloride	1.544
Potassium chloride	1.490
Rubidium chloride	1.494

TABLE VII. ISOTROPIC CRYSTALS FOR THE DETERMINATION OF REFRACTIVE INDICES OF LIQUIDS BY IMMERSION METHODS*

Refractive Index	Name	Formula
1.326	Sodium fluoride	NaF
1.339	Potassium fluosilicate	K_2SiF_6
1.352	Potassium fluoride	KF
1.370	Ammonium fluosilicate	$(NH_4)_2SiF_6$
1.410	Potassium cyanide	KCN
1.439	Sodium alum	$NaAl(SO_4)_2 \cdot 12H_2O$

* From Volume 1 of "Handbook of Chemical Microscopy," Émile M. Chamot and Clyde W. Mason, Wiley, 1938.

TABLE VII (Continued)

Refractive Index	Name	Formula
1.456	Potassium alum	$KAl(SO_4)_2 \cdot 12H_2O$
1.459	Ammonium alum	$NH_4Al(SO_4)_2 \cdot 12H_2O$
1.481	Potassium chromium alum	$KCr(SO_4)_2 \cdot 12H_2O$
1.485	Ammonium ferric alum	$NH_4Fe(SO_4)_2 \cdot 12H_2O$
1.490	Potassium chloride	KCl
1.494	Rubidium chloride	$RbCl$
1.504	Sodium uranyl acetate	$Na(C_2H_3O_2) \cdot UO_2(C_2H_3O_2)_2$
1.515	Sodium chlorate	$NaClO_3$
1.544	Sodium chloride	$NaCl$
1.553	Rubidium bromide	$RbBr$
1.559	Potassium bromide	KBr
1.564	Chromium sulfate	$Cr_2(SO_4)_2 \cdot 18H_2O$
1.571	Barium nitrate	$Ba(NO_3)_2$
1.586	Strontium nitrate	$Sr(NO_3)_2$
1.617	Sodium bromate	$NaBrO_3$
1.640	Ammonium chloride	NH_4Cl
1.641	Sodium bromide	$NaBr$
1.642	Cesium chloride	$CsCl$
1.647	Rubidium iodide	RbI
1.657	Potassium chlorostannate	K_2SnCl_6
1.667	Potassium iodide	KI
1.678	Ammonium chlorostannate	$(NH_4)_2SnCl_6$
1.698	Cesium bromide	$CsBr$
1.703	Ammonium iodide	NH_4I
1.711	Ammonium bromide	NH_4Br
1.736	Magnesium oxide	MgO
1.755	Arsenic trioxide	As_2O_3
1.775	Sodium iodide	NaI
1.782	Lead nitrate	$Pb(NO_3)_2$
1.788	Cesium iodide	CsI
1.825	Potassium chloroplatinate	K_2PtCl_6

At 20°C, according to Table VIII, s-tetrachloroethane has a refractive index of 1.4943, which is very close to the value for rubidium chloride. When crystals of the latter are observed in a drop of s-tetrachloroethane, the Becke line will not be very pronounced. Suppose, however, the same liquid is employed with potassium chloride; then the Becke line should indicate that the crystal has an index lower than that of the immersion medium. On the other hand, if a pronounced Becke line should indicate that the crystal has an index higher than the s-tetrachloroethane, you could infer that the solid specimen is sodium chloride. This, of course, is based on the assumption that the sample is known to be one of these three salts.

2. Oblique illumination method. As mentioned in the text, one advantage of this method over the Becke line method is that a medium- or

Table VIII. Liquids for Refractive Index Determinations

(Partial list suggested by the Eastman Kodak Co., and supplied by them in 25-ml, glass-stoppered bottles)

	n_D 20° C
Methyl alcohol	1.3288
Water	1.3330
Acetone	1.3592
Ethyl acetate	1.3727
n-Hexane	1.3755
n-Heptane	1.3872
n-Butyl alcohol	1.3991
n-Butyl chloride	1.4022
1,4-Dioxane	1.4223
Methylcyclohexane	1.4235
Ethylene glycol	1.4318
Ethyl citrate	1.4434
Ethylene chloride	1.4453
Trimethylene chloride	1.4476
Cyclohexanone	1.4507
Cyclohexanol	1.4678
Diethanolamine	1.4782
Triethanolamine	1.4853
p-Cymene	1.4908
s-Tetrachloroethane	1.4943
Toluene	1.4957
Benzene	1.5017
Ethyl iodide	1.5138
Anisole	1.5178
Trimethylene bromide	1.5238
Chlorobenzene	1.5250
Methyl iodide	1.5310
Ethylene bromide	1.5383
o-Nitrotoluene	1.5466
Nitrobenzene	1.5526
Tri-o-cresyl phosphate	1.5582
Bromobenzene	1.5602
o-Toluidine	1.5725
Aniline	1.5864
Bromoform	1.5973
o-Iodotoluene	1.6095
Quinaldine	1.6120
Iodobenzene	1.6205

Note: The designation "n_D 20° C" denotes the refractive index as determined by the yellow light of the sodium D line, at 20° C.

even a low-power objective can be employed. Obviously, by using a lower degree of magnification (for example, the 24-mm or 32-mm objective), correspondingly larger particles are required. Frequently, it may prove desirable to apply both tests, but this should cause very little inconvenience since the illumination can be arranged to permit rapid change from symmetrical to unilateral oblique.

Apply the oblique illumination method to potassium chloride in benzene and to potassium chlorate in benzene. Remember to keep the N.A. of the system as low as consistent with adequate definition.

Draw sketches to represent the appearance of both crystals as viewed by the oblique illumination method.

Recrystallize some sodium alum on a clean slide and try the oblique illumination test using a drop of n-decylchloride, levo-dipropyl malate or hexahydro-p-cymene (menthane). Each of these has a refractive index of 1.4380 at 20°C.

On another slide test similar crystals in n-butyl bromide or trimethylene glycol. (Index for each, 1.4398 at 20°C.)

Note regarding immersion liquids for refractive index determinations: For those who plan to perform a large number of tests which require immersion liquids it may prove advantageous to procure an appropriate series of "Shillaber's Certified Index of Refraction Liquids." These are available in uniform bottles covering the range 1.460 to 1.640 in intervals of 0.002. Although the complete series includes 91 liquids, they may be purchased in any number desired. These liquids are of low volatility, chemically inert, and stable during storage.[1]

Those who prefer to use organic liquids of which the values have been reported in the literature will find about two thousand listed in Lange's *Handbook of Chemistry.* In many instances this handbook cites several different liquids for a given index value. Frequently, however, the compounds are not readily available. Furthermore, there is a rather wide variation in the temperatures which apply.

B. IMAGE DISPLACEMENT METHODS

1. Direct method. Following the procedure outlined in the text, determine the refractive indices for two liquids provided by the instructor. If none are supplied, choose any convenient liquids for which the indices are available. Preferably select non-corrosive liquids of relatively low volatility. The temperature of the liquid, which may be assumed to be that of the laboratory, should be recorded.

If the depth of the cell is not known, it must be measured. This should be accomplished by mounting the slide so that it sets on edge, whereupon the depth of the cell can be measured by means of a calibrated ocular micrometer.

A sodium vapor lamp should be employed if available, or at least a yellow filter.

---

[1] Shillaber's immersion liquids are available through R. P. Cargille, 118 Liberty St., New York 6, N. Y.

In order to estimate the refractive index of a liquid at different temperatures, remember that the value increases as the temperature is lowered, and decreases as the temperature is raised. For many liquids the average change n for one degree of change in temperature is approximately 0.0004.

The data should be recorded in a form similar to Table IX.

TABLE IX.   MEASUREMENT OF REFRACTIVE INDEX

Sample No. 1.

Trial No.	Depth of Cell	Image Displacement	Apparent Depth	Measured n	Temperature	n at 20° C (calc.)
1.						
2.						
3.						
Av.						

Sample No. 2.

Trial No.	Depth of Cell	Image Displacement	Apparent Depth	Measured n	Temperature	n at 20° C (calc.)
1.						
2.						
3.						
Av.						

2. Displacement of reference liquids. In accordance with the method described in Chapter VI of the text, prepare a curve for use in determining refractive indices of unknowns by the measurement of image displacement. At least three reference liquids should be selected, but if the curve is to cover an extended range of indices a larger number will be advisable. There may be irregularities in different sections of the fine-adjustment micrometer screw. Consequent errors may be reduced by recording image displacements for a larger number of reference liquids.

The reference liquids should be distributed over the general range within which future measurements are to be made. Shillaber's certified liquids (cf. page 201) are well adapted for the purpose because, within their range, they can be supplied for almost any desired value. Further advantages are their low volatility, inertness, and general uniformity throughout the series. However, the other liquids can be used quite successfully. If it is not feasible to have their values accurately measured in a good refractometer, it becomes all the more urgent to make certain of their purity. Otherwise the values found in the recent literature may not apply. For a limited range, a serviceable group of reference liquids includes distilled water, 1,4-dioxane, triethanol amine, monochlorobenzene, nitrobenzene, and aniline.

If possible, the measurements should be made by sodium light or by light coming through an appropriate yellow filter. A time should be chosen when the temperature of the laboratory is most likely to remain constant, or nearly so. The apparatus and the liquids should have been in the laboratory sufficiently long to have attained the same temperature. The only way to know the temperature of the liquids is to use a good thermometer. Periodically the room temperature should be checked.

The image displacement value recorded for each reference liquid should be the average of several different trials. For each reference liquid it is necessary to record the refractive index n_1, as published in the literature, and the temperature T_1, at which the value applies. For use in constructing the reference curve it is necessary to calculate the index n_2 which applies at the temperature T_2 of the experiment. All of the pertinent data should be recorded in Table X below.

TABLE X

Temperature of experiment, T_2 _____

Illumination employed _____

Ocular _____   *Objective* _____   *Tube length* _____

Reference Liquid	Average Displacement	Reported n_1	T_1	n_2 at T_2 (calc.)

After all the data have been assembled in Table X, the reference curve is constructed by plotting the average displacements of the reference liquids against their respective refractive indices. Subsequently the refractive index of any liquid may be found by measuring the image displacement it causes, and then referring to the curve. Before determining the refractive indices of any unknowns the student should test the reliability of the curve by checking on one or more liquids of known index.

TABLE XI. REFRACTIVE INDICES OF VARIOUS LIQUIDS

Liquid	n_D	Temperature (°C)
Corn oil	1.4733	25
Cotton-seed oil	1.4743–1.4752	25
Linseed oil	1.4797–1.4802	25
Olive oil	1.4657–1.4667	25
Soy bean oil	1.4723–1.4756	25
Sunflower seed oil	1.4657–1.4721	
Tung oil	1.515–1.520	25
n-Propanol	1.3854	20
iso-Propanol	1.3776	20
BUTYL ALCOHOLS		
n-Butanol	1.3991	20
iso-Butanol	1.3968	17.5
sec-Butanol	1.3924	22
tert-Butanol	1.3878	20
AMYL ALCOHOLS		
n-Amyl alcohol	1.4101	20
iso-Butyl carbinol	1.4085	15
tert-Amyl alcohol	1.406	20
Pentanol-2	1.4053	20
2-Methyl butan-3-ol	1.3973	20
Pentanol-3	1.4124	14.7

Admittedly the preferred practice, when giving the refractive index of a liquid at only one temperature, would be to conform with some uniform system and cite all of the indices for the same temperature. Although some workers have attempted to report their index measurements consistently at 20° or 25°, the literature abounds in values reported for many other temperatures. The range in the temperatures cited in Table XI is not unusual. Approximate values for a desired temperature can be calculated as mentioned previously.

Natural oils which are not specific chemical compounds may vary in their values. Thus in the case of olive oil, the examination of a large

REFRACTIVE INDEX

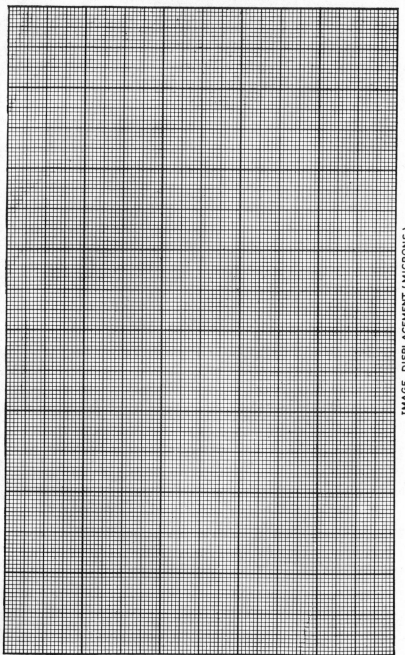

IMAGE DISPLACEMENT (MICRONS)

FIG. 6. CALIBRATION CURVE BASED ON TABLE X.

number of specimens of known purity has shown that at 25° the refractive index may be as low as 1.4657 or as high as 1.4667. If a sample should exhibit a value outside these limits, it should be viewed with suspicion.

After the student has prepared his calibration curve for the refractometer cell, typical laboratory problems to be assigned by the instructor would be the following.

1. Three samples submitted to the student may be n-butanol, sec-butanol or tert-butanol. Determine the identity of each liquid by a refractive index measurement.

2. Determine whether a submitted sample is normal- or iso-propanol.

3. In a storeroom part of each label on two bottles has been destroyed, but the bottles are known to contain either normal or tertiary amyl alcohol. Identify the contents of both bottles.

4. Determine whether a given sample is cottonseed oil or olive oil.

Note: In exercises such as the foregoing it is important to use sodium light or a yellow filter, and to make proper allowance for any deviations in temperature.

EXPERIMENT 17

PERCENTAGE OF STARCH IN ADULTERATED FLOUR

(Reference: Chapter VI)

This experiment applies the technique of Wallis in determining the percentage of potato starch in an adulterated sample of wheat flour.

The first requisite is an appropriate reference mixture. It is suggested that the flour sample contain 70 per cent of ordinary flour with 30 per cent potato starch as the "adulterant." Although any convenient quantity may be prepared, the samples should be kept fairly small in order to conserve on oil. On an analytical balance weigh out accurately 0.0300 gram of potato starch and 0.0700 gram of flour. Transfer these to a glass mortar, taking precautions to avoid any loss in making the transfer. To this, add exactly 0.1000 gram of the lycopodium powder. Next, suspend these solid ingredients in castor oil, following the procedure outlined in Chapter VI of the text.

During cold weather the oil may become rather viscous. Under such conditions the oil should be heated until it attains a temperature of 20° or 25°, after which the container is suspended in a 20° or 25° water bath until required. The volume of oil used with this quantity of lycopodium should equal 20 ml, but a little more may be added if required in bringing the particles into uniform suspension or in transferring the suspension to a labeled flask.

The instructor should provide a sample of "adulterated" flour containing from 15 to 35 per cent potato starch. Using 0.1000 gram of this sample and 0.1000 gram of lycopodium, prepare a suspension by the same procedure followed in compounding the reference liquid. The same volume of oil should be used.

The reference liquid and the test sample are now ready for counting. This is executed as explained in Chapter VI. It is desirable that all counts be made under similar conditions. If the laboratory is cold, the liquids should be brought to a temperature of 20° or 25° before samples are transferred to the slides.

After the percentage of starch in the "adulterated" sample has been calculated, the result should be checked against a second reference liquid. To illustrate, if the first analysis should indicate 22 per cent starch, then a reference liquid should be prepared using 0.0220 gram starch, 0.0780 gram flour, and 0.1000 lycopodium in the same volume of oil used in the previous suspensions. The ratio between starch grains and pollen grains in this new reference liquid is determined as in previous liquids. This new ratio now serves as the basis for calculating the percentage of starch in the unknown. The result may not agree with the first estimate but it should be more nearly correct.

Mastery of the Wallis method merely requires patient repetition.

EXPERIMENT 18

USING THE KOFLER HOT STAGE

(Reference: Chapter VI)

A. GENERAL DIRECTIONS

The electrically heated stage (A), together with the removable metal rim (B) and the glass cover (C), forms the actual heating chamber. Through the rheostat (O) the stage is connected with the 115-volt a-c or d-c power supply. For melting point determinations the sample is placed on a 1½ × 1 inch slide (P) and covered with a cover slip (PC). The glass baffle (D) covers the mounted sample to insure more uniform heat distribution. A calibrated thermometer (M) is inserted through an opening which extends toward the central lightwell (Z) of the Kofler stage. The two calibrated thermometers (M) cover the ranges +30°C to +230°C and +60° to 350° respectively. Both thermometers should bear the serial number of the stage on which they are being used, because they have been calibrated for only one specific stage. A metal guard (N) protecting the thermometer is screwed into the guard socket (NS). In order to secure the Kofler stage in the proper position relative to the optic axis (ZA)

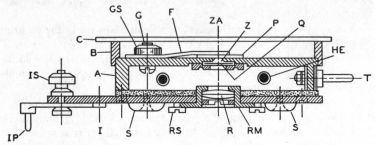

FIG. 7. CROSS SECTION OF KOFLER MICRO HOT STAGE

of the microscope, the pins (IP) are inserted in the holes provided for the microscope stage clips.

Near the rim of the hot stage the post (G) with a knurled screw (GS) serves for attaching certain accessories, such as the fork (F) or sublimation blocks (J–I and J–S). The center of the stage is provided with a

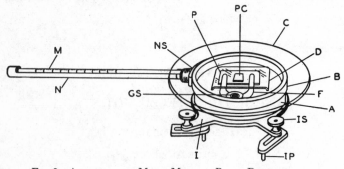

FIG. 8. ASSEMBLY FOR MICRO MELTING POINT DETERMINATION

lightwell (Z), which is closed toward the heating chamber by means of a Pyrex plate (Q). Beneath the latter there is a condensing lens system (R) so that the substage condenser of the microscope is not required when using the Kofler stage.

Preferably, the microscope on which the Kofler apparatus is mounted should have a metal stage, since hard rubber may be damaged by heat. However, if a metal stage is not available, a sheet of Transite, drilled

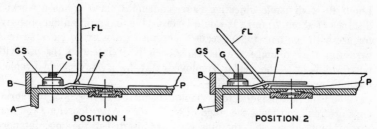

FIG. 9. MANIPULATION OF FORK AND LIFTER

with two holes, can be placed over the hard rubber stage for protection.

The objective should have a working distance in excess of 6 mm, since this is the height of the heating chamber when the glass cover (C) is in

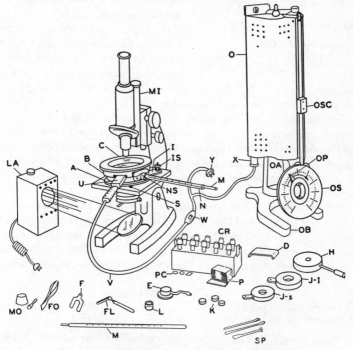

FIG. 10. No. 6886 A — MICRO HOT STAGE — KOFLER

place. A 24-mm objective affords ample working distance. If a 10-× objective is desired, it will be necessary to make a careful check on the working distance because it may be less than 6 mm. The Bausch &

Lomb 10-× divisible objective is recommended since it has a working distance of about 7 mm. It would be desirable to obtain an old objective for use with the hot stage, because continued exposure to elevated temperatures may damage the lenses, especially if intended for use with polarized light. The ocular employed may be a Huygenean eyepiece having a magnification up to 15-×.

When the hot stage is to be mounted on the microscope, the spring clips are removed from the stage of the latter. After loosening the hot-stage thumbscrews (IS), the pins (IP) are inserted in the holes intended

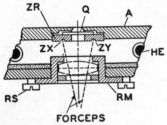

FORCEPS

Fig. 11. Cleaning of Glass Plate Q

for the microscope stage clips. The micro hot stage is then placed so that the lightwell (Z) is centered in respect to the optic axis (ZA) of the microscope. By tightening the screws (IS) the apparatus is firmly secured to the microscope stage.

The two calibrated thermometers supplied with the instrument embrace different temperature ranges, the lower one being more appropriate for temperatures up to about 180°C, while the other may be employed from about 150°C upward. For use, one of the thermometers is carefully inserted into the guard tube socket (NS). It must be thrust in as far as possible, but care must be exercised not to apply so much force as to crack the thermometer bulb. The guard tube (N) is then passed over the thermometer and screwed into the socket (NS). The guard tube should not be omitted, because the thermometers are calibrated with this guard in place.

The rate of heating is controlled by varying the resistance used in the vertical rheostat (O). This, in turn, is regulated by turning the control knob. The dial (OS) can be calibrated so that the approximate setting for any desired temperature can be used. Although there may be fluctuations because of changes in the line voltage, the values which follow will serve as a rough guide.

Desired melting point (°C):	50	100	150	200	250	300	350
Position on dial:	22	2)	34	38	42	47	56

The older models however are equipped with a vertical scale instead of a dial.

When the Kofler apparatus is used for the first time, or if it has not been used for a protracted period, the thermometer should not be inserted until the hot stage has been heated long enough to expel the moisture absorbed by the insulating material inside the heater. This is readily ac-

Index of A. H. T. Co.   Cat. Numbers in Figs. 7-8-9-10-11

C	No.	6888C	Glass Cover for Stage
CR	"	6889C	Set of 8 Test Reagents
D	"	6888D	Heat Baffle (Bridge)
E	"	6888E	Vacuum Sublimation Chamber
FO	* "	5556	Cover Glass Forceps 115%, Long
H	"	6888H	Cooling Block
J-s	"	6888J	Sublimation Block, Type A (small)
J-I	"	6888J	Sublimation Block, Type B (large)
K	"	6888K	Sublimation Dishes
L	* "	7052	Micro Slide Rings (Glass)
LA	* "	6924B or 6933D Microscope Lamp
M	"	6888M	Thermometer, Stage Calibrated High or Low Range
MI	*		Microscope, if possible with Metal Stage.
Mo	* N°	7329K or 7329M Micro Mortar with Pestle.
O-		8735	Vertical Rheostat.
P-	N°	6888P	Micro Slides, 1-1/2 x1 inches
PC	"	7020	Micro Cover Glasses, 15%, No 1 (square)
	"	7022	Micro Cover Glasses, 12%, No 1 (round)
	"	7022	Micro Cover Glasses, 18%, No 2 (round)
SP	* "	9008	Set of Micro Spatula

Note: Parts Marked with * are not supplied under No. 6886A

The Following Are Letters Used to indicate the Parts of Micro Hot Stage Under Cat. No. 6886A.-6886B, & 6887A.

A	Metal Stage	RM	Lens Mount
B	Metal Rim	RS	Screw for RM
F	Fork	S	Feet (Transite)
FL	Lifter for Fork	T	Contact Pins
G	Threaded Post	U	Plug to Stage
GS	Screw for G	V	Cord
HE	Heating Element	W	On-Off Switch
I	Arm of Stage	X	Plug to Rheostat
IS	Screw	Y	Plug to Current Supply
IP	Pin on Slotted Arm	Z	Light Well
N	Guard Tube	ZA	Optical Axis
NS	" " Socket	ZR	Glass Plate Ring
Q	Glass Plate	ZX	Groove
R	Lenses	ZY	

complished by allowing the stage to heat up to about 200° for 10 minutes or so. During this interval, of course, the thermometer and the guard tube are not attached to the stage.

B. DETERMINATION OF MELTING POINT

The apparatus should be set up in a place which is practically free from drafts. It is not advisable to work too close to a window.

A very small quantity of the sample is placed on a clean, dry 1½ × 1 inch slide. If the crystals or particles are large, they must be pulverized. This may be done directly on the slide by means of a micro spatula. The number of particles included within the field of vision should not be numerous. In order to secure intimate contact between the sample and the slide, a 9-mm No. 1 cover glass is pressed down firmly with the blade of a micro spatula.

After the microscope has been focused on the slide, the slide is searched for a suitable field, after which the bridge or heat baffle (D) is placed in position. Finally, the stage cover (C) is laid on the rim of the Kofler stage, and the microscope is refocused.

Ordinarily the temperature may be raised fairly rapidly until within 10° or 20° of the anticipated melting point. Thereafter the rate should be retarded considerably. While various authorities suggest a rate of approximately 2° per minute for the last 5° or 6°, the United States Pharmacopoeia recommends a rate not in excess of 0.5° per minute. This, of course, concerns capillary melting point determinations.

After having melted a specimen, the stage and accessories may be too hot to touch with the fingers. If it is planned to follow immediately with another determination, the glass parts are carefully removed with appropriate tweezers. The cooling of the hot stage is then hastened by placing the metal cooling block (H) on top.

With the Kofler apparatus the manufacturer supplies a set of eight test reagents with certified melting points. These reagents not only cover a wide range of values but also represent a variety of types. A description of their melting characteristics is included with each set. The student should obtain certified reagents and the corresponding report from the instructor in charge. After carefully reading over the report, he should essay determinations on the samples suggested by the instructor. If the value is not in agreement with the report, the determination should be repeated. Remember that it is important to avoid rapid heating near the melting point, otherwise the temperature indicated by the thermometer will not be the actual temperature of the sample.

After trying several of the certified samples, the student should determine the melting point of at least one unknown, preferably one having a melting point fairly close to that of one of the certified specimens used. Obviously, the samples should be free from any adsorbed moisture. It is therefore advisable to store samples in a desiccator some time before using. In some instances the melting of a sample is more easily observed between crossed Nicols (or Polaroids) (cf. Experiment 19).

C. SUBLIMATION

There are various means for carrying out sublimations beneath the microscope. In subliming directly from a slide, a cell may be formed by placing a glass ring (L) around the sample and covering with a No. 2

cover glass. The whole unit can then be covered by the heat baffle (D) and the glass stage cover (C).

Another procedure employs a microsublimation dish (K) and a Fisher sublimation block (J-S or J-I). The block is laid on the hot stage, and the dish is placed in the central opening of the block. The receiver consists of a cover glass placed over the dish.

D. VACUUM SUBLIMATION

In using the Kofler-Dernbach vacuum sublimation chamber (E) the sample may be laid in the center of the base plate if desired. As in other sublimations, the receiver may be a No. 2 cover glass of appropriate diameter. This receiver may be laid over a glass ring, or it may be supported by two small glass strips of the required thickness. Depending upon the distance the experimenter requires between sample and sublimate, the supporting strips may be cut from cover glasses or from a glass slide. When the assembly is ready, it is covered with the chamber, using an appropriate sealing agent on the ground edges. (A silicone vacuum grease is recommended.) The side arm of the sublimation chamber is then connected with the manometer and the vacuum line.

EXPERIMENT 19

POLARIZED LIGHT

(Reference: Chapter VII)

For this experiment there should be available some form of polarizing microscope, preferably one with a rotating stage. A petrographic microscope or a chemical microscope designed to accommodate a selenite plate would be ideal. However, lack of one of the conventional models does not necessarily preclude the possibility of performing some of the observations which involve polarized light.

An ordinary biological microscope can be converted into a simple polarizing instrument by purchasing a Polaroid polarizer-analyzer set. Such sets can be obtained from the various scientific supply houses. Those who prefer to devise their own outfit can do so without much difficulty. Two square inches of Polaroid sheet can be purchased from a supply house. The polarizer is made by cutting a Polaroid disc of such diameter that it readily slips into the substage filter holder. To construct the frame of the "cap analyzer," obtain a round pill box which is just large enough to fit snugly over the ocular of the microscope. Using a cork drill of appropriate diameter, cut a hole slightly larger than the diameter of the eyelens of the 5-× ocular. Carefully center this opening. Over the window (inside) place a small square of Polaroid. The Polaroid may be held in place by a tiny drop of glue placed in each of the four corners of the square. To prevent scratching the Polaroid when it is rotated on the ocular, attach a clean cover glass to the under side.

The surface of Polaroid film should not be touched with the fingers. It should be protected from dust, moisture, and chemical fumes.

A. DETECTING ANISOTROPIC SUBSTANCES

1. Attach the polarizer to the microscope and arrange for parallel axial illumination, using the 4-mm objective. If the microscope is equipped with a cap analyzer, slowly rotate it until the field appears practically dark. The Nicol prisms of the polarizer and analyzer are now said to be "crossed." If Polaroid film is used instead of Nicol prisms, the Polaroids are "crossed."

Observe the exact position of the analyzer, and then slowly rotate it until it has made one complete turn (360°). How many times did the field become dark in making one complete turn of the analyzer?

1 (alternate). If the microscope is equipped with a "tube" analyzer, the foregoing procedure must be modified. This type of analyzer is brought into position by sliding it through a slot in the body tube of the microscope. Usually a tube analyzer cannot be rotated. It is possible, however, to rotate the substage polarizer. Insert the analyzer into the body tube and turn the substage polarizer to a position which results in a dark field. This probably occurs when an index on the rim of the polarizer coincides with the figure 360 (generally in the front center). Now slowly rotate the polarizer through one complete turn and note how many times the field becomes dark.

2. Place a small square (about ½ inch) of clean, unwrinkled cellophane on a slide and protect it with a cover glass. (A much better plan is to make a permanent mount. Place a very small drop of Canada balsam in the center of a clean slide and lay the cellophane square on top. Over this place another drop of balsam. Next let a clean cover glass fall on the latter drop of balsam. By means of the little finger gradually apply pressure to the cover glass so that the cellophane is spread out flat, and the excess balsam is expelled. The slide can be used immediately. After it has been allowed to dry for a few days the excess balsam around the edge of the cover glass can be cleaned away with a bit of cloth moistened with xylene or toluene.) With the polarizer and analyzer in crossed position (that is, with a dark field) place the cellophane specimen beneath the objective. Rotate the slide and observe the effects which result in making one complete turn of 360°. Repeat the test using a very thin piece of mica as the specimen.

3. Suspend a few potato starch grains in a drop of water on a slide, and protect the preparation with a cover glass. Examine the starch with ordinary light, and then examine between crossed Nicols, that is, with the polarizer and analyzer in crossed position.

4. Prepare small crystals of sodium chloride or potassium chloride by allowing a drop of solution to evaporate on a slide. Examine the crystals between crossed Nicols. (Remember that it is important to exclude any rays which do not come from below the stage.) Are any of the crystals illuminated? Rotate the crystals by turning the slide or by rotating the stage. The crystals should remain dark in all positions since they do not exhibit double refraction. Both potassium chloride and sodium chloride belong to the isometric system; they are isotropic.

The foregoing tests demonstrate the fact that even the simplest type of polarizing microscope enables the observer to place quickly a transparent substance in one of two classes, viz., isotropic or anisotropic.

B. PARALLEL EXTINCTION

1. On a clean slide place a few very small crystals of pyrogallic acid, anthraquinone, quinine sulfate, or picric acid. Only a very small quantity should be dusted on the center of the slide so that the crystals appear separated from each other, rather than in matted clusters. Observe the specimen between crossed Nicols. Select a distinct crystal, and, after bringing it to the center of the field of view, slowly turn the slide so as to cause the crystal to rotate about the center of the field. Eventually a position is reached where the crystal image vanishes or is blacked out. This is referred to as an "extinction" position. For the crystals suggested for this exercise, extinction occurs when the long axis is parallel with the plane of vibration of one of the Nicol prisms (either the polarizer or the analyzer). All of these crystals exhibit the phenomenon of parallel extinction. After noting the position of the crystal, rotate the crystal through 360°. How many times does the crystal suffer extinction during one complete turn?

When making observations with polarized light, it is very desirable to employ an ocular which is provided with two cross-hairs. Normally these should lie parallel with the vibration planes of the crossed Nicols and, consequently, parallel with the extinction positions of the crystals mentioned above.

C. OBLIQUE EXTINCTION

1. Obtain some very small crystals of copper sulfate pentahydrate by allowing a solution to evaporate on a slide. Examine between crossed

Nicol prisms, and observe the effect produced when a given crystal is rotated. In contrast to the crystals studied previously, the copper sulfate pentahydrate exhibits oblique extinction.

2. Prepare manganese formate by adding an excess of manganese carbonate to a small volume of 1:1 formic acid. Having allowed time for the carbonate to react, filter the mixture and transfer a few drops to a clean slide. As soon as there has been sufficient evaporation to result in the separation of crystals, examine the specimen between crossed Nicols. The thin, colorless tablets should exhibit oblique extinction.

3. As another example of a substance which shows oblique extinction, select a few crystals of Epsom salt, $MgSO_4 \cdot 7H_2O$. Since very small grains are required, crush the substance by placing on a slide and applying pressure to a second slide which is placed on top. The object is not to grind the grains into a fine powder. Applying a steady pressure to the upper slide causes the crystal to break down along its cleavage planes. Place the specimen under the microscope and search for small slender fragments having straight edges. When these are rotated between crossed Nicols, oblique extinction is observed. It is important that the grains examined be very thin.

4. Not all hydrates of $MgSO_4$ will exhibit oblique extinction. If time permits, you may check on this by examining crystals obtained under different conditions.

From the foregoing exercises it becomes evident that the polarizing microscope not only enables one to distinguish between isotropic and anisotropic substances but, under favorable conditions, may further distinguish between two major groups of anisotropic crystals. Substances which exhibit parallel extinction are "uniaxial" and usually crystallize according to the tetragonal or hexagonal system. Uniaxial crystals are so named because they possess one axis along which no double refraction occurs. Crystals which show oblique extinction are "biaxial" and possess two axes along which double refraction does not occur. These crystals belong to the orthorhombic, monoclinic, or triclinic system. A uniaxial crystal possesses two different refractive indices; one value for the ordinary ray and another for the extraordinary ray. For a biaxial crystal there are three refractive index values. A description of the procedure to follow in determining the refractive indices of birefringent crystals is beyond the scope of this work.

D. PLEOCHROISM

A very interesting property exhibited by some colored anisotropic substances is pleochroism. When viewed by polarized light pleochroic crystals change color as they are rotated.

1. Prepare thin crystals of cupric acetate by allowing a drop of hot, saturated solution to cool on a clean slide. Examine the preparation by

polarized light, that is, with the polarizer of the microscope in place but with the analyzer removed. In what way do the various crystals differ in color?

Select one of the thin crystals and observe the color changes which result as it is rotated through 360°.

Introduce the analyzer and determine whether cupric acetate exhibits parallel or oblique extinction. Refer to tables in a chemical handbook to find the system to which cupric acetate crystals belong. Does this confirm the type of extinction which you found? Explain.

2. Several other crystals should be examined for pleochroism. A few appropriate compounds are azobenzene, o-nitrophenol, sodium cyanide, and silver chromate. The latter may be prepared directly on the slide by the reaction of a drop of 2 per cent silver nitrate with one drop of dilute potassium dichromate. In all cases, the crystals examined should be rather thin.

E. SELENITE PLATE

The selenite plate, first-order red plate, or gypsum plate (see Chapter VII) may be mounted in an oblong metal plate or in a circular metal cap. The former type is for use with a microscope provided with an appropriate slot in its body tube. The cap type is intended for an instrument having a cap analyzer, that is, one which is placed over the ocular. In both cases the gypsum plate must be placed somewhere between the polarizer and the analyzer. One use of the selenite plate is to detect substances which are only weakly birefringent.

When the selenite plate is placed between crossed Nicol prisms, the color of the field should be red or a rich blue, depending upon which of the two colors is its "sensitive tint." When a crystal lies in its extinction position, between crossed Nicols and a selenite plate, the color of the crystal should be identical with the sensitive tint of the selenite plate.

Examine thin crystals of sodium fluoride between crossed Nicols. Rotate the crystals to determine their extinction position. Next introduce the gypsum plate and try to determine whether sodium fluoride exhibits parallel or oblique extinction. Does the crystal system mentioned in your chemical handbook confirm your interpretation?

Before deciding that a substance is isotropic it should be checked with a selenite plate.

F. INTERFERENCE

For a considerable period mineralogists have utilized interference figures and certain other optical properties in the identification of minerals. The subject has been systematized to such an extent that by determining a few optical properties on a properly prepared thin section of rock the component minerals can be identified within a comparatively short time. The success of the method depends upon the fact that there are available rather extensive tables which serve as a key.[1] More recently similar methods have been adopted by certain chemical investigators particularly in connection with alkaloids, sugars, synthetic fibers, and other specialized fields. Although the specialized technique of optical crystallography is not within the province of this brief work, the exercises which follow will convey to the student a qualitative concept of certain interference figures. Detailed discussions of the subject may be found in such standard works as Winchell and Johannsen.

1. Since the figures to be observed depend upon the behavior of strongly convergent polarized light, the microscope must be equipped with a substage condenser, as well as with Nicol prisms (or their Polaroid equivalents). If the condenser is provided with a supplementary lens for decreasing its focal length, it should be swung into position.

With the analyzer removed from the microscope, focus the 4-mm objective on the slide bearing a small piece of wrinkle-free cellophane mounted in a drop of balsam or glycerol. A permanent preparation, such as suggested in part A-2 of this series of experiments, will serve admirably. After focusing, remove the ocular and adjust the analyzer to the "crossed" position. Instead of placing the eye just above the draw tube (or over the cap analyzer), peer into the tube from such height that, when rotating the specimen, interference figures will be seen. This may be at a height of 8 or 10 inches above the tube.

The interference figures may appear as a pair of dark parabolas which approach each other to form a cross and then recede toward different quadrants as the specimen is rotated. It will be found advantageous to view the figures through a double convex or a plano-convex lens, which is supported an appropriate distance above the microscope. A 250-mm lens may be used. By means of a ring stand it may be supported at the proper height to have the rear element of the microscope objective in focus.

Describe carefully what is observed as the specimen makes one complete rotation of 360°. These phenomena are biaxial interference figures. Although interference figures are very useful for identifying or characterizing minerals and numerous chemical compounds, the procedure just described is not sufficiently refined for such work.

2. On a slide let a drop of a xylene solution of iodoform, or hot saturated aqueous KH_2SO_4, recrystallize. Examine crystals, both with and without a selenite plate; compare with uniaxial interference figures described in Fig. 7.11 (p. 111).

3. Repeat step 2 with crystals obtained from hot saturated $BaCl_2$, or $ZnSO_4 \cdot 7H_2O$. Examine for biaxial interference figures. Also examine an extremely thin section of muscovite (mica).

[1] Cf. Larsen and Berman, "The Microscopic Determination of the Nonopaque Minerals," *U. S. Geological Survey Bulletin No. 848* (1934).

EXPERIMENT 20

GENERAL PROCEDURES EMPLOYED IN CHEMICAL MICROSCOPY

(Reference: Chapter VIII)

A. FILTRATION AND RECRYSTALLIZATION ON A SLIDE

By means of a micropipet place in the center of a clean slide one drop of a 2 per cent silver nitrate solution acidified with nitric acid. Beside this drop place a drop of dilute hydrochloric acid (ratio of acid to water, approximately 1:3). Using a fine glass needle, cause the acid drop to flow into the silver nitrate. This should result in the formation of a curd-like precipitate. If the precipitate is examined under the microscope, no distinct crystals can be observed.

While waiting for the precipitate to settle to a more compact mass, prepare a supply of filter slips by cutting wedges from a sheet of ordinary filter paper. These may be in the form of isosceles triangles approximately 1 cm wide and 2 cm high.

To remove the excess liquid from the silver chloride precipitate, apply the tip of a paper wedge to the edge of the preparation. If one wedge is not sufficient, a second may be applied. Now apply a drop or two of distilled water to the residue on the slide. After waiting for a brief interval to permit the water to take up some of the acid remaining in the system, again draw off the resulting solution by means of a filter wedge. By repeating this process several times the precipitate can be washed free from any excess reagent. The method is of limited application because many fine precipitates are drawn into the fibers of the paper.

To the well-washed precipitate, add a drop of diluted ammonium hydroxide. (One volume of the concentrated ammonium hydroxide should be diluted with 2 volumes of water.) Stirring with a glass needle should cause the silver chloride to dissolve. If necessary, add another drop of the ammonium hydroxide to bring about solution. In case the volume of liquid has attained unwieldy dimensions, transfer a single drop to another slide by means of a micropipet. When exposed to the air for a while, ammonia escapes from the solution and crystals of silver chloride are deposited. Describe their appearance as seen under the microscope, using a 16-mm objective.

B. SEPARATION OF A MIXTURE

Prepare a small volume of a solution containing about 1 per cent silver nitrate, 3 per cent lead nitrate, and a little nitric acid. Place a drop of this solution on a clean slide, and add hydrochloric acid to precipitate the metals as before. After removing the liquid with a filter wedge, cover the residue of mixed chlorides with 2 drops of water, and heat the preparation over a microburner until the solution seems near boiling. (*However, do not actually boil.*)

Remove the hot solution, which contains lead chloride, by means of a filter tube, and transfer to another slide. If the volume is large, transfer one small drop of the solution to another slide for testing. Place a drop of potassium dichromate solution beside the test drop, and cause the reagent to flow into the latter by means of a glass needle. The formation of yellow precipitate indicates the presence of lead. Although the particles of this precipitate may seem to have no definite structure when viewed through a 16-mm objective, the small distinct crystals can be resolved by using the 4-mm objective. The preparation should be covered with a cover glass when using the high-power objective.

C. HANGING-DROP TECHNIQUE

Since the hanging-drop technique finds frequent application in some fields, the microscopist should acquire some skill in its performance. To illustrate the procedure we shall employ it in detecting the release of ammonia, but there are numerous other tests in which it can be applied.

Drop a few small particles of ammonium sulfate into a microcrucible. Apply a small drop of 2 per cent platinic chloride solution to the center of a $1\frac{1}{2} \times 1$ inch slide. After carefully inverting the slide, place it on top of the crucible so that the reagent drop hangs suspended in the center. Now, while raising the hanging-drop slide with one hand, use the other hand to introduce a drop of 10 per cent NaOH from a capillary pipet. Replace immediately the hanging-drop slide on top of the crucible. It is important to prevent any of the sodium hydroxide from touching the rim of the crucible, since this would react in the same manner as ammonia. After allowing 5 minutes for the ammonia to react with the hanging-drop, turn the slide right side up and examine under a 16-mm objective. The presence of small tetrahedra reveals that ammonia was released by the reaction mixture.

For reactions which depend upon the absorption of a gas by a liquid, as in the foregoing procedure, a number of variations are possible. Instead of supporting the hanging-drop slide on a microcrucible, it may be placed over a glass ring which is resting on an ordinary slide. In some cases the ring should be fixed to the slide by means of a thin film of silicone stopcock grease. One advantage of this arrangement is that the entire assembly can be placed under the microscope so that changes in the hanging drop can be observed without removing it from the reaction chamber.

D. SUBLIMATION

For some types of work microsublimation is an important procedure, and the microscopist should therefore be prepared to apply this means of separation with whatever facilities are available.

Examples of substances which can be sublimed readily include phloroglucinol, salicylic acid, phenothiazine, phthalimide, quinone, anthranilic acid, etc. For practice one may work with a known sample consisting of an intimate mixture of finely powdered table salt and phloroglucinol, in the ratio of approximately 5 to 1.

At the end of a clean slide place a short piece of a broken slide; one inch from the end place a small quantity of known sample. (This may be a pile measuring approximately 1 mm in diameter and 0.5 mm in height.) To complete the assembly, cover with another slide, with one end resting on the bit of broken glass. Applying the thumb and the index finger at the end where the two slides meet, carefully heat the sample over the flame of a microburner. The heating should be gradual. Within a few minutes the upper slide may be removed, turned right side up, and examined for any sublimate.

FIG. 12. SPRING CLAMP FOR PERFORMING SUBLIMATIONS FROM A MICRO CRUCIBLE TO A SLIDE. (*Will Corporation, Rochester, N.Y.*)

Although a special clamp is available for performing sublimations from a microcrucible to a glass slide (Figure 12), the lack of such a clamp need not deter one from performing sublimations from a crucible. It is a simple matter to form a crucible support from a 12 inch length of heavy copper wire. At one end the wire is shaped to form a loop having a diameter slightly smaller than the top of the crucible. This is conveniently done by bending it around a glass tube or a cork drill of appropriate diameter. About 8 inches behind the loop the far end of the wire is bent forward so that 2 parallel lengths of wire serve as a handle to hold between the thumb and index finger.

When using this simplified wire holder the sublimation from crucible to slide is carried out more conveniently if the slide measures only $1\frac{1}{2} \times 1$ inch. To keep the slide comparatively cool, a small beaker of cold water is placed on it during short periods of heating the crucible.

E. BOILING POINT DETERMINATION

Prepare a thin-walled glass tube about 10 cm long and having an inside diameter of 3 mm. One end should be sealed. An inner tube will also be required. For this, draw out soft glass tubing to obtain a thin-walled tube about 15 cm long and 0.5 mm in diameter. Near one end cautiously apply a microflame so that the walls fuse together, dividing the tube into two parts. Now cut off part of the short end of tubing 3 mm from the seal, thereby leaving a small cell or chamber. The upper end is bent over at such a height that when it hangs in the wider tube the small chamber will not quite touch the bottom (Figure 13).

To carry out a determination, use a micropipet to place in the larger tube enough of the sample liquid to extend to the constriction of the inner tube when hung in position. Now attach the assembly to a thermometer by means of thin strips of Scotch tape, and place in the heating bath of a melting point apparatus. Raise the temperature of the bath slowly until bubbles of air and, finally, bubbles of vaporized sample issue steadily from the bottom of the small chamber. Remove the flame so that the bath begins to cool. Eventually the stream of bubbles will cease and the liquid will move up into the small tube. The temperature of this point is recorded as the boiling point.

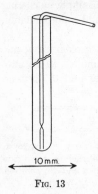

10 mm.

Fig. 13

In order to obtain reproducible results the apparatus must be protected against drafts while the heating is in progress. This may be accomplished by placing an appropriate shield of asbestos around the assembly. The analyst should also keep in mind the fact that if the boiling point is to be of greatest value the usual "stem correction" should be applied, and the corrected boiling point should be calculated for "normal" pressure (cf. Chapter VIII).

EXPERIMENT 21

IDENTIFYING THE CONSTITUENTS OF A PROTECTIVE COATING: TEST FOR INDIVIDUAL METALS

(Reference: Chapter IX)

A. DESCRIPTION OF PROCEDURE

1. In testing for the presence of zinc or cadmium the analyst may employ the following procedure. By means of a capillary pipet deposit a drop of the solution to be tested, which should contain a trace of free nitric acid, toward one end of a well-cleaned slide. If the composition of the test drop is likely to include more than a trace of strong acid, add a gran-

ule of sodium or ammonium acetate to serve as a buffer. Warming the slide and stirring the drop will facilitate solution of the buffer. For microscopic tests in general, the best results require the test drop to be of such magnitude that, when spread out by stirring with a glass or platinum needle, it will measure about 5 mm in diameter and 1 mm in depth. **A shallow test drop is important** because the depth of focus of 8- and 16-mm objectives is very small.

The reagent employed in this test should be a fairly concentrated aqueous solution of potassium mercuric thiocyanate, but it need not be saturated. Place a small reagent drop close to, but not touching, the test drop. Then place the slide beneath the microscope objective. By means of a fine glass needle, carefully draw a channel from the reagent drop to the test drop. The dense reagent drop will flow into the test drop, forming zones representing several different ratios of reagent to test material. As the concentration of the appropriate ions exceeds the solubility product constants, characteristic crystals of the zinc or cadmium derivatives will separate.

Another interesting test for zinc depends upon the formation of sodium-zinc carbonate, $3Na_2CO_3 \cdot 8ZnCO_3 \cdot 8H_2O$, which separates as characteristic colorless tetrahedra and triangular plates. Render the test drop, which may contain zinc nitrate, alkaline by exposing it to ammonia fumes. This may be done by inverting the slide over an open bottle of ammonium hydroxide. The drop should be permitted to absorb sufficient ammonia to redissolve the precipitate which is first formed. Then turn the slide right side up, and add finely powdered sodium bicarbonate to the center of the test drop. By tapping the edge of the slide it can be jarred sufficiently to disperse the bicarbonate through the liquid. Do not stir the drop with a needle because this may bring about the sudden separation of submicroscopic crystals. The sodium bicarbonate should be added in slight excess, so that some of the solid remains in suspension. If the characteristic crystals are not found within a few minutes, re-examine the slide 5 or 10 minutes later. Certain metals, such as cadmium, may interfere with this test.

2. When testing for tin the metal should be present as a very dilute solution of stannic chloride in dilute hydrochloric acid. The reagent, rubidium chloride, is employed in the form of an aqueous solution. Combine one drop of the reagent with a test drop according to the procedure followed before in detecting zinc or cadmium. If preferred, the test may be performed by dropping a small particle of the solid reagent into the test drop. Since the crystals of rubidium chlorostannate (Rb_2SnCl_6) are very minute, use a 4-mm objective to observe the preparation.

3. In testing for lead the test drop, which may be very dilute, should contain the lead ion in dilute nitric acid, that is, approximately 5 per cent.

Apply the test drop to a clean slide in the manner described in the test for zinc. Then drop a fragment of the solid thiourea into the sample. The characteristic crystals will separate if the lead ion is present. As little as 0.02 mg may give a positive test.

4. The triple nitrite test for copper should be performed on a sample having a fairly high concentration. For this reason, place a drop of the original sample (which may contain the cupric ion combined with nitrate or acetate ion) on a clean slide and carefully evaporate just to dryness, using a microflame. Cover the residue with a small drop of 30 per cent (approx.) acetic acid solution, and add a particle of sodium acetate. After a clear solution results, add a fragment of lead acetate. Finally, when this has dissolved, add a granule of potassium nitrite (KNO_2) to the center of the resulting solution. Within a few seconds the characteristic crystals of triple nitrite should begin to separate if cupric ion was present in the original sample.

Since the triple nitrite crystals may appear in the form of very minute squares and rectangles, employ an 8-mm objective if available.

5. The nickel dimethylglyoxime test is readily performed on a dilute solution of one of the common nickel salts such as the nitrate or chloride. First render a drop of the solution alkaline with concentrated ammonium hydroxide. After gently warming the preparation, transfer the clear solution to a clean slide, using a capillary. Any undissolved residue is subjected to a second extraction with ammonium hydroxide. Should the combined alkaline extract form a drop of unwieldy dimensions, remove a convenient volume for use as a test drop. Close to the latter place a drop of saturated aqueous solution of dimethylglyoxime. After causing the test drop to flow into the reagent, *gently* warm the preparation. A deep pink or magenta precipitate of nickel dimethylglyoxime will separate. While this may at first appear amorphous, distinct slender prisms will gradually develop.

6. To perform the test for chromium in the form of chromate or dichromate ion, place a drop of a soluble chromate or dichromate solution, acidified with nitric acid, beside a drop of 2 per cent silver nitrate solution on a clean slide. As the reagent is caused to flow into the test drop, dark reddish crystals of silver chromate or silver dichromate separate. It is believed that the latter compound is formed when much nitric acid is present; otherwise the chromate results. In either case the crystals may not be well formed, but this renders the test no less conclusive. Should better crystals be desired, they may be recrystallized from a little ammonium hydroxide or hot nitric acid. This is accomplished by covering the chromate or dichromate residue with a drop of nitric acid (acid to water approx. 1:2) and heating the preparation, without boiling, over a microflame. Should the residue fail to dissolve, add another drop of acid and follow by further heating. As the solution cools, the crystals will separate.

An alternate test for chromium consists in substituting 5 per cent lead acetate solution for the silver nitrate in the foregoing test. A yellow precipitate of lead chromate (or dichromate) is formed in the presence of chromium. As a rule no distinct crystals are observed. This preparation should be viewed by reflected light.

7. Gold is readily detected by the use of a solution of pyridine hydrobromide in an excess of hydrobromic acid. This reagent is very simply prepared by mixing 1 volume of pure pyridine with 9 volumes of the 40 per cent hydrobromic acid (or approximately $7\frac{1}{2}$ volumes of the 48 per cent acid). To demonstrate this test, cause a drop of the reagent to flow into a drop of very dilute chlorauric acid solution (gold chloride in water). The resulting precipitate ($C_5H_5N \cdot HBr \cdot AuBr_3$) may vary from yellow or orange to a dull red color and may consist of thin, elongated, almost rectangular plates which exhibit oblique extinction and are pleochroic. Some of the crystals may appear as feathery crosses and may be golden yellow when viewed between crossed Nicols. Other metals do not interfere with this test.

8. The test drop employed in detecting silver should contain the metal as silver nitrate in a solution which is strongly acidified with nitric acid. After placing a cover glass over the test drop, allow a drop of hydrochloric acid to flow under the cover. Draw off the mother liquor and wash the residue with several successive drops of water acidified with nitric acid. *This washing is important.* Finally dissolve the washed residue in ammonium hydroxide solution, and set aside the preparation to permit spontaneous evaporation of ammonia. Gradually there will separate tiny cubes and octahedra of silver chloride, resulting from the decomposition of $AgCl \cdot 2NH_3$. In spite of their small dimensions the crystals are readily seen because they have a high refractive index (2.07).

9. A very convenient test for palladium is carried out on a solution of its chloride. For this purpose, dissolve the metal in aqua regia (3 volumes conc. hydrochloric acid to 1 of nitric), and evaporate the resulting solution to near dryness. After adding a little hydrochloric acid to the residue, again evaporate the product to near dryness. Then take up the moist residue in the minimum volume of water. This solution serves as the test sample. If necessary, add sufficient hydrochloric acid to render the preparation acid, but excess acidity must be avoided. Upon the addition of a few granules of KCl to a test drop thus prepared, long, slender, yellow prisms are formed. The latter exhibit brilliant polarization colors. In some cases the preparation may have to stand for some time before the prisms are formed. Under some conditions small, deep orange or reddish crystals may be formed instead of the slender, yellow prisms.

10. In our test for platinum the metal should be present as chloro-platinic acid (also referred to as platinic chloride). Using potassium chloride solution as the reagent, allow a drop to flow into the test drop, which consists of a moderately dilute solution of chloroplatinic acid. Characteristic octahedra of potassium chloroplatinate (K_2PtCl_6) will separate. Rubidium chloride may be substituted for potassium, thereby obtaining rubidium chloroplatinate, which has a more intense color.

B. APPLICATION

In order to observe the characteristic crystals formed in the various reactions, apply the appropriate tests to each of the following solutions.

1. Dilute solution of zinc nitrate. Try both the potassium-mercuric thiocyanate and the sodium bicarbonate reagent.
2. Dilute solution of cadmium nitrate.
3. A solution containing both zinc and cadmium ions, approximately in the ratio 5:1. (The test for zinc may be obscured if too much cadmium is present.)
4. A very dilute solution of stannic chloride. (Use rubidium chloride as reagent.)
5. Dilute solution of cupric ion, for example, 0.1 per cent copper nitrate, copper acetate, etc.
6. Solution containing the nitrates of both copper and zinc.
    a. On one drop perform the triple nitrite test for copper.
    b. On a second drop demonstrate the presence of zinc, by the formation of sodium-zinc carbonate.
7. Dilute nickel chloride or nickel nitrate solution.
8. Dilute solution of sodium or potassium chromate; also, try the test on potassium *di*chromate.
9. Solution of gold chloride (chlorauric acid). Try a 0.5 per cent solution and also 0.01 per cent.
10. Platinic chloride. Using a 0.5 per cent solution (approx.), try both KCl and RbCl as reagents. Both tests can be performed simultaneously on the same slide. Repeat the tests on a more dilute solution.

Solution of palladium in aqua regia. If the free element is not available, a suitable test solution can be prepared from commercial palladium chloride solution by the following procedure. Place a drop of 1 per cent palladium chloride solution on a clean slide and evaporate to dryness. After the slide has cooled, cover the residue with a drop of aqua regia and gently heat the preparation so that the liquid is slowly evaporated. Finally dissolve the resulting residue in a small drop of aqua regia, which then serves as the test drop.

Note: Until the student has acquired some first-hand experience in the preparation of microscopic crystals, it is advisable to have the instructor pass judgment on each slide prepared. Whenever samples of known composition fail to yield the characteristic crystals, the tests should be repeated. In the event of persistent failure, the student should have the instructor check his procedure for possible errors in technique.

EXPERIMENT 22

IDENTIFICATION OF A METALLIC COATING

(Reference: Chapter IX and Experiment 21)

A. INEXPENSIVE METALS

The sample furnished to the student may be a piece of hardware, kitchenware, etc., or it may be merely some odd piece of metal having the required coating. Appropriate samples include common pins, nails, bolts, pie pans, "tin" cans, fencing wire, metallic papers. Each sample submitted should first be tested by the instructor or some other responsible chemist. It is inadvisable to *assume* the identity of a protective coating.

In order to take a sample, the student will require an etched slide or some other piece of ground glass. Rub the object being tested across the etched end of the slide several times in order to obtain a few streaks. (Should there be any reason for not taking a streak sample, it is entirely feasible to scrape a minute particle from the surface of metal being examined. The edge of a glass slide can be used for the purpose. The particle taken should be very small; otherwise solution of the sample may have to be carried out in a microcrucible because the volume of liquid will be too large to manipulate on a slide.) Bring the sample into solution by adding 2 drops of dilute nitric acid (1 volume conc. acid to 2 volumes H_2O) and heating very gently over a very small flame. When *most* (not all) of the moisture has been evaporated, add 2 more drops of acid and resume gentle heating until evaporation has been just barely completed.

Treat the residue with 2 drops of water to bring about solution of any lead, zinc, or cadmium nitrate. Should any tin be present, it will be in the form of the oxide, which is insoluble. If there is such a residue, it is reserved for later testing. Remove the solution, which may contain lead, zinc, or cadmium ions, by means of a microfilter tube. A small drop is subjected to the thiourea test for lead. In the absence of lead the remainder of the solution may be used in the potassium mercuric thiocyanate test for zinc and cadmium; but if the lead test is positive, this metal must first be removed. In this case slowly evaporate the clear solution to near dryness. When the slide has cooled sufficiently, add 2 drops of concentrated sulfuric acid to the residue. Then carefully heat the preparation over a very small flame, so that the excess acid is "fumed down." Any lead present is thereby converted into the insoluble lead sulfate.

Treat this residue with water to take up the soluble sulfates; transfer the clear solution to another slide and evaporate to near dryness. After adding a drop of nitric acid to the resulting residue, again evaporate the product to near dryness. Take up the resulting residue of nitrates in the minimum amount of water and test for zinc and cadmium.

If the nitric acid treatment of the original sample yielded any insoluble residue, the presence of tin may be assumed. To perform a confirmatory test for this metal, first convert the oxide into stannic chloride. To do this, fume down the residue twice with a drop of hydrochloric acid. Finally take up the resulting residue in dilute hydrochloric acid and subject to the rubidium chloride test.

Note: The student must remember that the foregoing scheme of analysis is intended for substances which contain no metals other than lead, tin, cadmium, and zinc.

Electroplated utility ware which contains copper, either as the pure metal or in the form of brass, can be recognized by the color. There may, of course, be some doubt as to whether the plating is pure copper. A yellow or copper-colored sample, therefore, should be treated according to the following procedure.

Dissolve the sample in nitric acid and eventually bring into aqueous solution in the form of nitrates, just as in the procedure followed in the testing of "white" metals. Use one drop of this solution in the detection of zinc by the formation of sodium-zinc carbonate. If the typical crystals are not found, re-examine the slide at the end of 10 or 20 minutes. The presence of copper does not prevent the separation of the sodium-zinc carbonate crystals. Furthermore, even after the preparation has become dry, these crystals may still appear quite distinct.

In the case of inexpensive yellow or copper-colored plated wear it may be superfluous to perform a specific test for copper. The color, alone, should indicate its presence. Also, when the solution is rendered ammoniacal in the test for zinc, cupric ion will impart the rich blue color of the complex ion unless the concentration is very low. However, should further confirmation be desired, the triple nitrite reaction can be carried out in the usual manner even with zinc ion present.

B. NICKEL AND CHROMIUM

Using a stainless steel knife blade or the edge of a glass slide, remove a tiny fragment of metal from the object under examination and transfer to a size 0000 porcelain microcrucible. Add about 2 drops of aqua regia (1 volume nitric acid to 3 volumes hydrochloric acid). Gently heat the crucible over a microflame, but do not evaporate the mixture to dryness. While the material is still somewhat moist, add a little concentrated nitric acid to the crucible. Resume heating until most of the liquid has been evaporated. Dissolve the residue in a little water to form the test solution.

To detect nickel, transfer one drop of test solution to a clean slide and render alkaline with concentrated ammonium hydroxide solution. The dimethylglyoxime test is then performed as previously described.

Another drop of the test solution is subjected to the silver chromate test for chromium.

C. PRECIOUS METALS

If feasible, take the sample in the form of one or two streaks on an etched slide. Any silver or palladium present can be brought into solution by treating the streak with a large drop of diluted nitric acid (acid to water = 1:2). Solution may be facilitated by careful heating (not boiling). Should any copper be present this, too, will be attacked by the acid. Transfer a portion of the clear solution to each of two clean slides, reserving any undissolved metal on the original slide for later tests (gold and platinum). Subject one portion of the solution of nitrates to the hydrochloric acid test for silver. Should the test be negative, use the other drop of solution for the palladium test. For this purpose, first evaporate the solution to dryness. Then cover the product with aqua regia and heat gently until all of the liquid has evaporated. Dissolve the resulting residue in a fresh drop of aqua regia to form the actual test drop. The palladium is finally detected by the potassium chloride test.

If the original sample possessed a yellow (or golden) color, it may have contained copper, in which case the nitric acid solution may appear blue. The presence of copper should be confirmed by the triple nitrite reaction. However, since it is assumed that we are dealing with electro-plated ware, the test for copper may be omitted if silver or palladium is found present.

The metal which was not attacked by nitric acid may be gold or platinum. After covering the residue with 2 drops of aqua regia, subject the preparation to gentle heating until all of the liquid has been expelled. Repeat this treatment with aqua regia and take up the final residue in water. The solution may contain chlorauric acid or chloroplatinic acid.

The latter may be detected by means of potassium chloride or rubidium chloride, as explained previously. Another drop of this solution is used in the test for gold by means of the pyridine hydrobromide reagent.

After having analyzed several metallic samples of known composition, the student should test at least one "unknown."

EXPERIMENT 23

DETECTING SODIUM, POTASSIUM, AND AMMONIUM IONS

(Reference: Chapter IX)

A. OUTLINE OF PROCEDURES

The reagent employed in detecting sodium is a saturated solution of uranyl acetate in water which has been strongly acidified with acetic acid. A 1:4 ratio of acid to water will be satisfactory.

Evaporate to dryness on a slide one drop of the solution to be tested. This should be done slowly, using a very small microflame. If the test solution is too dilute to permit the evaporation of a single drop to deposit an adequate film on the slide, apply a second drop to the first residue and evaporate. When the slide has cooled sufficiently, place a drop of the reagent solution close to, but not touching, the residue. By means of a glass needle, cause the reagent to flow in a channel across the solid sample. Gradually, if sodium is present, the characteristic crystals of sodium uranyl acetate will appear. In using uranyl acetate to test for potassium, the same procedure is followed. This test for potassium is not as sensitive as when applied to sodium.

An effective test for the potassium ion consists in the formation of acid potassium tartrate. The reagent is a fairly concentrated solution of tartaric acid to which a few per cent of sodium tartrate has been added. The procedure is similar to that employed with uranyl acetate. An important precaution in this test, however, is to have a rather thick deposit of the sample. As mentioned previously, increased thickness is obtained by the evaporation of several successive drops. Since mineral acids interfere with this test, some sodium acetate should be added to the test solution if, for any reason, mineral acids may be present. The ammonium ion should be absent because ammonium bitartrate crystals are similar to, although not identical with, those of the potassium salt.

In testing for ammonium ion, place one or two drops of test solution in a microcrucible and cover with a bit of acid-washed, freshly ignited asbestos. Immediately after adding a drop of 10 per cent NaOH, cover the crucible with a slide bearing a small hanging-drop of dilute hydrochloric acid. Gentle warming of the crucible will facilitate the evolution of ammonia if the sample contains the ammonium radical. The hanging-drop of acid will convert the NH_3 into ammonium chloride. When the slide is turned right side up, test the drop with a drop of 5 per cent chloroplatinic acid solution. The gradual appearance of tetrahedral crystals serves as a positive test for ammonium ion. In case the sample is a solid, place a particle thereof in the crucible and cover with a drop of distilled water; from there on the procedure is just as outlined before. It is important that the solution in the crucible be kept out of contact with the slide which bears the hanging-drop. If the original sample contained potassium, such contamination would eventually result in the formation of crystals similar to those formed by the ammonium ion.

Although the foregoing procedure is generally recommended for detecting ammonium ion as the chloroplatinate, the following modification has proved quite satisfactory over a period of years. Carefully place one drop of test solution on the bottom of the crucible. Using an appropriate pipet, add a drop of 10 per cent NaOH with the right hand, while the left hand holds a 1½ × 1 inch slide bearing a *small* hanging-drop of 5 per cent chloroplatinic acid. Immediately after the NaOH has been added, cover the crucible with the reagent slide. After a few minutes, remove the slide for examination under the microscope. Add another drop of NaOH to the crucible. Then heat to expel all possible traces of ammonia. Dissolve the residue in one or two drops of water and carefully acidify with HCl; transfer a drop of the resulting solution to a clean slide and add a drop of chloroplatinic acid. If tetrahedra appear now, they indicate that the original sample contained K ion, since all the ammonia was expelled previous to the final test.

B. APPLICATIONS

1. Using pure samples known to contain only one metallic radical, perform each of the tests outlined in part A.

2. Apply the uranyl acetate test to a mixture containing the chlorides (or acetates) of Na and K in the ratio of 5:1; repeat the test on a mixture in which the ratio is 1:5. Can this single reagent be employed to detect both metals in a mixture?

3. Prepare a test solution containing approximately 2 per cent NaCl, 2 per cent KCl, and an equal concentration of NH_4Cl. Render a 2-drop sample acid with dilute HCl, after which add a slight excess of 5 per cent chloroplatinic acid. After a few minutes, remove the clear liquid from the precipitate, using a filter stick if necessary. Now devise a means for demonstrating the presence of sodium in the filtrate, and potassium and ammonium ions in the precipitate.

EXPERIMENT 24

TEST FOR COMMON ANIONS

(Reference: Chapter IX)

A. PROCEDURES

1. Halide ions. *a. Detection of chloride ion.* Add a small quantity of powdered potassium dichromate to a drop of the test solution on a slide. Taking the usual precautions, evaporate the drop to dryness. Add a small drop of concentrated sulfuric acid to the dried residue, and quickly place a glass ring [1] over the preparation. The reactants should be in the center of the circle. Place a 1½ × 1 inch slide bearing a hanging drop of water over the glass ring and allow the entire assembly to stand for about 10 minutes. If the original sample contained any chlorides, the mixture will react to form chromyl chloride. The latter is absorbed by the hanging drop of water and is subsequently hydrolyzed to yield hydrochloric acid and chromic acid, H_2CrO_4.

Eventually the hanging-drop slide is turned right side up, and the preparation is evaporated to dryness over a microflame. This expels the HCl but leaves a thin film of chromic acid. To detect the latter, cover the film with a droplet of water, after which add a tiny particle of silver nitrate. In the presence of chromic acid a reddish precipitate of silver chromate is formed. To obtain characteristic crystals of the latter, dissolve the precipitate by exposing to ammonia fumes. Later, as the NH_3 escapes from the solution, the crystals of silver chromate will separate.

If a glass ring is not available, the test can be performed in a microcrucible. In this case care must be exercised to prevent the assembly from toppling over when the crucible is covered with the slide which bears the hanging drop of water.

To insure the reliability of the chromyl chloride test, it is necessary to prevent any of the reagent potassium dichromate from finding its way into the hanging drop of water. (Why?)

---

[1] Some of the scientific supply houses are able to provide glass rings measuring about 18 mm in diameter and 7 mm in height. It is not advisable to use a ring which is less than 7 mm high.

b. Bromide ion. Place the test drop on a slide and render strongly acid by the addition of a drop of dilute sulfuric acid (approx. 1:4). Place a glass ring over the drop and cover the ring with a $1\frac{1}{2} \times 1$ inch slide which bears a hanging drop of a solution of *m*-phenylenediamine hydrochloride or a solution of aniline hydrochloride. Remove this slide momentarily to add a pinch of potassium dichromate to the reaction mixture on the lower slide and then replace. Any bromide ion in the test drop should be released as bromide. As the vapors of the latter diffuse into the hanging drop of reagent, characteristic crystals of the bromo derivative should be formed. The formation of these crystals can be observed through the microscope.

Just as in the test for chloride ion this reaction may also be carried out in a microcrucible if a glass ring is not available. When this substitution is made, the hanging-drop slide should be left on the crucible for 5 or 10 minutes before transferring to the microscope for inspection.

c. Iodide ion. Place the test drop which may contain iodide ion on a slide and add a few grains of potato starch, followed by a droplet of dilute acetic acid and a granule of sodium or potassium nitrite. Any iodine liberated during the reaction will promptly cause the starch grains to assume the characteristic lavender to blue or black color.

d. Fluoride ion. The silicon tetrafluoride, which is the intermediate compound formed in this test, is produced from the interaction of a fluoride, sulfuric acid, and a few grains of quartz or silica. Sand may be used, but it has been claimed that some sea sand contains fluorine.

Drop a small quantity of the solid sample, a few granules of crushed quartz or sand, and one or two drops of concentrated sulfuric acid into a microbeaker and promptly cover with a $1\frac{1}{2} \times 1$ inch slide carrying a hanging drop of water. If no reaction is apparent, warm the container briefly. At the end of 5 or 10 minutes, examine the hanging drop for a white precipitate, formed by the separation of silicic acid during the hydrolysis of silicon tetrafluoride. To confirm the test for fluorine, add a few granules of NaCl to the center of the preparation on the slide. Any fluosilicic acid present will then react to form characteristic crystals of the insoluble fluosilicate. The crystals may appear in the form of beautiful six-pointed stars, hexagonal plates, etc.

Instead of performing this test in a microbeaker it may be carried out in a microcrucible or in the special Feigl gas absorption tube.

2. Other anions. *a. Nitrate ion.* Cause one drop of the reagent, which is a solution of nitron in 30 per cent acetic acid, to flow into a drop of the test solution. Nitrates will cause the prompt formation of characteristic needles. Should the crystals leave any doubt concerning the presence of nitrate ion, remove the liquid portion by applying several wedges of filter paper, and then test the dry residue with diphenylamine reagent. If the nitrate radical was present, a deep blue color will be formed. The diphenylamine reagent is merely a solution of diphenylamine in concentrated sulfuric acid.

b. Sulfide ion. This test is readily performed by employing any type of micro gas chamber and a hanging drop of reagent. Apply a small drop of lead acetate solution to the center of a clean 1½ × 1 inch slide. Invert the slide and hold it over the mouth of a bottle of ammonium hydroxide until a white precipitate forms. To the sample drop in a microcrucible, add 2 or 3 drops of acetic acid, after which immediately cover the crucible with the prepared reagent slide. The release of hydrogen sulfide, indicating the presence of sulfide in the test drop, will be made manifest in the hanging drop by the appearance of a few dark specks of lead sulfide or by the darkening of the entire drop. Frequently a characteristic metallic sheen is produced. It should be observed that, in order to release the hydrogen sulfide, sufficient acid must be added to render the sample drop distinctly acidic.

3. Chromate and dichromate ions. When a drop of 2 per cent silver nitrate solution flows into a drop of solution which contains chromate ion or dichromate ion, a dark red precipitate is formed. Once it has been established that one of these ions is present, a new test drop is placed on another slide and tested with a drop of manganese acetate solution. The formation of a brown precipitate, gradually giving way to fine needle-like crystals and opaque particles, indicates the presence of chromate ion.

A solution of dichromate ion does not give rise to crystals when treated with manganese acetate. However, very dark particles may be observed in the preparation after most of the water has evaporated.

B. APPLICATIONS

1a. The student should familiarize himself with the several tests for halide ions by working on known solutions containing individual halides.

b. Determine whether a given sample of table salt has been "iodized."

c. Determine which halides are present in a sample of rock salt or ice-cream salt.

d. Obtain an "unknown" mixture from the instructor and analyze it for halide ions.

2a. Demonstrate the presence of nitrate radical in a "grain" of gunpowder.

b. Test minute samples of several depilatories for the presence of sulfides.

c. After performing the manganese acetate test on known specimens of chromate and dichromate, identify two "unknowns" furnished by the instructor.

EXPERIMENT 25

ALCOHOLS

(Reference: Chapter X)

IODOFORM REACTION

To carry out the iodoform test under the microscope the following special equipment should be provided.

1. A hanging-drop slide having a concavity at least 1.75 mm deep.
2. A flat-topped, steam hot plate or a metal heating block which can be maintained at 90–100°C.
3. Capillary pipets having an outside diameter of just about 1.5 mm.
4. A cooling block.

The sample consists of only 2 small drops as delivered from one of the capillary pipets. The latter are filled by capillary action rather than by suction. Holding the pipet in a nearly horizontal position, apply the tip to the surface of the liquid. The amount which flows into the tube can be readily controlled by varying the angle of inclination. A finger placed over the mouth of the pipet retains the liquid until released. When the finger is removed, not all of the liquid flows out of the pipet, even when the latter is in a vertical position. After a bit of practice, however, the analyst will be able to ascertain the correct amount of sample to take into the capillary in order that the desired 2-drop sample may be delivered.

To the sample on the reaction slide, add a pinch of anhydrous sodium carbonate. This is easily done by means of one of the small microspatulas marketed commercially, although a very convenient spatula for taking up an appropriate amount of the carbonate is made by flattening the end of a short length of 20-gage platinum wire. The latter may be sealed in the end of a glass tube, or it may be inserted in one of the conventional needle-holders used by bacteriologists.

In order partly to disperse the sodium carbonate in the liquid, rotate the slide, after which add, from a micropipet, 2 drops of a solution of iodine in potassium iodide. This reagent should be about 0.2N. At this stage it is important that none of the reactants be permitted to spread to the plane surface of the hanging-drop slide.

To prevent loss of the liquid by evaporation, place an ordinary micro-slide over the reaction mixture in such a manner as to leave a small opening to serve as a vent. Then carefully transfer the combination to a metal heating block (regenerating block) operating between 90–100°C, or to the water bath. The water in the latter should be boiling vigorously.

After 3 minutes, remove the slides to a cooling block. In the absence of a regulation cooling block a pile of glass plates may be used for the purpose.

After a short interval to allow the mixture to cool, carefully lift the upper slide from the reaction slide and invert. Examine this cover slide for microscopic crystals of iodoform which may have sublimed from the reaction mixture. As a rule the crystals resemble six-pointed "snow stars," but occasionally they may appear as thin hexagonal plates. While it is true that the crystals are frequently imperfect, they can always be identified as belonging to the hexagonal system.

If none of the iodoform has sublimed to the cover slide, the crystals can be found in the residual reaction mixture on the hanging-drop slide.

Students in chemical microscopy who have applied the foregoing procedure to "unknowns" containing not over 2 per cent of an appropriate organic ingredient have found it fully as reliable as most qualitative tests, even when working under the stress of a "practical" final examination.

Perform the iodoform test on dilute solutions of each of the following compounds.

Methanol
Ethanol
Methyl acetate (or ethyl acetate)
Acetone
Isopropyl alcohol
Two "unknowns" furnished by the instructor

EXPERIMENT 26

ALDEHYDES AND KETONES

(Reference: Chapter X)

A. REDUCTION OF TOLLENS' REAGENT

Tollens' ammoniacal silver nitrate solution may be prepared as follows. Dissolve one gram of silver nitrate in 5 ml of distilled water and 5 ml of concentrated ammonium hydroxide solution. Mix this solution with 10 ml of a 10 per cent solution of sodium hydroxide. If the reagent is to be kept for another day, it should be put in an amber-colored bottle and stored in a dark place. For reliable results the reagent should be comparatively fresh.

To perform the test under the microscope, place a small drop of sample on a small piece of filter paper on a slide. The paper may measure about

5 × 10 mm; one side should present a ragged torn boundary rather than a clean-cut edge. The drop of sample should not flood the paper and overflow to the slide.

Apply one drop of the Tollens' reagent to the paper. The preparation is protected with a clean cover glass and set aside for about 10 minutes. In the presence of an appropriate reducing agent (viz. aldehyde) the silver in the complex ion is transformed to the metallic state. The latter will be in the form of very finely divided black particles. With an abundance of reducing agent there will be a copious black deposit, readily visible to the unaided eye. With very dilute solutions of reducing agents the particles of silver can be detected by the microscope.

B. SODIUM BISULFITE ADDITION PRODUCT

The reagent for this preparation is made by adding 2 ml of ordinary ethyl alcohol to 8 ml of a cold, saturated aqueous solution of sodium bisulfite. Should a precipitate form, the solution is filtered or centrifuged.

To perform the sodium bisulfite test on a microscopic scale, place a drop of the reagent beside a test drop on a slide. By means of a glass thread, run the two drops together. If crystals fail to appear spontaneously, stir the preparation vigorously with a glass thread.

The crystalline addition product formed with an aldehyde or ketone can be made to release the carbonyl compound by treating with a solution of sodium carbonate.

C. NITROPHENYLHYDRAZONES

Aldehydes and ketones, even in very dilute solutions, are readily detected by the formation of their corresponding nitrophenylhydrazones. Although any of the isomeric nitrophenylhydrazines may be employed, Fisher and Moor [1] consider the para compound as the most satisfactory reagent in general. The reagent is prepared by saturating a 15 per cent solution of acetic acid with the solid nitrophenylhydrazine. Preferably it should be used the same day, although it may give results even on the third day. None but glass stoppers should be used on bottles in which this reagent is kept.

To perform a test, put a drop or two of unknown sample into a microbeaker which measures about 1 cm in height. Then invert a clean slide (preferably the 1½ × 1 inch size) bearing a drop of the reagent solution over the beaker. Warm the beaker slightly to vaporize any aldehyde or ketone present. A convenient method for warming the beaker is to place the whole assembly on the flat top of a small water bath or on a metal heating block which is maintained at a temperature not in excess of 100°C. As the vaporized aldehyde or ketone rises to the hanging drop of

[1] R. Fisher and A. Moor, *Mikrochemie* 15, 74–86 (1934).

reagent, the hydrazone formation takes place. This requires a rather brief period. In some cases the crystalline hydrazones may separate from the solution only after cooling for 10 or 15 minutes, but generally their formation can be observed while the heating is in progress.

To identify, it will be necessary to obtain the melting point of the hydrazone. Wash the crystals with a few successive drops of water and quickly dry. The melting point should then be determined on individual crystals, not on aggregates. This is done on a Kofler stage, by heating rapidly until within about 10° of the anticipated value. From this point the rate of increase is retarded to about 5° per minute. This is further retarded so that it is barely 2° per minute at the actual melting point. A preliminary run may be desirable in order to apply the required control during the accepted melting point determination.

Satisfactory results have been obtained with water solutions of the following compounds: acetone, acetyl acetone, diacetone alcohol, isophorone, n-butyraldehyde, benzaldehyde, glyoxal, salicylaldehyde, and diacetyl.

Fisher and Moor [2] give the following melting points for p-nitrophenylhydrazones.

Compound	*M.P. (°C) of p-Nitrophenylhydrazone*
Formaldehyde	181
Acetaldehyde	142
Acrolein	157
Isovaleraldehyde	105
Propionaldehyde	124 after subliming (otherwise 112)
Crotonaldehyde	183–184 (not sharp)
Benzaldehyde	192
Furfural	127
Salicylaldehyde	226
Anisaldehyde	160–161
Vanillin	220 (approx.)
Acetone	148
Acetophenone	183–184

D. PHENYLOSAZONES

In order to adapt this reaction to the microslide it will be necessary to provide the latter with a shallow reaction cell. Of two simple methods, the author prefers the following one.

Cut a paper ring measuring 18 mm in outside diameter and approximately 14 mm inside diameter by means of cork drills of appropriate size. After spreading a thin layer of Dow-Corning stopcock grease on a slide, press the paper ring into the grease by means of a needle. Having coated one side of the ring, turn it over so that the opposite side can be coated.

[2] *Ibid.*

By means of a clean needle transfer the coated ring to the center of a clean microscope slide. To insure good contact between the slide and the greased ring, press a needle against the ring at several points. When fixing the ring to the slide, it is necessary to avoid getting grease on that area of the slide bounded by the inner edge of the paper ring. This means the ring must be dropped directly into its final position on the slide. Once the ring has lodged on the slide, it should not be moved sidewise since this, in effect, will apply grease to the floor of the microreaction cell.

To perform the osazone test, place 1 droplet of test solution and 2 droplets of reagent within the area bounded by the paper ring. The reagent solution is prepared by dissolving 1.4 grams of phenylhydrazine hydrochloride and 2.1 grams of sodium acetate in 10 ml distilled water, warming if necessary. The test solution should contain several per cent of the unknown. A 2½ per cent solution of glucose, for example, gives a good test. If preferred, the sample to be tested may be in the form of a few minute particles of solid instead of a drop of solution. Since the available space is rather restricted, the total volume of the reaction mixture must be correspondingly small. Introduction of droplets of proper magnitude is facilitated by using capillary pipets measuring 1.0 to 1.2 mm in outside diameter.

The reactants may be mixed by stirring with a glass thread, but generally this is unnecessary. An 18-mm circular cover slip is carefully dropped on the greased paper ring. Light pressure applied by a needle at several points along the periphery of the cover will effect a tight seal. If properly prepared, this microreaction cell does not lose any vapor during a 40-minute heating period on a gently boiling water bath or on a metal heating block operating at 90–100°C. If 1½ × 1 inch slides are used, the cells can be heated directly on the Kofler warm stage, thus permitting constant observation of the preparation until the first osazone crystals appear. It is quite convenient, however, to detect the time of appearance of the crystals by means of a hand lens.

With proper care, the quantity of crystalline product is adequate to permit washing and recrystallization from 50 per cent ethanol, so that a subsequent melting point determination can be performed on a Kofler stage. When working with sugars, however, the analyst is more generally interested in determining the time required for the osazones to separate from the hot reaction mixture. Assuming that the sugar concentration is the same in all tests, osazones separate from hot reaction mixtures in the following order.

1. Mannose (hydrazone instead of osazone).
2. Levulose.
3. Dextrose.

4. Xylose.
5. Arabinose.
6. Galactose.
7. Sucrose (osazone forms only after hydrolysis).
8. Raffinose.

The osazones formed by lactose and maltose are soluble in hot water and therefore separate only when the mixture is allowed to cool.

In an alternate method, which some workers may prefer, the sidewall of the reaction cell consists entirely of silicone stopcock grease. The ring of grease is readily applied to the slide by means of an appropriate "stamp." The latter merely consists of a thin cork ring which has been glued or cemented to a convenient support, such as a small block of wood or a cork stopper. The ring should have an outside diameter of 18 mm, while the inside diameter may measure 14 or 15 mm. This device is pressed into a thin layer of Dow-Corning stopcock grease and then is applied to a clean slide. Thus, by using it like a rubber stamp the silicone rings can be applied very quickly. In stamping the rings excess pressure must be avoided so that the depth of the cell will not be too shallow. Osazone formation is carried out according to the same procedure described previously.

E. APPLICATIONS

1. Following the procedure given in part A, carry out the reduction of Tollens' reagent on minute droplets of very dilute solutions of several known compounds. Determine whether aqueous solutions of the following give positive tests.

Benzaldehyde   Acetone
Vinegar n-Butyraldehyde

2. Report the effect of Tollens' reagent on four unknowns furnished by the instructor.

3. Following the procedure described in part B, prepare sodium bisulfite addition products of the following:

Benzaldehyde
Acetaldehyde (aqueous solution)
Acetone (2 per cent aqueous solution)
Formalin (dilute with about 8 volumes of water)

4. Dissolve a drop of benzaldehyde in the required volume of water. Placing 1 or 2 drops of this clear solution in a microbeaker, cover the latter with a slide bearing a hanging drop of p-nitrophenylhydrazine reagent and proceed as directed in part C.

When a residue appears in the reagent drop, turn the slide right side up and examine the hydrazone crystals under the microscope.

If a Kofler stage is available, and if time permits, determine the melting point of the hydrazone.

5. Perform the nitrophenylhydrazone test on several unknowns furnished by the instructor. In your report indicate which of these are aldehydes. (*Note:* Take advantage of their behavior with Tollens' reagent or Fehling's reagent.)

6. Prepare three micro reaction cells as described in part D of this experiment. Using 3 per cent solutions of glucose, fructose, and an unknown (provided by the instructor), perform the osazone test on each. Heating should be accomplished by laying the slides on the dry surface of a simple water bath or on a metal heating block maintained at 90–100°C. Observing the number of minutes required for osazones to appear in the cells containing the known sugars, determine whether the unknown is glucose or fructose.

If time permits, wash one of these osazone preparations with 2 successive drops of water, recrystallize from a few drops of 50 per cent alcohol, and determine the melting point on the Kofler stage.

EXPERIMENT 27

PHENOLIC COMPOUNDS

(Reference: Chapter X)

A. REAGENTS

The palladium chloride, chlorauric acid, and chloroplatinic acid used in this experiment should be in the form of approximately 2 per cent solutions. The ferric chloride solution may be 1 per cent or 0.5 per cent, and should be freshly prepared. All of these reagents are applied by placing one drop close to a drop of the test solution, which is then caused to flow into the reagent by means of a glass needle. Bromine, in the form of bromine water, may be applied in the same manner. The various hydroxy compounds being tested with the foregoing reagents should be in the form of aqueous solutions.

Although the conversion of phenols into *a*-naphthylurethanes is not a slide reaction and does not yield crystals which can be identified by mere appearance, it may be worth while to become familiar with the test if time permits. It is preferable to purchase the reagent in small units, such as 25 grams, so that the bulk of the supply need not be exposed to the atmospheric moisture too long. Although water does not interfere as much as it does with phenylisocyanate, for example, prolonged exposure *can* exert an effect. In this test the dry phenolic compounds should be employed.

B. PROCEDURES AND APPLICATIONS

1. If only a very limited amount of time can be assigned to the phenols, the test checked in the following table may suffice to impart a general impression of the behavior of this group.

Compound	Br–Water	Ferric Chloride	Palladium Chloride	Chlorauric Acid
Phenol	X	X	X	
Catechol*	X	X		
Resorcinol	X	X		
Hydroquinone		X		X
Pyrogallol	X	X	X	X
Phloroglucinol				
α-Naphthol			X	
β-Naphthol			X	

* After observing the color change caused by the reaction of catechol with ferric chloride, a small quantity of powdered sodium bicarbonate should be added to the preparation on the slide. Record the new color observed.

2. To prepare an α-naphthylurethane, mix 1 or 2 drops of the reagent and about half as much of the phenol in a small tube, such as a 3-inch test tube. After heating just at the boiling point (over a micro flame) for about 1 minute, set the preparation aside to cool and solidify. Should the mixture fail to solidify, even after scratching the inner walls of the tube with a thin glass rod, it may be necessary to heat for an additional period. Finally, to remove the urethane from the solid reaction product, shake the product with several successive portions of boiling ligroin. When working with small quantities these ligroin extracts are allowed to evaporate in a small (25-mm) watch glass, whereupon the crystalline urethanes will be deposited.

EXPERIMENT 28

CRYSTALLINE DERIVATIVES OF AMINES

(Reference: Chapter X)

A. SPECIAL REAGENTS

Among the common reagents for use with amines are saturated aqueous picric acid, dilute aqueous auric chloride solution (2–5 per cent), dilute aqueous platinic chloride and a 0.02-molar solution of 3,5-dinitrobenzoic acid in absolute alcohol. This may be prepared by dissolving about 1 gram (more precisely, 1.06 gram) of the dinitrobenzoic acid in 25 ml of alcohol.

Another interesting reagent is α-naphthylisocyanate. This should not be purchased in large containers unless the reagents will be used within a short time.

B. PROCEDURES

1. To test with aqueous picric acid, gold chloride, and platinic chloride, dissolve in dilute acetic acid (20–25 per cent). Good tests are generally obtained on solutions containing 1 or 2 per cent of the amine. In many instances the crystalline derivatives are obtained even when the amine concentration is much lower. With the three reagents just mentioned the tests are generally performed by allowing a reagent drop to flow into a test drop.

2. The formation of 3,5-dinitrobenzoates from many amines is very easily performed directly on the slide. To perform a test, place a small particle of the solid amine (possibly 2 mg) on a clean slide and cover with 1 or 2 drops of absolute alcohol. (If the amine is a liquid, a very small droplet can be applied to the slide by means of a fine-tipped glass rod.) If the sample does not dissolve promptly, solution may be facilitated by stirring with a glass needle. After the sample has gone into solution, apply 1 drop of the dinitrobenzoic acid solution. The resulting derivatives will gradually crystallize out of the solution. If a small quantity of the product is desired for a melting point determination, it would be advisable to treble the amounts of the reactants used. After allowing the preparation to evaporate to near dryness, wash in 2 small portions of alcohol to remove any excess reagent. Finally, recrystallize the product from warm alcohol (or other appropriate solvent), dry, and transfer to a capillary tube or a Kofler hot stage.

3. To prepare amine derivatives of α-naphthylisocyanate, place a small sample of the amine on a slide and treat with a drop of the reagent. If the derivative is desired for a melting point determination, treat the preparation with a few portions of ligroin to remove any byproduct.

C. APPLICATIONS

1. Test α-naphthylamine and β-naphthylamine with the picric acid, gold chloride, platinic chloride, and 3,5-dinitrobenzoic acid reagent. Which test could be applied in distinguishing between the two isomers?

2. Perform all of the tests described in part B on pyridine, quinoline, and α-picoline.

3. Which of the five reagents give positive tests with the following?

Acetamide

Thioacetamide

Urea

Benzidine

Thiodiphenylamine

Dimethylaniline

Acetanilide

EXPERIMENT 29

XANTHYL DERIVATIVES OF AMIDES

(Reference: Chapter X)

A. XANTHYDROL REAGENT

Dissolve 0.5 gram of xanthydrol in a solvent consisting of 5 ml ethyl alcohol, 2 ml glacial acetic acid, and 3 ml water. After thorough agitation, centrifuge the preparation or allow to stand overnight. Only the clear solution should be used. The reagent may deteriorate in time but appears to keep for a few months.

B. PROCEDURE

The reaction should be carried out in a closed microcell. This is especially true for those preparations which must stand for some time at room temperature or which are to be heated. To form such a cell, apply a circle of silicone stopcock grease to a clean slide as directed in Experiment 26D. Place a small quantity of the amide inside the circle. About 2–2.5 mg will be required, and the sample should be finely powdered if possible. Cover the amide with 1 drop of the xanthydrol reagent, and, after the liquid has spread somewhat, cover the cell with a cover slip. After a few minutes, examine the preparation under the 16-mm objective. If no crystals have formed by the expiration of 5 or 10 minutes, the process may be hastened by placing the slide on a water bath for 5 minutes. If desired, of course, it is entirely permissible to place the assembly on the water bath as soon as the cover glass has been placed over the cell. It is doubtful whether heating should be prolonged beyond 5, or at most 10, minutes. If a prompt result is not essential, the labeled assembly may be set aside overnight, which should be ample time for the derivatives of most amides to separate.

If it is desired to determine the melting point, as on a hot stage, the product should be rid of the mother liquor and then recrystallized from 65 per cent dioxane-water solution. Finally the crystals should be dried in an oven at 80° for approximately 10 minutes.

C. APPLICATIONS

Prepare the xanthydryl derivatives of the following at room temperature.

Acetamide   Urea
n-Butyramide or n-Valeramide   Thiourea

Which derivative separates first?
Which requires the longest period?

EXPERIMENT 30

SULFA DRUGS

(Reference: Chapter X)

A. SPECIAL REAGENTS

1. The picrolonic acid reagent is practically a saturated solution in 95 per cent ethanol. Keenan [1] recommends a 1 per cent solution of the solid in 95 per cent alcohol. If any residue remains after a reasonable time has elapsed, the preparation should be filtered to obtain a clear solution.

2. The chlorauric acid solution suggested by the same author [2] consists of 1 gram gold chloride in 20 ml of water.

B. PROCEDURES

1. Sulfapyridine. Place a very small quantity (considerably less than 1 mg) of powdered sample on a clean slide, and then cover with 1 drop of the 1 per cent alcoholic picrolonic acid solution. Apply cover slip and examine the preparation through the 16-mm objective and 10-$\times$ eyepiece. In the presence of sulfapyridine fine yellow needles separate in the form of rosettes.

For use with the chlorauric acid reagent, stir approximately 1 mg of the crushed solid sample into 1 drop of acetone and 2 drops of water on a slide. Although some residue remains, sufficient solid will dissolve to give a test. Place a drop of reagent adjacent to the test drop, and then draw into the margin of the solution by means of a fine glass rod or thread. When the preparation (without a cover glass is examined at a magnification of 100–150-$\times$, the presence of sulfapyridine is indicated

---

[1] *J. Assoc. Official Agr. Chem.* **25**, 830 (1942).
[2] *Ibid.* **24** (1941).

by the formation of yellow rods, blades, and X-shaped aggregates. Beautiful polarization colors are observed when the latter are placed between crossed Nicols or crossed Polaroids.

The reaction with picric acid enables one to distinguish between sulfapyridine and its sodium salt. For this purpose stir less than a milligram of powdered sample into 2 drops of 50 per cent alcohol on a slide. Promptly add a fragment of crystalline picric acid to the solution and immediately protect the preparation by a cover slip. In the presence of the sulfapyridine sodium salt fine, long, yellow crystals will develop. There may be clusters or rosettes. Sulfapyridine itself will not react.

2. Sulfathiazole. With picrolonic acid this drug yields crystals resembling those formed by sulfapyridine. The picric acid test yields long, fine, yellow needles, some of which may be curved. Dense rosettes may appear, as may also short stout rods.

When a drop of 95 per cent alcohol is added to a pinch of sulfathiazole on a slide, part of the sample will be recrystallized to yield characteristic prisms and hexagonal plates.

The chlorauric acid test yields no crystals with sulfathiazole, but an amorphous debris is thrown down by the reagent.

3. Sulfanilamide. With alcoholic picrolonic acid this drug does not yield any crystals, thereby differing from sulfapyridine and sulfathiazole.

In performing the picric acid test on sulfanilamide, Scudi [3] has suggested the following procedure.

Evaporate 1 drop of concentrated hydrochloric acid and 1 drop of a sulfanilamide solution to dryness, thus obtaining the hydrochloride, which melts at 235–237°. Treat this solid residue on the slide with a small drop of saturated aqueous picric acid solution. If sulfanilamide was present in the original sample, the picrate should now separate in the form of long, yellow needles, melting at 179–180°. This procedure should give a positive test for the drug on a single drop of solution in which the sulfanilamide concentration equals as much as 0.03 per cent.

Another test recommended by Scudi is the formation of acetylsulfanilamide. Cover a few small crystals of the drug or suspected sample with a drop of acetic anhydride. It may help if the mixture is stirred with a glass thread, but no heat should be applied. In due time the acetylsulfanilamide will be seen to separate in the form of sheaves of long needles. If care is exercised the crystals can be washed with ether, after which the slide is placed in a desiccator to permit the preparation to dry. The acetylsulfanilamide melts at 214°.

Although the chlorauric acid reagent does not yield characteristic crystals with sulfanilamide, there is a reaction, including the separation of a yellow, oily liquid.

[3] *Ind. Eng. Chem., Anal. Ed.* **10**, 346 (1938).

C. APPLICATIONS

1. Perform the various tests already outlined on known samples provided by the instructor.

2. Try the picric acid test on a small sample of sulfapyridine.

Suspend a second portion of sulfapyridine in 2 or 3 drops of water on a slide. While stirring the liquid with a glass needle, cautiously add some 5 per cent aqueous NaOH from a fine capillary pipet until most (or all) of the solid passes into solution. After transferring 1 or 2 drops of the clear solution of sodium sulfapyridine to a clean slide, the water should be expelled by heating on a water bath. Now perform the picric acid test on the residue. How does the behavior of the sulfapyridine differ from that of its sodium salt?

3. Identify two unknowns provided by the instructor.

EXPERIMENT 31

OBSERVATION OF FLUORESCENCE

(Reference: Chapter X)

The source of ultraviolet light may be a carbon arc or a Hanovia mercury arc ultraviolet lamp. Because of the heat generated the carbon arc should be provided with a suitable heat-absorbing filter. It will also be necessary to filter out the visible spectrum. In the case of the Hanovia lamp a Corning glass filter No. 5840, three mm thick will serve the purpose. For the carbon arc lamp the glass filter may have to measure 5 mm in thickness. The ultraviolet source should be tilted to permit the rays to fall on the stage of the microscope stage directly below the objective. Although radiation above 3650A is not considered especially harmful, direct exposure of the eyes should be avoided.

If quartz slides are not available, the glass slides to be used with ultraviolet light should first be tested for excessive fluorescence which would interfere with the observations. Scratches should be absent. Improperly cleaned slides, i.e., those with thin films of oil or soap adhering to the surface, may exhibit sufficient fluorescence to render them unsuited for the present purpose.

Although observations on fluorescence must be made in a darkened room it will be found desirable to have a dim lamp (for example a 7-watt bulb) some distance away from the microscope. The latter should be shielded from the lamp by means of a large square of cardboard or other suitable barrier. Before darkening the room the microscope should first be focused on a specimen in ordinary light so that only minor adjustments need be made when working with the ultraviolet. When all is in readiness extinguish the main room lights, turn on the ultraviolet source, and wait for a short time to permit the eyes to become adjusted to the darkness. To observe a given specimen merely place the slide under the objective and complete the focusing by means of the fine adjustment.

Using an 8-mm objective if possible (otherwise a 16-mm) examine small crystals of the following compounds. After the name of each compound in the table state the color of the fluorescence and indicate the relative brilliance. To express the latter use a scale ranging from x for the most feeble fluorescence to xxxx for the maximum brilliance observed.

Substance	Fluorescence color	Brilliance
Anthracene		
Dextrose		
Sucrose		
Urea (or urea nitrate)		
Phenanthrene		
Anthraquinone		
Strychnine		
Quinine		
Quinine sulfate		
Quinine salicylate		
Uranyl acetate (or nitrate)		
Lithium salicylate		
Strontium salicylate		
Salicylic acid		
Sodium salicylate		
Sulfathiazole		
Sulfapyridine		
Sulfanilamide		
Sulfaguanidine		

Some other substances the student may wish to examine include rosin, soap, uranium oxide, fluorite, drops of motor oil, olive oil, milk, etc.

With a sharp razor blade shave off an extremely thin section of cork. Lay this on a slide and observe the structure as revealed by fluorescence. Note the color and the intensity of the fluorescence.

In a similar manner obtain a very thin section of a small woody twig. (From a growing plant.) Examine for fluorescence. Next immerse the section in dilute primuline dye for several minutes. After removing the dye by rinsing the section in water repeat the examination for fluorescence. Is there any pattern apparent?

EXPERIMENT 32

ISOQUINOLINE IN CHEMICAL MICROSCOPY

(Reference: Chapter X)

A. REAGENTS

For use in chemical microscopy it is desirable to have the isoquinoline-thiocyanate reagent 0.2 M in respect to isoquinoline hydrochloride and 0.4 or 0.5 M in respect to thiocyanate. To prevent gradual separation of part of the solute, which may result at this concentration, it is advisable to work with a fresh reagent prepared from the following stock solutions.

1. 1 M ammonium thiocyanate solution.

2. 0.4 M isoquinoline hydrochloride solution, made by dissolving 26 g. of isoquinoline in 200 ml of 1 N hydrochloric acid, and diluting to 500 ml with distilled water.

Prepare the actual analytical reagent by mixing equal volumes of the two stock solutions a short time before using. This may involve merely a few drops of each, or a larger volume if needed.

B. PROCEDURE

To test for zinc ion, let a small drop of the prepared reagent flow into a droplet of dilute test solution on a slide. In the presence of various zinc salts, including the acetate, chloride, sulfate, and nitrate, characteristic crystals and clusters will separate. With zinc acetate, for example, good tests have been obtained on solutions containing 1 part zinc in 15,000. Nitrate ion appears to decrease the sensitivity of the test.

The test for cadmium is performed in the same manner, but the preparation should be observed with an 8-mm objective on account of the small dimensions of the crystals. Because of the lower sensitivity of this test the cadmium concentration should not be less than 1 part in 2,000.

The test for cobalt is rather intriguing. As a rule, very soon after the reagent is applied a blue oil-like liquid begins to separate, especially along the edge of the preparation. Gradually beautiful blue prisms and clusters develop, the length of time required depending upon the concentration of cobalt ion, the temperature, and (probably) upon the kind of anion present. Although the actual form of the crystals may vary in different trials, this is no handicap; the blue color itself is characteristic of cobalt. In cobalt chloride solutions satisfactory tests are obtained with the Co concentration as low as 1 part in 4,000. In sulfate solutions the sensitivity is reduced approximately one-half.

C. APPLICATIONS

1. Using approximately $M/50$ solutions, perform the isoquinoline-thiocyanate test on samples containing the acetate or chloride of zinc, cadmium, copper, and cobalt respectively. Compare the resulting microcrystals with the illustrations shown in Chapter X. Repeat the test on a $M/20$ solution of nickel chloride.

2. Prepare a sample by mixing one drop each of the cobalt and copper test solutions used in part 1. Perform the isoquinoline-thiocyanate test on one drop of the mixture. You should be able to detect both metals.

3. Perform the test on a sample prepared from equal volumes of the zinc and cadmium test solution. How do the resulting crystals compare with those which separated from solutions containing only one of these two cations? Could this test be used to identify a mixture of zinc and cadmium ions?

4. Alnico magnets contain not only iron, but also aluminum, cobalt, and nickel. Given a minute particle of this alloy, devise a procedure for demonstrating the presence of cobalt by means of the isoquinoline-thiocyanate reagent. Recall that ferric ion yields a deep red solution and dark crystals with this reagent As a clue, check on the relative solubilities of ferric oxalate and cobaltous oxalate.

5. Identify the cations in several appropriate unknowns containing Zn, Cd, Co, Cu, or Ni.

CONDENSED BIBLIOGRAPHY

Books

1. Allen, R. M., *The Microscope*, D. Van Nostrand, 1940.
2. Beck, Conrad, *The Microscope*, R. &. J. Beck (London), 1938.
3. Benedetti-Pichler, A. A., *Introduction to the Microtechnique of Inorganic Analysis*, John Wiley & Sons, 1942.
4. Brown, Thomas B., *Foundations of Modern Physics*, John Wiley & Sons, 2nd ed., 1949.
   This book contains interesting discussions on optics, polarized light, etc.
5. Todd, J. C., and Sanford, A. H., *Clinical Diagnosis by Laboratory Methods*, 11th ed., Saunders, 1948.
6. Chamot, E. M., and Mason, C. W., *Handbook of Chemical Microscopy*, 2nd ed., John Wiley & Sons, 1938.
   This two-volume set is sometimes referred to as the chemical microscopist's "bible". Volume I describes a variety of apparatus and general techniques. Volume II describes a large number of inorganic tests. The latter are illustrated with photomicrographs.
7. Clark, Walter, *Photomicrography by Infrared*, John Wiley & Sons, 1946.
8. Dake, H. C., and De Ment, Jack, *Fluorescent Light and Its Applications*. Chemical Publishing Co., Inc., 1941.
   Includes brief, simple discussions regarding applications in chemistry, criminology, medicine, microscopy, etc.
9. De Ment, Jack, *Fluorochemistry*, Chemical Publishing Co., Inc., 1945.
   A study of both theory and applications. Includes tables of data and a bibliography of several hundred references.
10. Emich, F., and Schneider, F., *Microchemical Laboratory Manual*, John Wiley & Sons, 1932.
    This work includes a number of techniques which do not belong to the field of microscopy, but which may be quite useful to the microscopist.
11. Fry, W. H., "Petrographic Methods for Soil Laboratories," *U. S. Department of Agriculture, Technical Bulletin No. 344* (1933).
12. Glick, David, *Techniques of Histo- and Cyto-Chemistry*, Interscience Publishers, Inc., 1949.
    Pages 99–108 present a brief but interesting discussion of fluorescence microscopy.
13. Hartshorne, N. A., and Stuart, A., *Crystals and the Polarizing Microscope*, Longmans, Green & Co., Inc., London, 1950.
14. Johannsen, Albert, *Manual of Petrographic Methods*, McGraw-Hill, 1918.
    This book includes descriptions of a number of general techniques and descriptions of interesting older microscope models.
15. Johns, J. B., *Laboratory Manual of Microchemistry*, Burgess Publishing Co. (Minneapolis), 1941.

16. Kofler, Ludwig, and Kofler, Adelheid, *Mikromethoden zur Kennzeichnung organischer Stoffe und Stoffgemische*, Universitätsverlag Wagner, G.m.b.H., Innsbruck, Austria, 1948.

   An important book for those interested in the techniques based on the Kofler micro hot stage.

17. Larsen, E. S., and Berman, Harry, "Microscopic Determination of the Nonopaque Minerals," *U. S. Geological Survey, Bulletin No. 848* (1934).

18. Lindsley, L. C., *Industrial Microscopy*, Wm. Byrd Press, 1929.

   This includes an interesting outline of the chemical microscopy of ten common alkaloids, as well as sections on natural fibers and commercial starches.

19. Munoz, F. J., and Charipper, H. A., *The Microscope and Its Use*, Chemical Publishing Co., 1943.

20. Pringsheim, Peter, *Fluorescence and Phosphorescence*, Interscience Publishers, Inc., 1949.

   A detailed presentation of the general subject, although not concerned with microscopy. Bibliography of approximately 2000 references.

21. Radley, J. A., and Grant, Julius, *Fluorescence Analysis in Ultra-Violet Light*, D. Van Nostrand Co., Inc., 1939.

   An interesting discussion of the theory, techniques, and applications in various fields.

22. Shillaber, C. P., *Photomicrography in Theory and Practice*, John Wiley & Sons, 1944.

   Very comprehensive.

23. Short, M. N., "Microscopic Determination of the Ore Minerals," 2nd ed., *U. S. Geological Survey, Bulletin No. 914* (1940).

24. Stephenson, C. H., *Some Microchemical Tests for Alkaloids*, J. B. Lippincott Co., (London & Phila.), 1921.

25. Wallis, T. E., *Analytical Microscopy*, Arnold & Co. (London), 1923.

   Includes various quantitative methods.

26. Welcher, F. J., *Organic Analytical Reagents* (four volumes), D. Van Nostrand Co., Inc., 1947–1948.

   Microchemical tests are suggested under many of the reagents. Extensive lists of references included.

27. Winchell, A. N., *Elements of Optical Mineralogy*, John Wiley & Sons, 1937.

28. Yagoda, Herman, *Radioactive Measurements With Nuclear Emulsions*, John Wiley & Sons, 1949.

   The techniques described in this volume show how the microscopist can utilize modern photographic emulsions to carry out quantitative radioactive measurements.

29. Eastman Kodak Company, *Photomicrography*.

30. Eastman Kodak Company, *Photography of Colored Objects*.

31. "Microanalysis of Food and Drug Products," Federal Security Agency, *Food and Drug Circular No. 1* (1944). (A book of approximately 170 pages.)

Papers

The perusal of various journals, especially "Analytical Chemistry," "The Analyst," and "Mikrochemie-Mikrochimica Acta" will reveal numerous papers dealing with chemical microscopy as applied to a wide variety of special fields. The worker who is interested in alkaloids, for example, will find a very comprehensive paper by W. F. Whitmore and C. A. Wood on the "Chemical Microscopy of Some Toxicologically Important Alkaloids" in Mikrochemie-Mikrochimica Acta

22, 249–334 (1939). Some other papers which should prove interesting are given below.

1. Alber, H. K., and Rodden, C. J., Microchemical analysis of colored specks and crystalline occlusions in soap bars, *Industrial & Engineering Chemistry, Analytical Edition* **10,** 47 (1938).
2. Allen, R. P., Technical microscopy in the rubber industry, *Ibid.* **14,** 740 (1942).
3. Arceneaux, C. J., Microscopic analysis of benzene hexachloride, *Analytical Chemistry* **23,** 906 (1951).
4. Benedetti-Pichler, A. A., and Cefola, M., Qualitative analysis of microgram samples, *Industrial & Engineering Chemistry, Analytical Edition* **15,** 227 (1943).
   This paper deals with the hydrogen sulfide group.
5. Benedetti-Pichler, A. A., Crowell, W. R., and Donahoe, C., Qualitative separations on a micro scale: separations in the alkaline earth group, *Ibid.* **11,** 117 (1939).
6. Bernstein, J. M., Microscopical identification of ultramarine blue in complex pigment mixtures, *Ibid.* **17,** 262 (1945).
7. Brubaker, D. G., Light and electron microscopy of pigments, *Ibid.* **17,** 184 (1945).
8. Buehler, C., Currier, E. J., and Lawrence, R., Identification of amines as 3,5-dinitrobenzoates, *Ibid.* **5,** 277 (1933).
9. Clark, G. L., and Tso, Tsong-Chi, Determination of persulfate in acid solution, *Ibid.* **21,** 874 (1949).
   A crystalline product is formed by the Zwikker reagent.
10. Clark, G. L., and Gross, S. T., Technique and applications of industrial microradiography, *Ibid.* **14,** 676 (1942).
11. Crossmon, G. C., Microscopical distinction of corundum among its natural and artificial associates, *Ibid.* **20,** 976 (1948).
12. Dollman, D. V., A simply constructed camera for use in photomicrography, *Chemist-Analyst* **38,** 80 (1949).
13. Donnay, J. D. H., and O'Brien, W. A., Microscope goniometry, *Ibid.* **17,** 593 (1945).
    The procedure requires a microscope provided with a graduated rotating stage.
14. Eisenberg, W. V., and Keenan, G. L., Microscopic identification of sodium and potassium by means of their crystalline picrolonates, *Journal of the Association of Official Agricultural Chemists* **27,** 177 (1944).
15. Exton, W. G., Quantitative microscopic urinalysis, *Journal of Laboratory and Clinical Medicine* **15,** 386 (1930).
16. Farrow, C. A., Hamly, D. H., and Smith, E. A., Phenolic resin glue line as found in yellow birch plywood, *Industrial and Engineering Chemistry, Analytical Edition* **18,** 307 (1946).
    Describes a procedure for rapid analysis of the glue line structure.
17. Feldstein, M., Klendshoj, N. C., and Sprague, A., 2-Anthraquinone sulfonate derivatives of morphine and codeine, *Ibid.* **21,** 174 (1949).
18. Ferris, S. W., and Cowles, H. C., Crystal behavior of paraffin wax, *Industrial and Engineering Chemistry* **37,** 1054 (1945).
19. Fischer, R., and Langhammer, T., Identification of metals (as salts) by the refractive index of precipitates obtained with organic reagents, *Mikrochemie-Mikrochimica Acta* **34,** 208 (1949).
    The method described uses a Kofler hot stage to find the temperature at which refractive index of a precipitate matches that of appropriate embedding liquid, as methylene iodide, which must first be standardized.
20. Foster, L. V., Microscope optics, *Analytical Chemistry* **21,** 432 (1949).

A review of developments in equipment for microscopy involving ultraviolet light, infrared light, and fluorescence.

21. Garner, W., Inorganic microanalysis, *Industrial Chemist* **4**, 357 (1928).
Very general.

22. Goetz-Luthy, N., Fusion analysis, a rapid method for identification of organic compounds, *Journal of Chemical Education* **26**, 159 (1949).

23. Goldbaum, Leo, Fractional sublimation on a removable transparent film, *Analytical Chemistry* **22**, 600 (1950).
This paper describes a method for the separation of micro quantities of mixtures. Shows the possibility of separating a mixture of caffeine and benzoic acid, or a mixture of phenobarbituric, acetylsalicylic, and salicylic acids, etc.

24. Goldstone, N. I., Chemicotoxicological examination of foods, *Ibid.* **21**, 781 (1949).
In this paper only the alkaloids involve microscopy.

25. Grabar, D. G., and McCrone, W. C., Application of microscopic fusion methods to inorganic compounds, *Journal of Chemical Education* **27**, 649 (1950).

26. Hassid, W. Z., and McCready, R. M., Identification of sugars by the microscopic appearance of crystalline osazones, *Industrial & Engineering Chemistry, Analytical Edition* **14**, 683 (1942).
Shows 20 photomicrographs.

27. Hauser, E. A., Polaroid Land Camera, *Journal of Chemical Education* **26**, 224 (1949).

28. Hauser, E. A., and le Beau, D. S., Microscopic studies of lyogels — Illumination by incident light, *Industrial & Engineering Chemistry* **37**, 786 (1945).
A method for observing ultramicroscopic particles.

29. Hubach, C. E., and Jones, F. T., Methadon hydrochloride, *Analytical Chemistry* **22**, 595 (1950).
Twelve photomicrographs showing crystalline compounds formed when methadon is precipitated by various reagents. Gives microchemical and optical properties.

30. Hutchings, L. E., A microscope cell for low-temperature work, *Journal of Chemical Education* **28**, 214 (1951).
For temperatures down to minus 40 degrees F.

31. Inouye, Kaoru, Sunderlein, Russell, and Kirk, Paul, Microscopy of the amino acids and their compounds: silver salts, *Industrial & Engineering Chemistry, Analytical Edition* **13**, 587 (1941).

32. Jones, F. T., and Mason, C. W., Microscopical qualitative analysis of antimony and bismuth: tetraethyl ammonium iodide as a reagent, *Ibid.* **8**, 428 (1936).
The reagent which must actually be provided is tetraethyl ammonium chloride.

33. Kaiser, E. P., and Parrish, W., Preparation of immersion liquids for the range $n_D = 1.411$ to 1.785, *Industrial & Engineering Chemistry, Analytical Edition* **11**, 560 (1939).

34. Keenan, G. L., Notes on the microscopy of some important alkaloids — part I: *Chemist Analyst* **39**, 33 (1950); part II: *Ibid.* **39**, 52 (1950); part III: *Ibid.* **39**, 79 (1950).

35. Keenan, G. L., Microscopic identification of morphine, *Ibid.* **38**, 59 (1949).

36. King, J., Simplified techniques for the employment of fluorescence microscopy, *Journal of the Royal Microscopical Society* **71**, 338 (1951).

37. King, J., and Weston, R. E., Fluorescence microscopy as an aid to food and drug analysis, *The Analyst* **75**, 397 (1950).

38. Kofler, A., Zur Polymorphie organischer Verbindungen, *Mikrochemie-Mikrochimica Acta* **34**, 15 (1949).

39. Kofler, A., Die Kristallisationsvorgänge in unterkühlten Mischschmelzen organischer Stoffe, *Mikroskopie* **3,** 193 (1948).

40. Kofler, A., Schmelzkurven mit Inflexionspunkten und Mischungslücken der flüssigen Phasen in organischen Zweistoffsystemen, *Zeitschrift für analytische Chemie* **128,** 544 (1948).

41. Kofler, L., Zur Vereinfachung der thermischen Analyse organischer Substanzen, *Ibid.* **128,** 534 (1948).

42. Laurie, A. P., Identification of pigments used in painting at different periods, *Analyst* **55,** 162 (1930).

43. Leary, J. A., Particle-size determination in aerosols by autoradiographs, *Analytical Chemistry* **23,** 850 (1951).

44. Levine, J., Microchemical identification of demerol, *Industrial & Engineering Chemistry, Analytical Edition* **16,** 408 (1944).

45. Loveland, R. P., Color photomicrography in the laboratory, *Analytical Chemistry* **21,** 467 (1949).

46. MacNevin, Wm. M., Theodore George Wormley—First American microchemist, *Journal of Chemical Education* **25,** 182 (1948).
   Biographical; concerns interesting pioneer in the microscopy of alkaloids.

47. Mathews, F. W., A microscope hot stage, *Analytical Chemistry* **20,** 1112 (1948).
   Describes construction of an instrument which proved satisfactory in the author's laboratory.

48. Mitchell, J., Jr., Microscopic identification of organic compounds, *Ibid.* **21,** 448 (1949).

49. McCrone, W. C., Application of fusion methods in chemical microscopy, *Ibid.* **21,** 436 (1949).

50. McCrone, W. C., Smedal, A., and Griffin, V., Determination of 2,2-bis-*p*-chlorophenyl-1,1,1-trichloroethane in technical D.D.T.: a microscopic method, *Industrial & Engineering Chemistry, Analytical Edition* **18,** 578 (1946).

51. Morehead, F. F., Modern microscopy of films and fibers, *American Society for Testing Materials Bulletin* **163,** 54 (1950).

52. Opfer-Schaum, R., The use of microsublimation in toxicological analysis, *Pharmazie* **2,** 540 (1947).
   Describes the use of the Kofler apparatus in the determination of barbital and phenobarbital in urine.

53. Rochow, T. G., Microscopy in the resin industry, *Industrial & Engineering Chemistry, Analytical Edition* **11,** 629 (1939).

54. Rochow, T. G., and Rowe, F. G., Resinography of some consolidated separate resins, *Analytical Chemistry* **21,** 461 (1949).

55. Ross, H. L., and Sehl, F. W., Determination of free silica, *Industrial & Engineering Chemistry, Analytical Edition* **7,** 30 (1935).
   The method described is quantitative. It is a modified immersion method but does *not* require a petrographic microscope.

56. Royer, G. L., Some applications of modern microscopy to the study of chemical phenomena and in the dyeing and printing of textiles, *American Society for Testing Materials Bulletin* **165,** 46 (1950).

57. Royer, G. L., Chemical microscopy in dyeing and finishing, *Analytical Chemistry* **21,** 442 (1949).

58. Royer, G. L., Maresh, C. M., and Harding, A. M., Microscopical techniques for the study of dyeing, *Calco Technical Bulletin No.* **770,** Issued by the Chemical Division of the American Cyanamid Co.
   This bulletin contains numerous illustrations, including interesting reproductions of photomicrographs in color.

59. Salzenstein, M. A., and McCrone, W., A new microprojector, *Journal of Chemical Education* **28**, 184 (1951).
60. Schaeffer, H. F., Isoquinoline in chemical microscopy, *Analytical Chemistry* **23**, 1674 (1951).
   Describes use of isoquinoline in detection of cobalt, nickel, copper, cadmium, zinc.
61. Schuldiner, J. A., Identification of amidone, *Ibid.* **21**, 298 (1949).
62. Scudi, J. V., Identification of sulfanilamide, *Industrial & Engineering Chemistry, Analytical Edition* **10**, 346 (1938).
63. Seaman, W., Estimation of anthraquinone-1,8-disulfonic acid, *Ibid.* **11**, 465 (1939).
64. Stewart, V. E., Microidentification of metrazole in mixed aqueous solutions, *Ibid.* **11**, 345 (1939).
65. Tipson, R. S., Theory, scope, and methods of recrystallization, *Analytical Chemistry* **22**, 628 (1950).
66. Vold, M. J., and Doscher, T. M., A hot stage for microscopic observations between room temperature and 350° C., *Industrial & Engineering Chemistry, Analytical Edition* **18**, 154 (1946).
67. Wagenaar, M., Michrochemistry of saccharin, *Mikrochemie* **11**, 132 (1932).
68. White, E. P., Bromo complexes for the identification of metals and alkaloids, *Industrial & Engineering Chemistry, Analytical Edition* **13**, 509 (1941).
   Of special interest in connection with alkaloids.
69. Whitehead, T. H., and Bradbury, W. C., Qualitative scheme of analysis for the common sugars, *Analytical Chemistry* **22**, 651 (1950).
   Individual sugars are eventually identified under the microscope.

.   .   .   .

The papers which follow are concerned with procedures based on the methods of optical crystallography. In general, the methods require a petrographic microscope or a polarizing chemical microscope provided with a rotating stage.

70. Benedict, H. C., The polarizing microscope in organic chemistry, *Industrial and Engineering Chemistry, Analytical Edition* **2**, 91 (1930). Approx. 25 references are included.
71. Castle, R. N., and Witt, N. F., Polymorphism of sulfapyridine, *Journal of the American Chemical Society* **68**, 64 (1946).
72. Davies, E. S., and Hartshorne, N. H., Identification of some aromatic nitro compounds by optical crystallographic methods, *Journal of the Chemical Society* **1934** (II) 1830.
73. Dewey, B. T., and Plein, E. M., Identification of organic bases by means of the optical properties of diliturates: primary aromatic amines, *Industrial and Engineering Chemistry, Analytical Edition* **18**, 515 (1946).
74. Dewey, B. T., and Witt, N. F., Identification of alcohols by means of the optical properties of the esters of carbanilic acid, *Ibid.* **14**, 648 (1942).
75. Hultquist, M. E., and Poe, C. F., An optical crystallographic study of some derivatives of barbital and luminal, *Ibid.* **7**, 398 (1935).
76. Holmes, V., Optical crystallography of sugar derivatives, *Journal of the American Chemical Society* **54**, 2843 (1932).
77. Keenan, G. L., Microscopic identification of acetyl salicylic acid and salicylic acid, *Chemist Analyst* **38**, 31 (1949).
78. Keenan, G. L., Rapid microscopic method for the identification of dextrose and lactose in mixtures, *Ibid.* **38**, 10 (1949).
79. Keenan, G. L., Demonstration of biaxial interference figures with the polarizing microscope, *Ibid.* **36**, 17 (1947).

80. Plein, E. M., and Dewey, B. T., Identification of organic bases by means of the optical properties of diliturates: aliphatic amines, *Industrial and Engineering Chemistry, Analytical Edition* **15,** 534 (1943).
81. Poe, C. F., and Swisher, C. A., Optical crystallographic data for some salts of cinchonine, *Journal of the American Chemical Society* **57,** 748 (1935).
82. Poe, C. F., and Sellers, J. E., Optical crystallographic data of some salts of strychnine, *Ibid.* **54,** 249 (1932).
83. West, P. W., Polarized light microscopy, *Chemist Analyst* **34,** 76 (1945); **35,** 4 and 28 (1946).
84. White, B. J., Witt, N. F., Biles, J. A., and Poe, C. F., Optical crystallographic identification of sulfanilamide, *Analytical Chemistry* **22,** 950 (1950).

INDEX

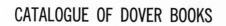

CATALOGUE OF DOVER BOOKS

BOOKS EXPLAINING SCIENCE AND MATHEMATICS

General

WHAT IS SCIENCE?, Norman Campbell. This excellent introduction explains scientific method, role of mathematics, types of scientific laws. Contents: 2 aspects of science, science & nature, laws of science, discovery of laws, explanation of laws, measurement & numerical laws, applications of science. 192pp. 5⅜ x 8.   S43 Paperbound **$1.25**

THE COMMON SENSE OF THE EXACT SCIENCES, W. K. Clifford. Introduction by James Newman, edited by Karl Pearson. For 70 years this has been a guide to classical scientific and mathematical thought. Explains with unusual clarity basic concepts, such as extension of meaning of symbols, characteristics of surface boundaries, properties of plane figures, vectors, Cartesian method of determining position, etc. Long preface by Bertrand Russell. Bibliography of Clifford. Corrected, 130 diagrams redrawn. 249pp. 5⅜ x 8.
T61 Paperbound **$1.60**

SCIENCE THEORY AND MAN, Erwin Schrödinger. This is a complete and unabridged reissue of SCIENCE AND THE HUMAN TEMPERAMENT plus an additional essay: "What is an Elementary Particle?" Nobel laureate Schrödinger discusses such topics as nature of scientific method, the nature of science, chance and determinism, science and society, conceptual models for physical entities, elementary particles and wave mechanics. Presentation is popular and may be followed -by most people with little or no scientific training. "Fine practical preparation for a time when laws of nature, human institutions . . . are undergoing a critical examination without parallel," Waldemar Kaempffert, N. Y. TIMES. 192pp. 5⅜ x 8.
T428 Paperbound **$1.35**

FADS AND FALLACIES IN THE NAME OF SCIENCE, Martin Gardner. Examines various cults, quack systems, frauds, delusions which at various times have masqueraded as science. Accounts of hollow-earth fanatics like Symmes; Velikovsky and wandering planets; Hoerbiger; Bellamy and the theory of multiple moons; Charles Fort; dowsing, pseudoscientific methods for finding water, ores, oil. Sections on naturopathy, iridiagnosis, zone therapy, food fads, etc. Analytical accounts of Wilhelm Reich and orgone sex energy; L. Ron Hubbard and Dianetics; A. Korzybski and General Semantics; many others. Brought up to date to include Bridey Murphy, others. Not just a collection of anecdotes, but a fair, reasoned appraisal of eccentric theory. Formerly titled IN THE NAME OF SCIENCE. Preface. Index. x + 384pp. 5⅜ x 8.   T394 Paperbound **$1.50**

A DOVER SCIENCE SAMPLER, edited by George Barkin. 64-page book, sturdily bound, containing excerpts from over 20 Dover books, explaining science. Edwin Hubble, George Sarton, Ernst Mach, A. d'Abro, Galileo, Newton, others, discussing island universes, scientific truth, biological phenomena, stability in bridges, etc. Copies limited; no more than 1 to a customer,
FREE

POPULAR SCIENTIFIC LECTURES, Hermann von Helmholtz. Helmholtz was a superb expositor as well as a scientist of genius in many areas. The seven essays in this volume are models of clarity, and even today they rank among the best general descriptions of their subjects ever written. "The Physiological Causes of Harmony in Music" was the first significant physiological explanation of musical consonance and dissonance. Two essays, "On the Interaction of Natural Forces" and "On the Conservation of Force," were of great importance in the history of science, for they firmly established the principle of the conservation of energy. Other lectures include "On the Relation of Optics to Painting," "On Recent Progress in the Theory of Vision," "On Goethe's Scientific Researches," and "On the Origin and Significance of Geometrical Axioms." Selected and edited with an introduction by Professor Morris Kline. xii + 286pp. 5⅜ x 8½.   T799 Paperbound **$1.45**

BOOKS EXPLAINING SCIENCE AND MATHEMATICS

Physics

CONCERNING THE NATURE OF THINGS, Sir William Bragg. Christmas lectures delivered at the Royal Society by Nobel laureate. Why a spinning ball travels in a curved track; how uranium is transmuted to lead, etc. Partial contents: atoms, gases, liquids, crystals, metals, etc. No scientific background needed; wonderful for intelligent child. 32pp. of photos, 57 figures. xii + 232pp. 5⅜ x 8.   T31 Paperbound **$1.50**

THE RESTLESS UNIVERSE, Max Born. New enlarged version of this remarkably readable account by a Nobel laureate. Moving from sub-atomic particles to universe, the author explains in very simple terms the latest theories of wave mechanics. Partial contents: air and its relatives, electrons & ions, waves & particles, electronic structure of the atom, nuclear physics. Nearly 1000 illustrations, including 7 animated sequences. 325pp. 6 x 9.
T412 Paperbound **$2.00**

THE STRANGE STORY OF THE QUANTUM, AN ACCOUNT FOR THE GENERAL READER OF THE GROWTH OF IDEAS UNDERLYING OUR PRESENT ATOMIC KNOWLEDGE, B. Hoffmann. Presents lucidly and expertly, with barest amount of mathematics, the problems and theories which led to modern quantum physics. Dr. Hoffmann begins with the closing years of the 19th century, when certain trifling discrepancies were noticed, and with illuminating analogies and examples takes you through the brilliant concepts of Planck, Einstein, Pauli, de Broglie, Bohr, Schroedinger, Heisenberg, Dirac, Sommerfeld, Feynman, etc. This edition includes a new, long postscript carrying the story through 1958. "Of the books attempting an account of the history and contents of our modern atomic physics which have come to my attention, this is the best," H. Margenau, Yale University, in "American Journal of Physics." 32 tables and line illustrations. Index. 275pp. 5⅜ x 8. T518 Paperbound **$1.50**

THE EVOLUTION OF SCIENTIFIC THOUGHT FROM NEWTON TO EINSTEIN, A. d'Abro. Einstein's special and general theories of relativity, with their historical implications, are analyzed in non-technical terms. Excellent accounts of the contributions of Newton, Riemann, Weyl, Planck, Eddington, Maxwell, Lorentz and others are treated in terms of space and time, equations of electromagnetics, finiteness of the universe, methodology of science. 21 diagrams. 482pp. 5⅜ x 8. T2 Paperound **$2.25**

THE RISE OF THE NEW PHYSICS, A. d'Abro. A half-million word exposition, formerly titled THE DECLINE OF MECHANISM, for readers not versed in higher mathematics. The only thorough explanation, in everyday language, of the central core of modern mathematical physical theory, treating both classical and modern theoretical physics, and presenting in terms almost anyone can understand the equivalent of 5 years of study of mathematical physics. Scientifically impeccable coverage of mathematical-physical thought from the Newtonian system up through the electronic theories of Dirac and Heisenberg and Fermi's statistics. Combines both history and exposition; provides a broad yet unified and detailed view, with constant comparison of classical and modern views on phenomena and theories. "A must for anyone doing serious study in the physical sciences," JOURNAL OF THE FRANKLIN INSTITUTE. "Extraordinary faculty . . . to explain ideas and theories of theoretical physics in the language of daily life," ISIS. First part of set covers philosophy of science, drawing upon the practice of Newton, Maxwell, Poincaré, Einstein, others, discussing modes of thought, experiment, interpretations of causality, etc. In the second part, 100 pages explain grammar and vocabulary of mathematics, with discussions of functions, groups, series, Fourier series, etc. The remainder is devoted to concrete, detailed coverage of both classical and quantum physics, explaining such topics as analytic mechanics, Hamilton's principle, wave theory of light, electromagnetic waves, groups of transformations, thermodynamics, phase rule, Brownian movement, kinetics, special relativity, Planck's original quantum theory, Bohr's atom, Zeeman effect, Broglie's wave mechanics, Heisenberg's uncertainty, Eigen-values, matrices, scores of other important topics. Discoveries and theories are covered for such men as Alembert, Born, Cantor, Debye, Euler, Foucault, Galois, Gauss, Hadamard, Kelvin, Kepler, Laplace, Maxwell, Pauli, Rayleigh, Volterra, Weyl, Young, more than 180 others. Indexed. 97 illustrations. ix + 982pp. 5⅜ x 8.
T3 Volume 1, Paperbound **$2.25**
T4 Volume 2, Paperbound **$2.25**

SPINNING TOPS AND GYROSCOPIC MOTION, John Perry. Well-known classic of science still unsurpassed for lucid, accurate, delightful exposition. How quasi-rigidity is induced in flexible and fluid bodies by rapid motions; why gyrostat falls, top rises; nature and effect on climatic conditions of earth's precessional movement; effect of internal fluidity on rotating bodies, etc. Appendixes describe practical uses to which gyroscopes have been put in ships, compasses, monorail transportation. 62 figures. 128pp. 5⅜ x 8. T416 Paperbound **$1.00**

THE UNIVERSE OF LIGHT, Sir William Bragg. No scientific training needed to read Nobel Prize winner's expansion of his Royal Institute Christmas Lectures. Insight into nature of light, methods and philosophy of science. Explains lenses, reflection, color, resonance, polarization, x-rays, the spectrum, Newton's work with prisms, Huygens' with polarization, Crookes' with cathode ray, etc. Leads into clear statement of 2 major historical theories of light, corpuscle and wave. Dozens of experiments you can do. 199 illus., including 2 full-page color plates. 293pp. 5⅜ x 8. S538 Paperbound **$1.85**

THE STORY OF X-RAYS FROM RÖNTGEN TO ISOTOPES, A. R. Bleich. Non-technical history of x-rays, their scientific explanation, their applications in medicine, industry, research, and art, and their effect on the individual and his descendants. Includes amusing early reactions to Röntgen's discovery, cancer therapy, detections of art and stamp forgeries, potential risks to patient and operator, etc. Illustrations show x-rays of flower structure, the gall bladder, gears with hidden defects, etc. Original Dover publication. Glossary. Bibliography. Index. 55 photos and figures. xiv + 186pp. 5⅜ x 8. T662 Paperbound **$1.35**

ELECTRONS, ATOMS, METALS AND ALLOYS, Wm. Hume-Rothery. An introductory-level explanation of the application of the electronic theory to the structure and properties of metals and alloys, taking into account the new theoretical work done by mathematical physicists. Material presented in dialogue-form between an "Old Metallurgist" and a "Young Scientist." Their discussion falls into 4 main parts: the nature of an atom, the nature of a metal, the nature of an alloy, and the structure of the nucleus. They cover such topics as the hydrogen atom, electron waves, wave mechanics, Brillouin zones, co-valent bonds, radioactivity and natural disintegration, fundamental particles, structure and fission of the nucleus,etc. Revised, enlarged edition. 177 illustrations. Subject and name indexes. 407pp. 5⅜ x 8½. S1046 Paperbound **$2.25**

TEACH YOURSELF MECHANICS, P. Abbott. The lever, centre of gravity, parallelogram of force, friction, acceleration, Newton's laws of motion, machines, specific gravity, gas, liquid pressure, much more. 280 problems, solutions. Tables. 163 illus. 271pp. 6⅞ x 4¼.
Clothbound **$2.00**

MATTER & MOTION, James Clerk Maxwell, This excellent exposition begins with simple particles and proceeds gradually to physical systems beyond complete analysis: motion, force, properties of centre of mass of material system, work, energy, gravitation, etc. Written with all Maxwell's original insights and clarity. Notes by E. Larmor. 17 diagrams. 178pp. 5⅜ x 8.
S188 Paperbound **$1.35**

SOAP BUBBLES, THEIR COLOURS AND THE FORCES WHICH MOULD THEM, C. V. Boys. Only complete edition, half again as much material as any other. Includes Boys' hints on performing his experiments, sources of supply. Dozens of lucid experiments show complexities of liquid films, surface tension, etc. Best treatment ever written. Introduction. 83 illustrations. Color plate. 202pp. 5⅜ x 8.
T542 Paperbound **95¢**

MATTER & LIGHT, THE NEW PHYSICS, L. de Broglie. Non-technical papers by a Nobel laureate explain electromagnetic theory, relativity, matter, light and radiation, wave mechanics, quantum physics, philosophy of science. Einstein, Planck, Bohr, others explained so easily that no mathematical training is needed for all but 2 of the 21 chapters. Unabridged. Index. 300pp. 5⅜ x 8.
T35 Paperbound **$1.85**

SPACE AND TIME, Emile Borel. An entirely non-technical introduction to relativity, by world-renowned mathematician, Sorbonne professor. (Notes on basic mathematics are included separately.) This book has never been surpassed for insight, and extraordinary clarity of thought, as it presents scores of examples, analogies, arguments, illustrations, which explain such topics as: difficulties due to motion; gravitation a force of inertia; geodesic lines; wave-length and difference of phase; x-rays and crystal structure; the special theory of relativity; and much more. Indexes. 4 appendixes. 15 figures. xvi + 243pp. 5⅜ x 8.
T592 Paperbound **$1.45**

BOOKS EXPLAINING SCIENCE AND MATHEMATICS

Astronomy

THE FRIENDLY STARS, Martha Evans Martin. This engaging survey of stellar lore and science is a well-known classic, which has introduced thousands to the fascinating world of stars and other celestial bodies. Descriptions of Capella, Sirius, Arcturus, Vega, Polaris, etc.—all the important stars, with informative discussions of rising and setting of stars, their number, names, brightness, distances, etc. in a non-technical, highly readable style. Also: double stars, constellations, clusters—concentrating on stars and formations visible to the naked eye. New edition, revised (1963) by D. H. Menzel, Director Harvard Observatory. 23 diagrams by Prof. Ching-Sung Yu. Foreword by D. H. Menzel and W. W. Morgan. 2 Star Charts. Index. xii + 147pp. 5⅜ x 8½.
T1099 Paperbound **$1.00**

AN ELEMENTARY SURVEY OF CELESTIAL MECHANICS, Y. Ryabov. Elementary exposition of gravitational theory and celestial mechanics. Historical introduction and coverage of basic principles, including: the elliptic, the orbital plane, the 2- and 3-body problems, the discovery of Neptune, planetary rotation, the length of the day, the shapes of galaxies, satellites (detailed treatment of Sputnik I), etc. First American reprinting of successful Russian popular exposition. Elementary algebra and trigonometry helpful, but not necessary; presentation chiefly verbal. Appendix of theorem proofs. 58 figures. 165pp. 5⅜ x 8.
T756 Paperbound **$1.25**

THE SKY AND ITS MYSTERIES, E. A. Beet. One of most lucid books on mysteries of universe; deals with astronomy from earliest observations to latest theories of expansion of universe, source of stellar energy, birth of planets, origin of moon craters, possibility of life on other planets. Discusses effects of sunspots on weather; distances, ages of several stars; master plan of universe; methods and tools of astronomers; much more. "Eminently readable book," London Times. Extensive bibliography. Over 50 diagrams. 12 full-page plates, fold-out star map. Introduction. Index. 5¼ x 7½.
T627 Clothbound **$3.50**

THE REALM OF THE NEBULAE, E. Hubble. One of the great astronomers of our time records his formulation of the concept of "island universes," and its impact on astronomy. Such topics are covered as the velocity-distance relation; classification, nature, distances, general field of nebulae; cosmological theories; nebulae in the neighborhood of the Milky Way. 39 photos of nebulae, nebulae clusters, spectra of nebulae, and velocity distance relations shown by spectrum comparison. "One of the most progressive lines of astronomical research," The Times (London). New introduction by A. Sandage. 55 illustrations. Index. iv + 201pp. 5⅜ x 8.
S455 Paperbound **$1.50**

CHEMISTRY AND PHYSICAL CHEMISTRY

ORGANIC CHEMISTRY, F. C. Whitmore. The entire subject of organic chemistry for the practicing chemist and the advanced student. Storehouse of facts, theories, processes found elsewhere only in specialized journals. Covers aliphatic compounds (500 pages on the properties and synthetic preparation of hydrocarbons, halides, proteins, ketones, etc.), alicyclic compounds, aromatic compounds, heterocyclic compounds, organophosphorus and organometallic compounds. Methods of synthetic preparation analyzed critically throughout. Includes much of biochemical interest. "The scope of this volume is astonishing," INDUSTRIAL AND ENGINEERING CHEMISTRY. 12,000-reference index. 2387-item bibliography. Total of x + 1005pp. 5⅜ x 8. Two volume set.
S700 Vol I Paperbound **$2.25**
S701 Vol II Paperbound **$2.25**
The set **$4.50**

THE MODERN THEORY OF MOLECULAR STRUCTURE, Bernard Pullman. A reasonably popular account of recent developments in atomic and molecular theory. Contents: The Wave Function and Wave Equations (history and bases of present theories of molecular structure); The Electronic Structure of Atoms (Description and classification of atomic wave functions, etc.); Diatomic Molecules; Non-Conjugated Polyatomic Molecules; Conjugated Polyatomic Molecules; The Structure of Complexes. Minimum of mathematical background needed. New translation by David Antin of "La Structure Moleculaire." Index. Bibliography. vii + 87pp. 5⅜ x 8½.
S987 Paperbound **$1.00**

CATALYSIS AND CATALYSTS, Marcel Prettre, Director, Research Institute on Catalysis. This brief book, translated into English for the first time, is the finest summary of the principal modern concepts, methods, and results of catalysis. Ideal introduction for beginning chemistry and physics students. Chapters: Basic Definitions of Catalysis (true catalysis and generalization of the concept of catalysis); The Scientific Bases of Catalysis (Catalysis and chemical thermodynamics, catalysis and chemical kinetics); Homogeneous Catalysis (acid-base catalysis, etc.); Chain Reactions; Contact Masses; Heterogeneous Catalysis (Mechanisms of contact catalyses, etc.); and Industrial Applications (acids and fertilizers, petroleum and petroleum chemistry, rubber, plastics, synthetic resins, and fibers). Translated by David Antin. Index. vi + 88pp. 5⅜ x 8½.
S998 Paperbound **$1.00**

POLAR MOLECULES, Pieter Debye. This work by Nobel laureate Debye offers a complete guide to fundamental electrostatic field relations, polarizability, molecular structure. Partial contents: electric intensity, displacement and force, polarization by orientation, molar polarization and molar refraction, halogen-hydrides, polar liquids, ionic saturation, dielectric constant, etc. Special chapter considers quantum theory. Indexed. 172pp. 5⅜ x 8.
S64 Paperbound **$1.65**

THE ELECTRONIC THEORY OF ACIDS AND BASES, W. F. Luder and Saverio Zuffanti. The first full systematic presentation of the electronic theory of acids and bases—treating the theory and its ramifications in an uncomplicated manner. Chapters: Historical Background; Atomic Orbitals and Valence; The Electronic Theory of Acids and Bases; Electrophilic and Electrodotic Reagents; Acidic and Basic Radicals; Neutralization; Titrations with Indicators; Displacement; Catalysis; Acid Catalysis; Base Catalysis; Alkoxides and Catalysts; Conclusion. Required reading for all chemists. Second revised (1961) eidtion, with additional examples and references. 3 figures. 9 tables. Index. Bibliography xii + 165pp. 5⅜ x 8.
S201 Paperbound **$1.50**

KINETIC THEORY OF LIQUIDS, J. Frenkel. Regarding the kinetic theory of liquids as a generalization and extension of the theory of solid bodies, this volume covers all types of arrangements of solids, thermal displacements of atoms, interstitial atoms and ions, orientational and rotational motion of molecules, and transition between states of matter. Mathematical theory is developed close to the physical subject matter. 216 bibliographical footnotes. 55 figures. xi + 485pp. 5⅜ x 8.
S95 Paperbound **$2.55**

THE PRINCIPLES OF ELECTROCHEMISTRY, D. A. MacInnes. Basic equations for almost every subfield of electrochemistry from first principles, referring at all times to the soundest and most recent theories and results; unusually useful as text or as reference. Covers coulometers and Faraday's Law, electrolytic conductance, the Debye-Hueckel method for the theoretical calculation of activity coefficients, concentration cells, standard electrode potentials, thermodynamic ionization constants, pH, potentiometric titrations, irreversible phenomena, Planck's equation, and much more. "Excellent treatise," AMERICAN CHEMICAL SOCIETY JOURNAL. "Highly recommended," CHEMICAL AND METALLURGICAL ENGINEERING. 2 Indices. Appendix. 585-item bibliography. 137 figures. 94 tables. ii + 478pp. 5⅜ x 8⅜.
S52 Paperbound **$2.45**

THE PHASE RULE AND ITS APPLICATION, Alexander Findlay. Covering chemical phenomena of 1, 2, 3, 4, and multiple component systems, this "standard work on the subject" (NATURE, London), has been completely revised and brought up to date by A. N. Campbell and N. O. Smith. Brand new material has been added on such matters as binary, tertiary liquid equilibria, solid solutions in ternary systems, quinary systems of salts and water. Completely revised to triangular coordinates in ternary systems, clarified graphic representation, solid models, etc. 9th revised edition. Author, subject indexes. 236 figures. 505 footnotes, mostly bibliographic. xii + 494pp. 5⅜ x 8.
S91 Paperbound **$2.50**

THE SOLUBILITY OF NONELECTROLYTES, Joel H. Hildebrand and Robert L. Scott. The standard work on the subject; still indispensable as a reference source and for classroom work. Partial contents: The Ideal Solution (including Raoult's Law and Henry's Law, etc.); Nonideal Solutions; Intermolecular Forces; The Liquid State; Entropy of Athermal Mixing; Heat of Mixing; Polarity; Hydrogen Bonding; Specific Interactions; "Solvation" and "Association"; Systems of Three or More Components; Vapor Pressure of Binary Liquid Solutions; Mixtures of Gases; Solubility of Gases in Liquids; of Liquids in Liquids; of Solids in Liquids; Evaluation of Solubility Parameters; and other topics. Corrected republication of third (revised) edition. Appendices. Indexes. 138 figures. 111 tables. 1 photograph. iv + 488pp. 5⅜ x 8½.
S1125 Paperbound **$2.50**

TERNARY SYSTEMS: INTRODUCTION TO THE THEORY OF THREE COMPONENT SYSTEMS, G. Masing. Furnishes detailed discussion of representative types of 3-components systems, both in solid models (particularly metallic alloys) and isothermal models. Discusses mechanical mixture without compounds and without solid solutions; unbroken solid solution series; solid solutions with solubility breaks in two binary systems; iron-silicon-aluminum alloys; allotropic forms of iron in ternary system; other topics. Bibliography. Index. 166 illustrations. 178pp. 5⅝ x 8⅜.
S631 Paperbound **$1.50**

THE KINETIC THEORY OF GASES, Leonard B. Loeb, University of California. Comprehensive text and reference book which presents full coverage of basic theory and the important experiments and developments in the field for the student and investigator. Partial contents: The Mechanical Picture of a Perfect Gas, The Mean Free Path—Clausius' Deductions, Distribution of Molecular Velocities, discussions of theory of the problem of specific heats, the contributions of kinetic theory to our knowledge of electrical and magnetic properties of molecules and its application to the conduction of electricity in gases. New 14-page preface to Dover edition by the author. Name, subject indexes. Six appendices. 570-item bibliography. xxxvi + 687pp. 5⅜ x 8½.
S942 Paperbound **$2.95**

IONS IN SOLUTION, Ronald W. Gurney. A thorough and readable introduction covering all the fundamental principles and experiments in the field, by an internationally-known authority. Contains discussions of solvation energy, atomic and molecular ions, lattice energy, transferral of ions, interionic forces, cells and half-cells, transference of electrons, exchange forces, hydrogen ions, the electro-chemical series, and many other related topics. Indispensable to advanced undergraduates and graduate students in electrochemistry. Index. 45 illustrations. 15 tables. vii + 206pp. 5⅜ x 8½.
S124 Paperbound **$1.50**

IONIC PROCESSES IN SOLUTION, Ronald W. Gurney. Lucid, comprehensive examination which brings together the approaches of electrochemistry, thermodynamics, statistical mechanics, electroacoustics, molecular physics, and quantum theory in the interpretation of the behavior of ionic solutions—the most important single work on the subject. More extensive and technical than the author's earlier work (IONS IN SOLUTION), it is a middle-level text for graduate students and researchers in electrochemistry. Covers such matters as Brownian motion in liquids, molecular ions in solution, heat of precipitation, entropy of solution, proton transfers, dissociation constant of nitric acid, viscosity of ionic solutions, etc. 78 illustrations. 47 tables. Name and subject index. ix + 275pp. 5⅜ x 8½.
S134 Paperbound **$1.75**

CRYSTALLOGRAPHIC DATA ON METAL AND ALLOY STRUCTURES, Compiled by A. Taylor and B. J. Kagle, Westinghouse Research Laboratories. Unique collection of the latest crystallographic data on alloys, compounds, and the elements, with lattice spacings expressed uniformly in absolute Angstrom units. Gathers together previously widely-scattered data from the Power Data File of the ATSM, structure reports, and the Landolt-Bornstein Tables, as well as from other original literature. 2300 different compounds listed in the first table. Alloys and Intermetallic Compounds, with much vital information on each. Also listings for nearly 700 Borides, Carbides, Hydrides, Oxides, Nitrides. Also all the necessary data on the crystal structure of 77 elements. vii + 263pp. 5⅜ x 8.
S1013 Paperbound **$2.25**

MATHEMATICAL CRYSTALLOGRAPHY AND THE THEORY OF GROUPS OF MOVEMENTS, Harold Hilton. Classic account of the mathematical theory of crystallography, particularly the geometrical theory of crystal-structure based on the work of Bravais, Jordan, Sohncke, Federow, Schoenflies, and Barlow. Partial contents: The Stereographic Projection, Properties Common to Symmetrical and Asymmetrical Crystals, The Theory of Groups, Coordinates of Equivalent Points, Crystallographic Axes and Axial Ratios, The Forms and Growth of Crystals, Lattices and Translations, The Structure-Theory, Infinite Groups of Movements, Triclinic and Monoclinic Groups, Orthorhombic Groups, etc. Index. 188 figures. xii + 262pp. 5⅜ x 8½.
S2126 Paperbound **$2.00**

CLASSICS IN THE THEORY OF CHEMICAL COMBINATIONS. Edited by O. T. Benfey. Vol. I of the Classics of Science Series, G. Holton, Harvard University, General Editor. This book is a collection of papers representing the major chapters in the development of the valence concept in chemistry. Includes essays by Wöhler and Liebig, Laurent, Williamson, Frankland, Kekulé and Couper, and two by van't Hoff and le Bel, which mark the first extension of the valence concept beyond its purely numerical character. Introduction and epilogue by Prof. Benfey. Index. 9 illustrations. New translation of Kekulé paper by Benfey. xiv + 191pp. 5⅜ x 8½.
S1066 Paperbound **$1.85**

THE CHEMISTRY OF URANIUM: THE ELEMENT, ITS BINARY AND RELATED COMPOUNDS, J. J. Katz and E. Rabinowitch. Vast post-World War II collection and correlation of thousands of AEC reports and published papers in a useful and easily accessible form, still the most complete and up-to-date compilation. Treats "dry uranium chemistry," occurrences, preparation, properties, simple compounds, isotopic composition, extraction from ores, spectra, alloys, etc. Much material available only here. Index. Thousands of evaluated bibliographical references. 324 tables, charts, figures. xxi + 609pp. 5⅜ x 8.   S757 Paperbound **$2.95**

THE STORY OF ALCHEMY AND EARLY CHEMISTRY, J. M. Stillman. An authoritative, scholarly work, highly readable, of development of chemical knowledge from 4000 B.C. to downfall of phlogiston theory in late 18th century. Every important figure, many quotations. Brings alive curious, almost incredible history of alchemical beliefs, practices, writings of Arabian Prince Oneeyade, Vincent of Beauvais, Geber, Zosimos, Paracelsus, Vitruvius, scores more. Studies work, thought of Black, Cavendish, Priestley, Van Helmont, Bergman, Lavoisier, Newton, etc. Index. Bibliography. 579pp. 5⅜ x 8.   S628 Paperbound **$2.45**

Prices subject to change without notice.

Dover publishes books on art, music, philosophy, literature, languages, history, social sciences, psychology, handcrafts, orientalia, puzzles and entertainments, chess, pets and gardens, books explaining science, intermediate and higher mathematics, mathematical physics, engineering, biological sciences, earth sciences, classics of science, etc. Write to:

Dept. catrr.
Dover Publications, Inc.
180 Varick Street, N.Y. 14, N.Y.